'Kneel down and place your hands upon the snake's head,' her mother ordered. 'He, too, is the beginning.'

Marie did as she was bid and was surprised to find the mottled skin of the great body warm and a little rough to her touch. The snake flicked its tongue out, but made no other movement.

'Do you swear that from this day forth you will be the servant of Vodun, that you will guard his secrets and serve him faithfully?' her mother demanded. 'And do you swear to do as you are bid by me in all things?'

'I swear,' said Marie Laveau.

'You may sit down again. There are some other things that I still have to tell you.'

Marie returned to the stool, a heavy weight constricted her chest. 'I do not feel well, Mama,' she said faintly.

'Then I will not keep you much longer,' her mother replied. 'Listen carefully to what I say. Never forget the importance of money or the importance of men of power. You must learn to cultivate and manipulate these men. With them you can afford no emotions. They are both target – and enemy!'

Margot Arnold

Marie, Voodoo Queen

A MAYFLOWER BOOK

GRANADA
London Toronto Sydney New York

Published by Granada Publishing Limited in 1981

ISBN 0 583 13399 1

A Granada Paperbacks UK Original
Previously published in USA by Pocket Books
under the title *Marie*
Copyright © Margot Arnold 1979

Granada Publishing Limited
Frogmore, St Albans, Herts AL2 2NF
and
3 Upper James Street, London W1R 4BP
866 United Nations Plaza, New York, NY 10017, USA
117 York Street, Sydney, NSW 2000, Australia
100 Skyway Avenue, Rexdale, Ontario, M9W 3A6, Canada
PO Box 84165, Greenside, 2034 Johannesburg, South Africa
61 Beach Road, Auckland, New Zealand

Set, printed and bound in Great Britain by
Cox & Wyman Ltd, Reading
Set in Intertype Times

Granada ®
Granada Publishing ®

To 'The Wild Bunch'
(Bea, Emmy, Gail, Harriett & Steve)
For The Gift Of Their Friendship

Part I
1844-1853

Chapter One

'Now is the beginning. Come. We must talk. We will not be disturbed.' The deep, authoritative voice of her mother sent a thrill of excitement through Marie-Belle, and, without question, she followed the tall, stately figure into the dusty, sunfilled courtyard of the small house on St Ann Street. No one ever questioned her mother.

She had been feeling excited and important all week long – ever since her fourteenth birthday, when her courses had started at last and she had at the same time become a woman. It had been an event that brought relief, for she had borne in anxious silence the brunt of barbed comment from her already maturing sisters for some time. Now, on top of that, came this summons for a *tête-à-tête* with her mother – an almost unheard-of occurrence. Conscious of the eyes of her brothers and sisters upon her, burning with curiosity and touched with envy, she straightened her shoulders and tried to emulate her mother's graceful swaying walk as she followed closely after her.

Her mother reached the shade of the magnolia tree, which filtered the faint warmth of the late-February sun into bold patterns on the dust, and sat down on a stool made of solid wood, fashioned in a curious hourglass shape and deeply carved with intricate, sinuous patterns; it had been brought all the way from Africa. She spread her bright, multi-flounced skirt around her, settled the crisp white cotton blouse off her magnificent shoulders, and motioned Marie-Belle to an ordinary three-legged stool facing her. 'We will talk in English,' she announced.

Marie-Belle's heart sank slightly. It was awesome enough talking alone with her mother in their native French, let alone the foreign tongue of the Anglos.

Sensing the girl's hesitancy, her mother said sharply, 'The

nuns at the convent have been teaching you English, have they not?.

'Yes, Mama,' Marie murmured.

'Well, then, we will talk in it, because it is the language of the future.' A slight look of distaste crossed her mother's face. 'It is a language which you must speak without hesitation.'

'Yes, Mama,' Marie-Belle said again.

'You are a woman now,' the older woman said. Marie nodded proudly, two spots of colour spreading on the high cheekbones, bringing the vivid young face even more to life.

A momentary silence fell as the two looked at one another; only in the great black, long-lashed eyes and a certain proud angle of the head were they similar. Though this year of 1844 would see her forty-seventh birthday, Marie Laveau was handsome still: her features strong and definite, her mouth full-lipped, sensuous, and startlingly red against her creamy skin. In the daughter there was no such budding promise of it: her figure small and childlike, her features still childishly rounded, but beneath lay fine bone-work – the high cheekbones, the thin aquiline nose, and the delicate, fine-lipped wide mouth. Soon the beauty would bloom.

Finally, the mother broke the heavy silence. 'Who am *I*?' she said.

Marie-Belle's mind raced. What did her mother want her to reply? Certainly not that she was her mother – that would be absurd. What should she say? The Widow Paris – the name her mother used when she went to church and talked with the nuns at her school? Marie Glapion – which was what she had called herself when Père Louis had been with them; the name of the family? No, she did not think she wanted either of those. The name that the hordes of people, black and white alike, used when they came rapping at the door seeking her mother's services? Intuitively, she felt that must be right. 'You are Marie Laveau,' she said slowly.

Her mother inclined her head approvingly, and Marie-Belle's heart rose – perhaps this was not going to be so difficult after all. But the next question surprised her. 'And who are you?' her mother said.

10

'Marie-Belle Laveau,' she said promptly, and was dismayed at the vigorous negative shake of her mother's head, which set the great golden hoop earrings tinkling.

'No,' her mother said firmly. '*You* are Marie Laveau. Together we are Marie Laveau – this you must not forget. No longer are you Marie-Belle, only Marie Laveau.'

'Oh, I see !' she said, not seeing at all.

'And *who* am I?' her mother persisted mercilessly.

Marie's mind reeled. Now what did her mother want? Marie Laveau, daughter of State Senator Charles Laveau and the beautiful Marguerite Durcantel? Marie Laveau, mother and supporter of fifteen assorted Parises and Glapions? Marie Laveau, prison-visitor, healer of the sick, hairdresser, fortune-teller, seer? Her mind came up against another idea, backed away from it, and then knew that this was what her mother was seeking. 'You are Queen of the Voodoos,' she whispered.

'There is no need to whisper. It is nothing to be ashamed of. It is a matter of great pride,' her mother said sharply and with emphasis, 'as you will find when one day you are Queen of the Voodoos. It means that we are women of power and of Powers.' She looked keenly at the girl. 'Do you know why it must be you and not any of those?' She waved a dismissive hand towards the house, where sundry shadowed forms could be seen pressed in curiosity against the windows.

Marie did not reply at once, but this time she did know the answer. From the time she was very little, she had realized the difference – that she saw things that no one else saw, heard things they did not hear, knew what they did not know: the difference that set her apart from them all. 'Because I have the powers, too,' she said simply.

Her mother nodded in satisfaction. 'Perhaps, then, you can tell me why *you* are Marie *Laveau*,' she said slyly.

Marie's heart began to beat uncomfortably fast. This was something she had never understood; she had seen her baptismal certificate once and it had said only that but all the rest had different names, the two Paris children, now gone from the household, and the remaining children all Glapions;

even François, the youngest who had been born a few months after Père Louis's death in 1835. Some, like her older brother Jean, used both Glapion and Laveau, but even in school she had never gone by any other name than that of her mother. 'I don't know,' she confessed, 'but I have often wondered. Was it because you wanted it like that?'

A strange expression passed over her mother's face. 'No – it was something that had to be. I must tell you now. Père Louis was not your father.'

A pang of sorrow shot through Marie. Even though she had only been five years old when Père Louis had died, she remembered him vividly as a constant source of warmth and comfort, as someone who was always there when he was needed. She had always thought of him as her father; she would have *liked* to have been his child. 'Then who was my father?' she demanded stiffly.

'A man of power, a man of great power,' her mother said quietly, and again the unsettling expression flitted across her handsome face. 'And the answer lies in your skin.'

Marie glanced involuntarily down at the hands clasped tightly in her lap. She was darker, much darker, than her mother, whose creamy skin turned the colour of ripe bananas in the sun, and only the darker pigmentation around the eyes and the long nails, bluish at the moons, hinted at the other strain that ran so deep and strong within; her skin, by contrast, was the colour of ripe peaches, which turned to copper under the sun. 'He was an Indian,' her mother said softly, as if to herself, 'an Indian from far away, a man who came seeking Dr John, and with Dr John he found me, for Dr. John was my teacher in the secret things, just as I will be yours.' She paused and sucked in her breath. 'When I saw them work together it was a revelation – I had never seen such force. His was the force of the earth – not of water, as mine is.' Again she paused and appeared to go off on a tangent. 'My mother used to say there was Indian in me, too, and he said the same thing, but I don't know ...' She looked wonderingly at her own creamy hands. 'Anyway, he wanted me and I him for that time, because it had to be

12

so, and between us we brought forth you, who should have the powers of earth and water – great powers, greater than mine alone or his alone.' She gave her daughter an un-fathomable look, the remarkable irises of her dark eyes con-stricting into half-moons, and for a moment she looked like a lioness about to spring.

'Then where is he?' Marie said through stiffened lips.

'I don't know,' her mother said, and she suddenly shivered in the sunbright courtyard. 'He wanted me to go back with him to his people, back to the desert. I tried to tell him it was no good, that for my power I must stay here, only here, between the waters. And, besides, there was Louis.' Her stern expression softened at the name. 'I loved Père Louis, loved him very much, and then there were the others, too – I could not leave them, either. This he did not understand; he wanted only you and me. When he saw I would not go, he flew into a terrible rage and left – but I thought he would soon be back. Then came the time of the fever. You were just a baby, so you do not remember, but for two years it raged here, the yellow fever, and then came the cholera. When one stopped, the other started, over and over and over. Father Dominic and Dr Clapp and I, we worked until we ourselves well-nigh dropped. And then when it was gone, *he* was gone. He left a message with Dr John for me – he said that one day he would return . . .' Again she shivered and stopped. 'He called himself Don Thomé di Sonora, but I do not think that was his real name,' she whispered.

Suddenly she got to her feet and said in a brisker, louder voice, 'Well, now you know. We must talk of the future.' And she went off towards the shady side of the courtyard, where a long box stood by itself. Marie-Belle closed her eyes. Her thoughts were in a whirl and her senses were acutely heightened, so that all the familiar sounds and smells took on new clarity and meaning – the crooning of the hens scratching about in the dirt of the courtyard; the complaints of the roosters penned in their cages against the sunny wall; the acrid smell of chicken droppings mixed with the sweet smell of late-blooming camellias and early Jasmine banked against the long wall of the courtyard; and the light breeze

13

riffling through the waxen leaves of the magnolia, just now coming into bud, bringing with it street cries and the noise of wheels and horses, all muffled by the barricade of the house itself. This day, this scene, this indescribable feeling within her, as if somehow she had been split in two, was something she would never forget.

She opened her eyes as her mother reseated herself and opened the box which she had dragged between them. The great gold and brown coils within heaved up and the great python stretched and slid quietly on to the earth. The hens scattered in sudden fright and, running into a corner, stood huddled together clucking dolefully. The python's head raised up and for a moment, the opaque black eyes stared directly into Marie's, and then it slowly turned towards her mother, the forked tongue gliding in and out in greeting as she crooned to it and extended her hands. The head briefly bowed over them, and then slowly sank to the ground to lie inert and happily bask in the sunshine.

'You have heard much of God at the convent?' her mother said conversationally.

'Why, yes!' Marie murmured, fascinated by the great serpent stretched out before her, of which, up to now, she had only had brief and occasional glimpses.

'There is no harm in what you have heard,' her mother said in a condescending tone, 'so long as you remember that God has many faces and many names, and that *our* power comes from the Vodun and that the snake, his symbol, is the vehicle through which it comes.'

'How do you know that?' Marie asked, still fascinated by the snake.

Her mother seemed taken aback by the question. 'I just *know*, that's all – I have no idea how it comes; it simply does. The way to Vodun and great power is long and hard – sometimes even dangerous – and I will not disguise from you that you will have to work very hard to become as I am. Nor is that all you will have to do ...' She hesitated, as if uncertain of how to proceed. 'You see, one thing you must know at once is that we cannot command the power at will, it commands us, and sometimes it will not come however

14

hard one tries. But the people who come to us seeking help expect it in us *all* the time, and you have already seen how many of them there always are ...' She sighed heavily. 'Sometimes I think the whole world is one vast cry for help.' She paused. Then: 'So when the power will not come, then it is that we must rely on our own wits. I am Queen of the Voodos because I have learned how to use mine to best advantage – there is not a household in New Orleans of any consequence in which I do not have a source of knowledge: there is nothing that happens in this city of any importance that I do not know of. And all this you must learn, too, and learn how to use.' She paused again. 'But first, in order to see how it all works together, you must become a hairdresser for the important ladies – just as I became one at about your age. This will give you the entrée and the insight into the great houses, and there you will listen and learn. Both apprenticeships must start at once, so you will not be returning to school – all that is behind you now.'

The girl's face fell and Marie Laveau said quickly, 'This disappoints you? You will be sorry to leave the nuns?'

The young Marie thought about it for a while. 'Not really,' she said at last, 'but I shall be sad not to be with Jacqueline.'

'Jacqueline Delambe? The one whose father keeps a shop down by the market on Decatur Street?'

Marie nodded. 'She's my best and dearest friend, and I love her very much.'

Her mother gave a dismissive shrug. 'There is no reason why she should not continue to be. After all the Vieux Carré is not such a big place; you can still see her.'

'Yes, Mama.' But she knew somehow it would not be like that.

'So are you ready to begin?'

Marie nodded slowly.

'Then kneel down and place your hands upon the snake's head,' her mother ordered. 'He, too, is the beginning.'

She did as she was bid and was surprised to find the mottled skin of the great body warm and a little rough to her touch; she had expected only cold and clammy smoothness.

15

The snake flicked its tongue out, but made no other movement. 'Do you swear that from this day forth you will be the servant of Vodun, that you will guard his secrets and serve him faithfully?' her mother demanded. 'And do you swear to do as you are bid by me in all things?'

'I swear,' said Marie Laveau.

'You may sit down again,' her mother said graciously. 'There are some other things I still have to tell you.'

Marie returned to the stool. A heavy weight constricted her chest, so that she panted slightly, and her head was bursting with so many new thoughts that she felt if her mother went on much longer it would split asunder. 'I do not feel very well, Mama,' she said faintly.

'Then I will not keep you much longer,' her mother replied. 'Just quiet your mind and listen carefully to what I say. Power and wealth go together and feed on one another – one cannot survive without the other. So, never forget the importance of money or the importance of men of power. But the men of power change as the world changes, and to keep your own power you must foresee these changes and prepare for them. It may not always be so, but for now, here in New Orleans, the power lies with the men of the old Creole families – these you must learn to cultivate and manipulate, but you must remember that you can never be *friends* with them; with them you can afford no emotions. They are both target and enemy. If you need help from a man, you must seek it among the Negroes or our own people – there you may find many true friends, many true helpers. Do you know why this is so?'

'Because Vodun is the god of the Negroes?' Marie said without thinking.

'God knows no *colour*!' her mother exploded. 'Didn't the nuns at least have the sense to teach you that much?' She glared balefully at the girl, who shrank into frightened silence. 'No,' she went on. 'It is *because* the white men hold all the power; it is in the very way they think, not only about us but about their own women. We are their ornaments, or toys, or breeding stock, or something to be used – but we are of no real consequence.'

'But if they think of us like that,' Marie said plaintively, 'I don't see how we ever can manipulate them as you say we must.'

'We can do so with a woman's weapons,' her mother said with scorn. 'And the chief weapon we have is other women, *their* women.' She laughed sardonically. 'When you go to their houses, you will soon see what I mean and how it is done. So, we will make a start tomorrow. I think I have said enough for today. There is but one thing more . . .' She took something from a pocket concealed in her voluminous skirt and held it out to the girl. 'Here. These are for you, and you must wear them from now on.'

It was a pair of golden hoop earrings similar to, but smaller than, the ones she herself wore. Marie took them gingerly and saw they were chased, as were her mother's, with the design of a snake swallowing its tail. 'Oh, thank you, Mama!' With a bright glance at her mother, she worked the small golden rings out of her pierced ears and put on the golden hoops, turning her head from side to side to hear them jingle. 'They're lovely!' she exclaimed. 'I'll never take them off, never.'

Her mother nodded in satisfaction. 'You may go now, but think well about all I have said, Marie.' To emphasize the dismissal, she got up and began coiling the inert snake back into its chest.

Marie got up also and walked slowly back into the house. Inside the back door, a clamouring horde of her brothers and sisters immediately descended. 'What were you doing with the snake?' 'Why did Mama give you those earrings?' 'What did the snake feel like?' 'Is Mama angry with you?'

Her arm was seized roughly and shaken, and she turned to face Celeste, her older sister by two years. 'What was Mama talking to you about all that time? Tell me!' Celeste demanded imperiously, her eyes full of envy and malice.

Marie had always known that Celeste did not like her, but now, looking into the burning dark eyes, she realized for the first time the extent of her hatred. She opened her mouth to let forth the torrent within her, then closed it again and

17

stared steadily at Celeste, who would never be as old as she was at this moment. 'Mama and I were talking about my future,' she said primly. 'I am to leave school and become a hairdresser.'

Chapter Two

The widow Paris's plans for her daughter did not get off to the early start she had anticipated. That first night Marie went to bed quite worn out by her experiences of the morning, but whichever way she tossed and turned on her small pallet bed, she could not get to sleep. She sighed and gazed in frustration at the plain whitewashed ceiling. I'll try the family litany, she thought; that usually does it. She began to whisper to herself the roll call of the large family, seeking in the familiar boredom of its names and numbers the first waves of drowsiness.

'Marguerite Paris, eldest child of St Jacques Paris and Marie Laveau,' she murmured, 'born 10 January 1821, married Marc Crocker 1840. Jacques Paris born February 1823, unmarried. Jean Laveau Glapion born 10 May 1825, eldest child of Louis-Christophe Daumeny de Glapion (she had always loved the swing of that name). Daumeny born 18 March 1826. Marie-Philome born 2 February 1827. Celeste born 4 January 1828. Marie-Belle born 21 February 1830 . . .' She hesitated on her own name and added with a strange feeling of sadness, 'Daughter of Thomé di Sonora.' But she would not think about that now. With determination she went on: 'Twins, Solange and Desirée, born and died 1831. Amelie born 4 September (or as was it 5 September?) 1832. Twins again born and died 1833 – she had never known their names. Charles-Louis born 4 August 1834. Marie-Jeanne born 9 September 1835. And François born 24 June 1836.' Poor little François, who had never even seen his father – not any more, she suddenly realized, than she had seen hers. It was an unhappy thought to end on, and she found she was just as wide awake as before.

She turned on her side and looked enviously at her sleeping sisters: Marie-Philome, who was the eldest girl left at home and who was beautiful, like her mother; Celeste, who

19

was dark and plain and disagreeable; quiet Amelie, Marie's own junior by two years; and little Marie-Jeanne, the next to youngest Glapion, who was only eight and who so strongly resembled Père Louis, the father she did not remember. Although she still thought of them as her sisters, they seemed like strangers to her, beings from another world – a world she had left behind.

She looked around the familiar room which held her earliest memories, as if seeing it for the first time. It was very plain. Besides the five beds, its only furnishings were a huge wardrobe and two washstands standing side by side, their slop pails beneath. It was a long, low room that made up, with a similar room next door which housed all her brothers, most of the top storey of the house. The only other rooms were a tiny one in which the slave Patty slept and an even smaller storeroom. The house had never appeared small to her before, but now it seemed insufferably so: cramped and too full of people – people pressing in upon her so that she could not even breathe. She longed to be alone, and the bright moonlight from the window giving on to the courtyard beckoned to her.

With infinite care not to disturb her sleeping sisters, she got up and dressed and crept silently down the stairs. The layout of the ground floor was quite different from the upstairs and even more cramped. It was divided into two front parlours, each with its separate front door. The family lived in the parlour to the left and the small dining room behind it; the parlour on the right was 'out of bounds' to them. This was where the clients came to seek Mama's help and advice, and where the services were held at times. Beyond this there lay another sacrosanct area – her mother's bedroom, opposite and of similar size to the dining room. Beyond these lay the kitchen, to the left, and the storeroom, in which the hired man, Christophe, slept. The stairs came down directly into the family parlour, and she flitted through it, pausing in the narrow passage a moment to listen at her mother's door, her heart beating madly. Then she carefully unbolted the back door and stepped into the moonlight that turned the yard to silver.

She was conscious of a lightening of the burden on her, and she felt drawn towards the magnolia tree now barring the silver with its blackness. She crossed the yard, stirring up a few sleepy protests from the hen coop, and stood looking down unseeingly at where the great snake had lain that morning. She felt that somehow there was something extremely important for her to do. Automatically, she started to walk around and around the tree, scenting the air as an animal might until she found a spot that felt different to her than anywhere else. There she sank down on to the ground and sat cross-legged. Her hands clasped her knees lightly.

She knew she must wait there. She must wait for whatever it was that was coming. She must wait for as long as it took to come ...

'*Madame, Madame*, please come quick!' The young Negro Christophe pounded on Marie Laveau's bedroom door, as the slave girl Patty snivelled and whimpered behind him in the narrow passage. The urgent summons brought Marie Laveau to the door, a light duster thrown over her nightgown, her long, wavy black hair falling in disarray upon her shoulders. Still, even under these most adverse of circumstances – though her waist showed the thickening of too many pregnancies and her full breasts the slight flaccidity of too many sucklings – she was a magnificent figure of a woman, who looked much younger than her forty-seven years. Christophe dropped his eyes hastily and retreated, and at the sight of her, Patty broke into wailing speech.

'It's Miz Marie-Belle – she done give me the fright o' mah life. Ah was goin' to git kindlin' fo' de kitchen fire an' let de hens out, an' dere she was a-sittin' 'neath de tree lak she was made o' stone. Oh, Lawdy, she was damp with dew-fall lak she been sittin' there fo' hours – an' she don' even know me, she don' even see me. Ah calls to her an' Ah shakes her an' she don' even move. That snake done take her wits, mos' lak – ya got to do somethin' quick, Missus!' She burst into fresh sobs and continued to wring her hands.

'It's all right now, Patty. Don't take on so,' Marie Laveau said automatically and hurried out into the growing light of the new day. She went up to the slim, immobile form seated under the magnolia and stood gazing silently down at her daughter. The girl sat with her back rigid, her eyes blank, looking inward to another world, her breathing slow and almost imperceptible. She gave no sign that she was even aware of her mother's presence. Marie tried to probe her mind to read her thoughts, but it was as if there was an opaque barrier between them; she could pick up nothing. She frowned slightly, a submerged memory that she could not bring to the surface of her mind nagging at her, then wheeled about and returned to the house.

'Patty! Christophe! You go about your chores as always, but on no account are you to disturb Marie-Belle, do you hear? And you, Christophe, as soon as you've eaten, go fetch Crocodile. Tell him I want him here quickly.'

'But she goin' to ketch her death in dem damp clothes!' Patty wailed. 'An' how 'bout her breakfast? She jus' pecked at her dinner las' night. Didn't eat 'nuff to feed a mouse.'

'I said to leave her alone,' Marie thundered, and Patty retreated, muttering and snivelling to herself.

The same message was repeated to the family as they straggled down for the new day, although for them the veto was more complete. 'No one is to go into the courtyard – you understand? No one at all.'

'But what is she doing there, *Maman*?' asked François, his face a-gleam with the avid curiosity of an eight-year-old.

'That's none of your business,' his mother snapped worriedly.

'What shall I tell the nuns at school? That Marie-Belle has taken leave of her senses?' Celeste put in slyly.

'You'll say *nothing*! I'll be talking to the nuns myself today. Marie-Belle will not be going back to the convent.'

Celeste opened her mouth to say something else, but she was intimidated by the angry gleam in her mother's eyes.

Crocodile came in with Christophe through the back way and Marie shooed the family into the *salle-à-manger*, where the bowls of chicory and milk and of cornmeal mush were dispatched in a continuing hum of excited conjecture. Then she beckoned to the grizzled ex-slave and crossed to the kitchen window. 'What do you make of it?' she demanded. 'She's been like that since sometime during the night.'

The big Negro gazed impassively out. He was a large man, whose muscles still rippled impressively under the coarse shirt and whose lithe body belied the seared and scarred lines of his face. No one knew how old he was; he could have been any age from forty to sixty, although the latter was more likely. He had been brought as a slave from Africa in the early 1800s. Not that it was important. What was important was that he had brought from Africa many new things that had been half-forgotten in the long diaspora of the blacks, and so he was Marie Laveau's righthand man at the Voodoo ceremonies.

'Have you ever seen anything like it?' Marie demanded. 'Could it have been anything I said or did yesterday? She took the serpent oath.'

'How much did you tell her?' His voice was a soft, deep rumble.

'Not very much.' Hastily, she went over for him the conversation of the day before.

'So you told her of Don Thomé. Was that wise?' he murmured.

'I thought it as good a time as any – she would have learned about it herself soon enough.'

'Well, this is nothing of ours – I think you know that yourself,' he said thoughtfully. 'I should leave her and see what happens next. When are you planning to initiate her?'

'I was thinking of St John's Eve,' Marie said. 'She should be ready by then. I plan to have her come to the ceremonies from now on, starting this Sunday.'

He nodded and gave her a sidelong glance. 'You know you'll have to go very slowly, very carefully, for what you've got in mind?'

She made an impatient gesture of dismissal with her hand. 'I had no idea I would have to wait this long to begin. You know as well as I do that I haven't all that much time left to waste.'

'You've still a good ten years, I'd say,' he said mildly.

'*If* I'm lucky. And she won't be ready for five years, at least, and that's assuming nothing goes wrong.'

'You're really determined on this?' he questioned.

'I am.' The dark eyes clashed for a moment. Then his dropped and he turned away.

'Well, there is nothing to do here now. I'd best be going. I'll ask around about this. Maybe Dr John'll know something. If you need me, you know where to find me.'

The tension built throughout the day, working its havoc on the weaker minds, and after dinner that night Patty went into a fit of hysterics. 'She's a-goin' to kill herself!' she screamed. 'Not a bite to eat or a sup to drink, she's had! She's hexed an' ya don' do nothin'! You're killin her, killin' yo' own flesh an blood, ya witch-woman, ya! God goin' to curse ya to hell fo' this! God goin' to strike ya down!' She fell down on the kitchen floor and started beating her head against it, screaming and foaming at the mouth.

'Help me, Christophe,' Marie ordered. And as he held the struggling form, she forced a soothing draught between the girl's chattering teeth. 'All right, you can let her go, but don't hurt her,' Marie said heavily. And she watched as the violent jerkings and convulsions became slower and finally ceased as Patty slumped down into an inert heap.

'Carry her up to her room,' she said, and she followed him up the stairs. When he had laid the limp figure on the trestle bed in the small cubbyhole of a room, Marie crossed to the tiny round window and opened it, letting in the cool night air. 'You can go. She'll be quiet now. I'll stay with her a while.' She sat down beside the bed and took the slave's limp brown work-worn hand. She was more concerned about Patty than she was about Marie, who still continued her strange vigil outside, because she knew too well how close the little slave always stood to the edge of darkness, how tenuous was the hold her waking mind had on reality, and what terrors life had held for the small body.

Her mind went back to the day in April of 1834 when she had first set eyes on Patty at the Lalurie house on Royal Street. She had always had her suspicions about Delphine Lalurie, suspicions which had been borne out all too well that day when the fire had broken out, and what had been found as a result had sent the enraged mob speeding to the Lalurie house bent on revenge.

She had been summoned to see what she could do to calm the situation, but, hardened though she was by her visits to the city prisons and her work among plague victims, she, too, had been sickened and appalled by the broken, tortured bodies of the slaves that had been found in the holocaust. She had found Patty huddled in the corner of a smoke-filled attic above the kitchen, the ribs sticking out of her starved body, which was covered with the sores and scars of many beatings. And all the child had said, over and over again, was, 'Don' hit me no more, Missus. Ah won' tell.'

She had never told, but Marie had found out later from the other slaves who survived that Patty had been half of a 'matched pair', the quiet one of the duo. Her sister had been the spirited one, and for that spirit she had paid with her life. They told the tale of Delphine Lalurie, the blood-madness high in her, chasing the small slave from room to room with a bullwhip, until the child, in desperate pain and terror, had rushed out on to the roof and thrown herself into the courtyard below. She had lived for an hour after that, her back broken, and what Delphine had done to her during that hour defied telling – and she had made Patty watch ...

She had bought Patty for practically nothing after the flight of the Laluries and the selling off of their property. People wondered why on earth she was wasting her money for a slave who would never be any good to anyone even if she lived. The same people wondered ever since why she put up with things from Patty that she would tolerate from no other living person. But the truth of it was that she was fond of her, fonder, in fact, than she was of some of her own flesh and blood. Patty had become her creation – hers and Croco-dile's. Between them they had healed the body – that had been easy enough – but the damage done to the mind was something they could not so easily undo. So, they had done the only thing they could. By hypnosis they had blanked out Patty's memory – her first nine years had become through them a merciful nothingness, though some tiny corner of the brain, which they had been unable to reach, still retained the horror so nothing would ever induce Patty to go past the house at the corner of Royal and Hospital streets.

Patty stirred and moaned in her drugged sleep, and Marie Laveau gently patted the hand she held and smoothed the sweat-damp forehead. Then she got up wearily and sought her own bed.

The next morning brought no change. Marie still sat on in her own private world and her mother again sent for Crocodile. 'Did you find out anything?' she asked worriedly.

'I think so.' He gazed for a while at the small figure still in exactly the same position as the day before. 'I've been talking around, and according to some of the Indians this is quite common among their young people. Seems that when they get to a certain age they go off by themselves and fast or drink or do all manner of strange things to themselves until they get their "vision". As they tell it, they each get a sort of spirit who becomes what they call their "ally" and who helps them when they need it. That could be her father's blood coming out in her. I asked Dr John and he'd heard tell of it, too, but he said he'd never seen Don Thomé do anything like it. Still, that doesn't mean much – he was a man who didn't need help from anyone. Dr John says it could go on for days until something happens or she keels over from sheer exhaustion.'

'Well, *I* can't let it go on much longer,' Marie said nervously. 'She may do herself serious harm.'

'You may not have to. I think something may be happening. Have you noticed the chickens? Yesterday they were scratching about, as usual, paying her no mind. Now look at them.' He pointed silently to the hens. They were soundlessly huddled against the cages of the roosters, which were also completely silent. 'I should let her go for a while longer. If it is part of the powers in her, it might be dangerous to stop it.'

Within herself Marie could feel the change. Now something was happening, something was coming. A small ball of

26

light within her grew, expanded, began to reach out. There had been a long period of blank darkness, although she had long since been past hunger and thirst and the mere physical discomforts of the body. Time had ceased to be, and yet she was aware of things moving within it. Christophe was no longer Christophe, but a long, black whirling cylinder, Patty a round ball of yellow light, and she had followed their new appearances with part of her mind as they moved around her field of vision, delighting in their different forms. There had been something else, also – a large purple glow that had approached her and had sent out violet streamers towards her, but it had not been able to get through the barrier around her. She wondered if it could be her mother.

She had probed the cold mind of the sleeping snake, and had listened to the conversations of the chickens – she knew they were talking, but about what she did not know and soon lost interest. For a while she had been with an ant as it toiled its precarious path across the yard; a chicken had got it and she felt its ultimate blackness.

She had managed to float out of her body, rising high into the night sky towards the cold, glowing moon, until the magnolia tree and the house were like toys beneath her. She had looked northward over the twinkling lights of the city to the great darkness of the lake – a darkness that welcomed – and south to where the river lay encoiling the city like a great black snake, and there she sensed danger. She would have liked to have risen even higher, but there seemed to be a luminous chain that anchored her to the body beneath the tree. She had fought to free herself of it, but the chain had pulled her inexorably back.

At one point there had been something behind her within the magnolia. It had threatened and frightened her, so she had fixed her mind firmly upon a distant star, and when she felt around again it had gone.

Now the day was dimming and she knew something was near. A shadow had been forming in the bushes; it still was not defined, but it was growing. She concentrated hard upon it and it gained solidity. Little sparks of light flashed from its blackness, outlining the figure that presently took on the definition of a tall man.

It was now before her, long black braids lying on copper shoulders, a glint of gold at the neck: an Indian with a proud face and the glance of an eagle. Mind touched mind. 'What do you want of me?'

'What path do I follow?'

'Your own path.'

'The path my mother has shown me?'

'She has shown you no path, but with her you will go part of the way. She shall not harm you.'

'Are you my father?'

'No – but if your path be right, he will not harm you.'

'How shall I know that it is right?'

'You will know.'

'Will you help me to know?'

'I must help you, but the choice will only be yours.'

'Can you tell me more? I do not understand.'

'Not until you learn to ask the questions – then perhaps you will understand. But from now on I will be near.'

'Will I see you and know you?'

'No, you will not, but I will be there.'

The figure began to waver and lose definition. 'Don't go!' Marie cried, stretching out her hands to it. 'There is so much I have to ask, so much I don't know.' But she was talking to the empty evening as a light wind swirled up the dust of the courtyard.

She looked around herself in astonishment: What was she doing out here? She was aching and thirsty and ravenously hungry. She went to rise and almost fell forward on her face as her cramped limbs refused to obey her. A tremendous sense of achievement and of purpose spread through her, overcoming her physical pain with a sense of well-being. She stretched out her aching legs and tottered to her feet as unsteadily as a young colt, then hobbled painfully towards the back door and the beckoning warmth and light of the kitchen.

She leaned dizzily against the doorjamb and looked into the startled face of Marie-Philome, who was stirring a large pot on the stove, as Celeste, her back turned, sliced bread on the kitchen table. 'What's for dinner?' she asked, and sniffed ecstatically. 'Is that crab gumbo? I feel so hungry I could eat forever.'

Chapter Three

Marie was surprised to find that she had been absent for almost three days, and she basked happily in the relieved welcome her family gave her return to normalcy. Even Celeste was amiable to her for a change. Only her mother seemed a little put out. Due to the late start, there was little time to prepare her for her introduction into the world of Voodoo, and her mother was constantly pouncing upon her and muttering a new set of instructions into her bewildered ear.

As Sunday evening approached, her sense of excitement, as well as her own importance, grew. Marie Glapion had always kept this part of her life completely separated from her family. None of them had ever been allowed to attend even the small services she sometimes held in the front parlour for one or two individuals. Though they knew of the big services out by the lake, they had no idea of what these consisted, nor of what part their mother played in them. Sometimes they had sneaked off on a Sunday afternoon to watch the dancers in Congo Square at the edge of the quarter by North Rampart Street, but while this was exciting – with the strange vibrant rhythms and the sense of release coming full-throated from the mouths of the chanting slaves – they knew it was not the actual rites, which would hardly have been tolerated in broad daylight by the ever-suspicious city fathers. The rites themselves were still part of the secret life of the city, a secret that its white masters either did not know or did not wish to know.

The day dragged by and the rest of the household retired to bed. Just after ten, Marie, dressed in a new dress of light violet, and her mother, arrayed richly in dark purple, threw on cloaks against the raw chill of the February night and went silently out of the sleeping house. Christophe was out in front with the gig. Behind him, Marie could dimly make

30

out another flat cart which held several shadowy figures and was being driven by Crocodile. The snake, in its chest, was brought out and placed on that flat cart. Her mother motioned Marie to get in beside Christophe and mounted beside her without saying a word. And with a light jingling the procession was under way.

They jerked and bumped over the paving stones up St Ann Street, turned left down Burgundy, then on to the wide, tree-lined avenue of the Esplanade, where they turned north. Still in silence, they progressed beyond the newer *faubourgs* and the paving gave way to dirt, so that the gig ran smoother. They were now free of the city, but Marie could make out groups of people, some in bands, others singly, hurrying in the same direction. The faint glow of the gig's lantern lit some of the faces, and on all was the same expression of solemn expectancy and of a tense and urgent need. There were other carts and carriages on the road, too, all crowded with people, but these groups were more animated, and as they passed there could be heard the occasional burst of excited laughter, the clink of bottles, or the high-pitched buzz of many people talking at once.

Marie's own sense of excitement could not keep the silence a moment longer. 'Are all these people going to the ceremony?' she said. 'Are there always this many?'

Her mother seemed to rouse herself, nodded, and looked sleepily around. 'Usually there are more, many more – but tonight is a cold one, and it is not going to be a big ceremony. The big ones are the water ceremonies, like the one on St John's Eve. Tonight we will have only the fire ceremony and the dancing.' She smiled faintly. 'Tonight we will dance the Calinda – that will warm their blood!"

They had reached the slight rise of the Metairie ridge, and to the left over Bayou St John roiled a sluggish mist. Beyond, over a small bridge, Marie saw lights dancing among the grove of large, moss-draped trees and dim silhouettes of figures moving around under them. 'Look!' she exclaimed. 'What's that? Is that the place?'

Her mother peered in the direction of her pointing finger. 'No, that's the old Allard plantation, and those are the

31

duelling oaks – some fools fighting by lantern-light, most likely, or getting ready for a duel at dawn. What next, I wonder!' she snorted derisively. 'Well, tomorrow there'll be mourning wreaths on somebody's door and one less fool to feed.' Her tone was savage.

Silence once again descended and the scent of the marshes welled up out of the darkness, surrounding and embracing them with the faint sickliness of decay. The road twisted towards a flickering light in the distance. 'Ah, at least some-one has had the sense to get the fires started,' her mother observed. 'We'll soon be there.' They rattled across a wooden bridge which spanned Bayou Sauvage and the gig picked up speed. In a few minutes they had passed a couple of small bonfires, around which crowds were already huddled, and approached a larger blaze. By its light Marie saw they were on a small promontory sticking out into Lake Pontchartrain and that, in addition to the bonfires, pitch torches had been stuck around the perimeter of the prom-ontory providing a dancing, flickering illumination.

The gig came to a halt and Christophe jumped out and helped her mother down. 'Stay here!' her mother ordered. 'Christophe will come and get you when we're ready. And mind what I've said – you can take part in the dance before the ceremony and the ceremony itself, but once the Calinda starts you're to come back here to the gig and stay with old Bessie until it's over.'

'Oui, Maman,' Marie said absently as she tried to take in all that was happening. She watched with fascination as Crocodile and his helpers unloaded the flat cart, which con-tained drums of all sizes and shapes, a cage of roosters, and the snake in its crate. Seizing one of the pitch torches, Crocodile burned a large circle in the grass around the main bonfire, and Marie saw by its light that he was clad in a dark purple shirt with ruffled sleeves, the same shade as her mother's dress, and a pair of white, tight-fitting trousers. The drums were set up just outside the circle, and the drum-mers crouching over them started to tap out a slow, soft rhythm. The squawking roosters were lifted out of the crate by their pinioned feet, and the box containing the snake was dragged in front of her mother, who was now standing within the circle gazing into the heart of the fire. She saw other purple-clad figures ranging themselves behind her mother, all carrying white candles, and then Christophe was at her side. 'Your mother says it's time,' he announced and shoved a white candle into her hand.

With a fast-beating heart, Marie stepped into the circle and took her place with the others. There were a few Negroes in the group, but in the main they were mixed bloods of all shades from brown to cream, and she was amazed to see that at least one of the purple-clad figures was blonde and fair, a white Creole, beyond question. The rhythm of the drums quickened, and she could make out beyond the circle crowds of people pressing in upon it. Her companions began a slow shuffling dance around the fire, leaning towards the blaze and lighting their candles. Marie joined in, trying to imitate their movements. They circled the bonfire three times and then coiled themselves three times around the still figure of her mother, who was now standing a little above them on the chest containing the great python. They kept to the same slow shuffling step, and as Marie shuffled past she saw that her mother now had a thick cord of indigo-blue knotted around her waist, and Crocodile, who was standing just behind her to the right, had a similar one around his. The purple chorus shuffled into position behind them and began humming to the quickening rhythm: *'Badoum, badoum, badoum.'*

Suddenly, her mother raised her arms and gave a deep-throated call, and Crocodile sprang into action. Seizing one of the black roosters, which had been lying pinioned at his feet, he leaped into the centre of the circle and with a single blow of a shining machete struck off its head. A deep roar went up from the crowd as he sprayed the spurting blood into the heart of the flames, where it sizzled and spat sparks, and hurled the body after it. Then, quick as a flash, he had seized another, decapitated that, and, whirling around the circle, sprayed its blood into the crowd. Two more men, clad

33

as he was, sprang forward and did the same, and as they whirled by, Marie felt some of the warm drops hitting her bare arms and face.

The ground was beginning to tremble with the thudding of the drums and the answering thud of hundreds of feet. The purple chorus began to sway in unison and the humming grew louder, and then with a sudden gesture they hurled the candles into the fire. The drums stopped suddenly and for a moment there was dead silence. Then the chorus started to clap its hands in a soft pat-patting rhythm and her mother's voice rose deep and clear in the night air. *'Danse, danse, danse, la Calinda!'*

A Negress beside her took up the refrain in a stronger, higher voice: *'Danse, danse, danse, la Calinda!'*

The drums started up again on a wild, swift beat and the crowd took up the refrain with a roar: *'Danse, Calinda, boum-boum! Dance, Calinda, boum-boum!'*

The scene broke into pandemonium as bodies started gyrating, twitching, swaying, leaping to the beat. It coursed through Marie's veins, invading her mind, wiping out with its hypnotic call all conscious thought. She began to dance along with the others, a feeling of wild elation flooding through her. Never had she felt so free! Never had she been so happy! She whirled, she twitched, she jumped over other bodies now convulsively twitching on the ground, heedless of anything but the call.

A young, light-skinned Negro, stripped to the waist, leaped in front of her and, with a flashing grin, fitted his movements to hers, retreating and advancing, closer and closer, until they were almost touching. Around and around they moved, laughing and holding the perfect unison by the bond of their eyes. Suddenly she was plucked roughly from her feet from behind, and, opening her mouth to scream, she found herself looking up into the angry face of Crocodile, whose shirt was now open to the waist and whose face and chest were streaming with sweat.

Before she could say or do anything, he had thrown her over his shoulder like a sack of potatoes and started to elbow his way through the mass of bodies, oblivious to her kicks and struggles. He strode beyond the circles of light shed by the fires and into the shadows. Then he dumped her unceremoniously on to the floor of the gig and leaned over her. 'When your mother tells you to do something,' he hissed, 'you *do* it, Marie! Now, stay here and don't move until we're through.' And he strode off towards the light.

Marie crouched on the floor of the gig, panting and almost blind with fury. How dare he ...? How dare they ...? She would kill them for this ... She ... She became conscious of a huge form sitting on the gig seat, clapping its hands and humming softly to itself like a gigantic bumble bee. It was old Bessie. Her mother's instructions came back to her and the fever in her blood was suddenly quenched. She started to shiver violently and she felt around for her cloak, her teeth chattering.

'That you, Miz Marie?' The huge bee stopped its humming and wriggled on the seat. 'That's right, chile, wrap yo'self up. Don' do to get chilled after the dancin'. Does ya a power o' harm. Ya cuddle up to me now— Ah got warmin' fat enough fo' the both o' us.' She chuckled richly.

Marie drew a deep, quivering sigh and did as she was bid, snuggling up to the warm, massive thighs. She looked back wistfully to the dance and her eyes widened at the scene. People were tearing off their clothes as they danced; naked couples were running off into the dark hand in hand, only to reappear a few minutes later to plunge once more into the dancing crowd of writhing, sweating bodies. There was so much screaming and shouting going on that the hypnotic beat of the drums was now only a muffled counterpoint. Men with bottles in their hands were running around the outside of the great circle, taking huge swigs from them and spitting into the crowd, which screamed its approval.

Her eyes focused on the only quiet figure in the scene. Her mother still stood upon the snake chest, swaying gently to the rhythm, her head bent towards the flames. From time to time a figure would detach itself from the crowd and kneel before her, looking up. At such times her mother would bend forward, sometimes touching the hand of the individual, sometimes the head. At one point something obviously angered her, since she made a furious dismissive gesture and pointed a long accusing finger downwards. The figure before her cowered as if struck, and crawled away on hands and knees.

Marie began to feel immensely tired and her eyelids drooped. Nestled against Bessie's warmth, she dozed, coming awake from time to time to see the same scenes re-enacted and then to doze again.

Suddenly, she was wide awake. The drumming had stopped and there was a strange, whispering silence. She opened her eyes on a striking tableau. Outlined in the dying firelight was the tall figure of her mother, with two male figures at her side. The great snake was out of its box, and the three of them were lifting it slowly above their heads. Her mother held up the snake's head and turned slowly around in a circle. Then she threw back her head and gave a long, drawn-out call: 'Vodun!' she cried. 'Vodun!'

Again there was a whisper of sound as the crowd sank to its knees. 'Vodun,' it sighed, 'Vodun.'

The snake was slowly lowered and with it the fires were extinguished, as if by magic; the ceremony was over. By the dim light of the few remaining pitch torches, Marie could see the crowd silently breaking up, and within moments some of them were flitting by the gig. Once again she was struck by their expressions – all the tension, all the worry, had drained away, leaving their faces smoothed out and bland; they looked satiated, calm, at peace.

The passengers of the flat cart came straggling back in silence, carrying the snake chest, the empty rooster cage, and the drums; there was a weary droop to their shoulders. Beside her, with mighty wheezings and heavings, Bessie came to life and, climbing laboriously down from the gig, took her place among the bundles on the cart. With a groan it came to life under its heavy burden and moved slowly off.

Marie was alone in the dark and for a moment she was terribly afraid. The great body of which she had been a living part for a moment was no more, and she was an atom stripped of all its connections. Then with relief she heard soft footsteps on the grass, and Christophe and her mother reappeared and climbed up.

Now a new fear took hold of her: Would her mother be terribly angry with her? She moved over to make room and looked timidly up into the stern face. But all her mother said was, 'I hope you didn't get chilled sitting here all this time. Would you like some brandy to warm you up?'

She produced a small silver-topped flask, and on Marie's nervous shake of the head, shrugged and tipped it into her own mouth. Then she relaxed with a great sigh, drew her cloak around her, and nodded to the exhausted-looking Christophe, who set the gig in motion.

No mention was made of Marie's transgression on the interminable trip back into the city. Instead, her mother, who seemed amazingly fresh, talked about the ceremony, how it differed from other ceremonies, and, at amazing length, about crowd control. Most of what she said passed completely over Marie's exhausted mind, but a few remarks here and there stuck, and stirred in her amazement and awed respect for her mother's remarkable powers.

'When you are Queen,' her mother was saying calmly, 'you must always remember to organize everything beforehand so that you avoid as much as possible a mob getting out of control. A mob is not mindless, as some would say; a mob has a mind of its own, which can be very dangerous. It is not always possible to control it entirely – you'll see that when we get to the water ceremonies – but a small crowd like this presents no problems . . .'

Marie's mind reeled – a small crowd like this! Her thoughts were boggled by the idea of a large crowd. She slept some more and was only awakened as the gig hit the paving of the city, and they rattled back through its now entirely darkened streets.

When they finally drew up before the St Ann Street house, Marie felt she could not even summon enough energy to crawl down. She staggered into the house and up the narrow staircase. By the dim light on the landing, she saw that her arms were still runnelled with the rusty stains of the rooster's blood mixed with her own dried sweat, but she was far too tired to do anything about it – she wasn't even going to bother to undress.

Tiptoeing among her sleeping sisters, she flopped on to her bed with weary thankfulness. As she did so, Celeste opened a baleful eye and struggled up on to one elbow.

'Now you'll go to hell for sure,' she announced thickly and with immense satisfaction. 'Now you'll surely burn, you Voodoo woman, you!' And with a pleased sigh, she turned over and went back to sleep.

Chapter Four

The learning time had begun; now Marie's world had become entirely circumscribed by incantations and numberless rituals, by 'gris-gris' for every condition under the sun: gris-gris for love and for hate, for fertility and infertility, for virility and impotence; gris-gris for gain and for loss, to ward off sickness and to bring it, to end pain and to cause it – all with different ingredients, measures, and exact and exacting formulas. The information poured out of her mother in an unending cascade, as if some great dam had broken within – she could not wait to pour its contents into the receptacle of her daughter's mind. There was no time for Marie to miss her childhood, her school, her former friends; her mind was completely filled with the new world into which she was being inexorably led.

She was still finding it hard to adjust to her new relationship with her mother. From dawn to dusk they existed side by side, in either the front right parlour or her mother's bedroom: her mother talking, showing, explaining, she listening, endlessly listening. From the shadowed confines of the rooms, she would look out at the sun-filled spring now ripening into summer with the sense of something hopelessly, irrevocably lost, and yet she felt no urge to escape; the fascination of this new world was too strong, the sense of excitement too intense, to permit the smallest regret.

It was not just the hidden lore her mother confided in her; it was everything and anything – past, present, or future. She talked as if she had been long isolated in some kind of limbo and could not wait to impart her problems, her hopes, and her fears to a newfound kindred spirit, and to shift some of these burdens in the process. She was changing from the remote, awesome figure of Marie's childhood into a being of more human stature, and yet, with all the confidences, all the contact, there was still no sense of closeness.

This worried Marie. There were times she felt a reserve almost amounting to hostility towards her on her mother's part, as if the information *had* to be given, but to her not as a separate human being at all but merely as an extension of her mother. It was a most peculiar sensation, as if her mother were talking to herself and Marie had become invisible. Nor was this sensation dispelled in even their most intimate conversations, a fact which puzzled and even angered her. It did not help that the rest of the family, seeing her in her new role as confidante to their mother, resented it, and showed this resentment according to their various personalities, ranging from open hostility on the part of Celeste to timid withdrawal on the part of the younger children.

Sometimes this feeling of nonexistence made Marie feel uneasy. A typical instance took place one early summer's day when her mother was mulling over her future plans for the family, exhibiting in the process something which Marie had found to be characteristic of her, a strict sense of chronological order. 'Well, at least Marguerite and Jacques are established,' she said with satisfaction, 'even if Marguerite is far away in Biloxi. But her husband is a good, sound man and they should do well. Jacques has chosen the riverboats, which is not a metier I would have picked out for him myself, but in some way he is a lot like his father was – a man of very fixed ideas, Jacques Paris.' This thought seemed to displease her and she hurried on, dismissing her two eldest children without further comment. 'Jean and Daumeny are doing very well in their apprenticeship, and when it is over perhaps I can set them up in a little business of their own. They are both such hard workers, and anything in the ornamental ironwork line is booming just now.'

Her face softened into a smile at the mention of Jean's name, as it always did – emphasizing a fact Marie had long known, that of all the Glapion children, the eldest was his mother's favourite and this love was reciprocated fully. Jean Glapion worshipped his mother, and since the death of his father nine years before, he had strived to be the man of the family with single-minded zeal in spite of his tender years. 'I do hope they will not wish to marry too young,' Marie

40

Laveau went on. 'It is difficult enough for our sort to make their way, and certainly not with the added responsibility of a family.'

'I doubt whether Jean will ever marry at all,' Marie broke in dryly. 'He is far too attached to you ever to want to leave home, *Maman*.'

'Oh, you think so!' her mother exclaimed. 'But that would not be right, not right at all! He must marry in due time.' But she looked pleased, none the less. Then her face clouded. 'And it is high time I did something about Marie-Philome. She is seventeen now and I simply cannot keep her at the convent much longer; I *must* decide.' She sighed heavily. 'It is so difficult to know what is best to do. She is very beautiful and it seems a pity to waste such a gift on an early marriage to one of our own. Times have changed so . . .' She sighed again. 'In my mother's time, there was no option. In my time one at least had the possibility of marriage, and that was what was decided for me. But now . . . well, Marie-Philome *could* have both lover and husband . . . Perhaps if she came out at the next quadroon ball and found a good protector? It would be so nice if she lived the good life for at least a few years and then, with a nice *dot* at the back of her, could find some good man to settle down with . . .' She fell into silence.

'And what of Celeste?' prompted Marie, who was anxious to get on with the list and down to herself.

Her mother roused herself with an effort. 'Oh, Celeste — the poor unfortunate has neither beauty nor charm. There is nothing but to find her a livelihood and hope that her dowry will be sufficient to entice some man to marry her young. She is good with her hands, so I have been thinking of apprenticing her to a milliner – even if we're not allowed to wear hats, at least we can make them.' She gave a short, mirthless laugh. 'It's a very profitable trade, I am told. Yes, I think that is what I must do; when Marie-Philome leaves the convent, Celeste will, also. I must see to it, after your initiation is out of the way.' Again she fell silent and Marie waited tensely.

'As to Amelie,' her mother went on, shaking her head

slowly, 'She is of such a retiring and timid disposition I can see nothing ahead for her but a religious life – strange as that may seem coming from me. She is not fit for the buffets of this world, and though she and Marie-Jeanne are too young to plan for, at least Marie-Jeanne shows some promise of beauty and spirit. So much in her case will depend on how things turn out for Marie-Philome – a rich alliance or a poor marriage. Similarly with Charles-Louis and François – if Jean and Daumeny do go into the iron-working business, there may be places for them in that – but these are early days, early days yet to be worrying about that ...' Her words trailed off.

Marie's heart thudded uncomfortably fast. There it was again – she had been left out; once more she had become invisible! 'And what of me? What are your plans for me?' she managed to get out.

Her mother looked at her blankly for a moment. 'What do you mean? I've already told you – you are to be my successor.'

'But I am a woman, too!' Marie said heatedly. 'Am I not to have lovers? Am I not to marry? Like the others?'

The elder Marie looked somewhat shaken. 'Why,' she stuttered, 'of course. But in your case, you have so much to do, to learn – it is not the same with the rest. It is much too soon to talk of such things; you are still very young.'

'But not too soon to talk of Amelie and Marie-Jeanne,' Marie pointed out. 'Or am I such a special case I am to make my own plans?'

'When the time comes, plans will be made, never fear,' her mother said coldly. 'But for the moment there is nothing to discuss.'

There the matter ended, and they turned to other things, but again it left Marie with a sense of uneasiness, a feeling that all was not as it should be and that there were forces at work beneath the surface which were beyond her knowledge and comprehension.

It was the first small clash of wills, but a second was shortly to follow. This time it was on a more practical plane and one which sorely tried Marie's sense of pride.

42

Though spring had now turned into high summer, nothing further had been said about her hairdressing apprenticeship and it had almost faded from her mind. She had been kept so busy learning the contents of the numerous little drawers of the endless cabinets that lined her mother's room, accompanying her mother on many strange errands to dusky little shops full of queer smells and odd-looking merchandise, or going on trips into the bayous, where silent Indians or surly Negroes would slip out of the undergrowth to deliver equally strange packets of merchandise into her mother's hands. So it came as something of a shock when one day her mother announced that she would start learning the hairdressing trade tomorrow and that her mentor was to be none other than old Bessie. 'You'll go with her on her rounds and do nothing but watch at the start, and then gradually she will teach you all she knows and the tricks of the trade.'

At the thought of accompanying this mountainous figure – who had long been an object of fun-making in the neighbourhood – through the streets where she was so well-known, Marie protested violently: 'Oh, *Maman*, why do I have to learn from *her*? Please, can't it be someone else? I mean I *can't* be seen with her! You know how funny and queer she is! I just can't!'

'She may be old and queer, as you say, and not the most graceful object on the streets of New Orleans,' her mother said firmly, 'but she is very skilful. She goes to all the best houses because she is *better* than anyone else! – and as her apprentice you not only will learn well but will also gain connections with the right sort of people.'

'But can't you teach me?' Marie pleaded. 'After all, you were once a hairdresser yourself; you told me so.'

'It has been many years since I did so, and it's out of the question now.' Marie Laveau was stern. 'Besides, that is not the only consideration. I have agreed with Bessie that in return for her teaching, as soon as you are ready to take over, she will give up and I'll buy a little stall for her in the old market, where she can sit down all day and sell her shampoos and oils and creams. It is something she has

43

always wanted, particularly since her feet are so bad, and it will mean you will have all that business without the trouble of having to build it up for yourself, as I had to do.'

Marie continued to plead. Her imagination balked at the thought of accompanying that lumbering, grumbling figure throughout the neighbourhood. Her sense of injustice grew; not only had her mother so untimely torn her away from her childhood and her friends, but now she was proposing to make her an object of ridicule amongst them, as well. She expressed her resentment hotly.

Her mother was surprisingly mild and soothing in return. 'You don't have need to worry on that score,' she assured her. 'You will not have any trouble. You'll see.'

'How can you possibly know that?' Marie stormed.

'Because they know who you are,' her mother said quietly. 'And they are too afraid of me to make trouble for you. And soon, quite soon, they will be too afraid of *you*. St John's Eve approaches, and after it they will all know exactly who you are and what you are destined to be.'

Despite her mother's calm assurances, Marie was not comforted, and her pride was further rankled by the fact that her mother now insisted as a preliminary to her launching into her new trade that she should start to wear the 'tignon' when she went out. To soften this bitter pill, her mother presented her with six of the finest-quality Madras handkerchiefs and showed her half a dozen ways of tying them in attractive styles. But Marie still balked. 'I don't see *why* I have to wear those things,' she muttered rebelliously. 'I never have before, and it'll be bad enough as it is going about with Bessie. Why can't I wear a bonnet or a mantilla – or nothing at all?'

Her mother looked at her with grim amusement. 'Well, for one thing, since you are now officially grown up, some kind of a head covering is considered proper. For another, it is actually against the law for us to wear anything else. The wives of our city fathers, seeing the attraction we had for their menfolk, saw to that many years ago. In theory, if we disobey this law by wearing hats or jewellery in the streets, we can be publicly whipped – although it is a law that has

44

rarely been invoked. It is just there to remind us. As long as we do that, we have no trouble, but try disregarding such laws and you will soon see how precarious our foothold in society is.'

'How would they know?' Marie flared. 'I'm a lot fairer-skinned than many Creole women – my hair is straighter and my features are finer. How would they know?'

'Oh, they'd know, sure enough,' her mother assured her. 'All the people who matter know, and they would be quick enough to pounce. You might fool the Anglos who are swarming into the city, but you wouldn't fool *them*, and if you tried, you would be marked as a potential danger. That is the last thing we want.' She paused. 'You see, however distasteful this may be for you, it is necessary. It is part of the very elaborate game we play here in New Orleans – it's a game that one day will end, but that time has not yet come, and until it does we must observe the rules. You are now going into society, *their* society, and I want it to be apparent – at least on the surface – that Marie Laveau's daughter is playing the game just as I have always done. That will lull them into their own false sense of security, and it will leave us free to pursue our own ends, retain our own hold over them. Give them the tokens they want and you will reap a rich harvest.

'This is only the first instance of "knowing your place". Once you start meeting them there will be dozens of other instances where you will be shown it again and again, and sometimes it will be hard, very hard, to keep a still tongue and to keep your hands away from their throats. But, however hard, it will be worth doing – the snubs and the slights and the humiliations will balance out. When you've had a Creole aristocrat, who has at some time "put you in your place", literally grovelling at your feet begging for your help – as I so often have had in my life – *then* you'll know why the game is worth it.' She gave a little triumphant laugh. 'Then the power rises and the pride can surge. Then it is that *you* have the choice to create or destroy. There is no feeling quite like it.'

Silently, Marie picked up a tignon and tried it on in front

45

of her mother's mirror. She studied her reflection carefully, turning her head from side to side so that the golden hoop earrings tinkled. Then she turned to her mother with hooded, smouldering eyes. 'I will wear the tignon from now on,' she announced coldly, 'but one day I swear to you that I will walk the streets of New Orleans with my tignon studded with diamonds, and with diamonds on all my fingers – and when I do, no one will dare to say as much as a word against it or lift a finger against me. This will be, for this I have sworn.'

Marie Laveau looked at her daughter in silence. Then she gave a little shiver. 'Sometimes you frighten me, Marie,' she said. 'You really frighten me.'

Chapter Five

Patty had another bad spell, and Marie Laveau was sitting up with her as the little slave tossed and moaned on the narrow pallet bed. Actually, she was glad of the excuse to sit up, since she had been having difficulty sleeping lately, being much troubled in her mind. Patty, she reflected, was an unerring barometer for registering any change in the emotional climate of the household – and there had been many changes.

The trouble had started that evening when dishes and crockery in the kitchen had suddenly started to move and crash, apparently of their own volition. It had startled everyone and terrified Patty. It would even have startled Marie Laveau had she not already seen its like and remembered how it had been those many years ago in the house on Rampart Street. She had been full of frustration and inner anger, just as Marie-Belle was at this moment, and how things then soared and crashed and moved, to the terror of the household. She knew now that it was part of the powers, some unconscious force of the mind that caused the chaos – one of the many parts she did not understand and which could not be controlled. It had taken her some time to realize that she was the cause, albeit the unconscious cause, and it had been the first time she had realized that she had inherited far more from her grandmother, one of the Sirenes from Santa Domingo who had flooded into New Orleans in the aftermath of Revolution, than the dark strain in her blood. How different her life had been up to that time, how very, very different. If only . . .

Bitter words – 'if only'. She reflected, sighed, and stretched her hand out to the sleeping girl, as an act of comfort to herself. Remembrances of her parents and how it had been with them and with her came flooding back with aching clarity. There had been such bright plans: she was to

47

be sent away to Paris for schooling, to be 'finished'; her father had been so proud of her, her mother so hopeful of her future happiness. She had been raised as the child of a rich and powerful man – as indeed her father had been – cosseted and petted and pushed forward in her precocity; dandled on the knee of the great Lafayette himself during his triumphant return to New Orleans. There had even been talk of arranging a marriage for her through his auspices in France, where, since the triumph of Empress Josephine, a touch of colour was no bar to a good alliance. And then ... it had all stopped.

Marguerite Durcantel had a beauty as fragile as camellias, which had so ensnared the heart of Charles Laveau, but which had flared up into a final burst of hectic, flushed cheeks and fever-bright eyes; then the coughing and the blood; her mother gasping her life away and withering before their eyes like a flower untimely blighted. Finally, there was nothing but the stark white memorial in the old St Louis cemetery.

Even during her mother's final days she had sensed her father's withdrawal from them. Looking back over the wisdom of years, she could understand him now, even if she could not forgive him. Although he had grieved, almost as deeply as she, he had turned to his own world with an alacrity and a relief that had sickened and embittered her. From that time forth she had banished him from her life and her thoughts, just as she would have banished his blood from her veins had it been in her power to do so. She was her mother's daughter, only, more importantly, perhaps, the Sirene's granddaughter. She did not even give him the credit for her own remarkable powers of organization and business acumen, talents which were far more the attributes of a white state senator than a mulatto Voodoo priestess.

It was not that he had been ungenerous. After her mother's death he had given her free and clear the house on Rampart Street and provided her with money. But there had been no more talk of Paris, or marriage, arranged or otherwise, and she realized that his love for her had been but an extension of the great love he had felt for her mother. With

48

the death of one had come the death of the other. Thus, he had abandoned Rampart Street and its memories and abandoned her with it.

It was then that the furniture had moved and the crockery had crashed and the terrified household had sought the help of Père Antoine, thinking themselves bewitched.

In the darkness she stirred and her face softened its grim lines as the image of the stooped grey figure of the holy man rose before her. Dear Père Antoine – a saint if any human could be. How he had laboured then and thereafter for her. He had tried to ease her grief, banish her hate, smooth her path, and for as long as he had lived he had been a force in her life – a force drawing her to his God, the Christian God. It was not really his fault that the other forces had been stronger, had finally won – so much else had happened.

After a few months the disturbances had ceased – and she fervently hoped that this would be the case with Marie-Belle. The girl, after all, had not had the same stresses or the same griefs as she, and with this warning Marie now knew what to do. In her own case, Père Antoine had been the one to get her to spend some of the money her father had left with her to learn the hairdressing business, and with her mind channelled in a new direction, the upsets had ceased almost overnight – but not before what had been going on in the house on Rampart Street had reached the ears of Dr John.

With him drama and excitement had come into her life and she still thrilled to the memory of their first meeting. The slaves – who were afraid of him – had let him in secretly. She remembered how startling an appearance he had made in her mother's small, exquisitely furnished drawing room, his tall figure clothed in black broadcloth, with an elegantly ruffled white shirt and black silk cravat, from which glittered one of the largest diamond stickpins she had ever seen. Since he was also one of the darkest Negroes she had ever known, he had seemed like a gigantic black shadow towering over and commanding her.

He had wasted no time with niceties, stating bluntly what

she had begun to feel about herself. 'I knew your grandmother,' he had announced. 'She was a Mambo of great power; in you I feel the same. I have need of you. Your people have need of you. We can be useful to one another.'

It was true what he had said, for she could go where he could not, do things he could not do, and he had taught her well. Thus, she had commenced her double life – going to Mass in the morning, listening to the strictures of Père Antoine and helping him with his work, and in the evening entering that other world as black and as exciting as the night itself.

They had organized the slave dances in Congo Square, she and Dr John – a useful safety valve the white masters had thought, so long as it was carefully watched over, strictly controlled – and, under cover of this overt activity, under their very noses they had organized and established the covert ceremonies, the old hidden rites; and the element of the danger they were risking had added to the excitement.

She thought then that she could have both worlds, and for a few years it had seemed so, but it was not to be that easy. The rumours spread as they always did in New Orleans; some must have reached Père Antoine, because when she was twenty-one, he suddenly became adamant that she marry and settle down. At the same time the city fathers clamped down on the Congo Square dances and Dr John found it advisable to leave the city for a while until things cooled down. The idea of marriage had its attractions – for under Dr John's skilful guidance she found she had an appetite for men and knew full well the dangers involved in that. And when Père Antoine had presented Jacques Paris to her, she was doubly tempted – he was handsome, and she had always had a weakness for a handsome man.

On the surface it was a highly suitable marriage – he, too, was a quadroon. The son of a well-born white and his mulatto mistress, his education was equal to her own and he wished to establish himself in business. For her dowry she had the house on Rampart Street, its furnishings, and her not inconsiderable attractions. So, to the delight of Père Antoine, he presided over their marrriage at the cathedral church of St

Louis on 4 August 1819. It was a delight that she shared for only a few hours after the marriage.

Jacques had flown into a terrible rage on their wedding night when he had discovered she was not a virgin – Dr John had been her teacher in many things. Looking back over the four unhappy years they had spent together, Marie could recall few occasions when he was not either ranting in jealous tantrums or sulking silently. At first she had tried to make amends to his hurt pride, to be the sort of wife he demanded, but nothing she did ever seemed to please him. When Marguerite was born in 1821, she thought that, perhaps, would help, but if anything, it had aggravated the situation – for one thing he had wanted a son, for another she had found the baby so absorbing, so naturally satisfying that it had increased his jealousy. The experience of suckling the child had been to her a revelation, a new dimension in sensual satisfaction that almost outweighed the pleasures of the bed. But her pleasure had meant more resentment for Jacques, more withdrawal. And by the time his wanted male child was born in 1823, the child who bore his name and was so like him, it was already too late – by that time the rift was too wide and she had already met Louis, and had known what it was really to be in love.

Still – she stirred uneasily – she would have liked to have known for sure whether Jacques Paris was alive or dead, but there had never been any proof; he had disappeared without trace.

Things were working towards a crisis after the birth of Jacques. Dr John had meanwhile returned to town, the rites had started up again, and she had attended them. Although he was afraid of her and what she stood for, Jacques had threatened – he had threatened to inform the authorities on them. She had thought it just another empty threat, as so many of his had been, and had gone to the ceremonies as usual. But when she had returned in the small hours of the morning, he was not there, though all of his personal belongings remained. She never saw him again.

Naturally, she had made inquiries, but the only clue she had ever found did nothing to alleviate her unease. An old woman had told her she had seen him heading out of town towards Bayou St John – where they had been holding the rites. Beyond that there was nothing but silence, though she had always had the feeling that Crocodile and Dr John both knew more than they would ever tell.

To keep up appearances she had started to call herself the widow Paris and had spun some tale about Jacques going off upriver and being drowned in a boating accident. After Louis had moved in with her and Jean had been born, she had dropped even that pretence and had called herself Glapion. It had not mattered to her or to Louis that they had never legally been married – in their hearts they were married.

He was to her everything that Jacques had not been: a warm and tempestuous lover, a tender husband, and a compassionate and loving father. He was not all that good looking, or all that clever – in fact, he had never been much good at earning a living and had always had a reckless gambling streak. But she didn't mind, because it was soon evident that she was more than capable of supplying the needs of their ever-growing family.

There was a gay, slightly raffish tendency in him that she always had found endearing. He had fallen in with Jean Lafitte's men during the Battle of New Orleans and had never lost the devil-may-care attitude of those reformed pirates. Dominic You, Jean's righthand man, had been his closest friend and they were always involved in some escapade together. Jacques had insisted that their first son be called after his idol, the great pirate, even though the latter was long fallen from grace and sight.

She had never lost her taste for a handsome man of any colour, and he had understood and tolerated that, too, knowing that it meant little in terms of their own complete life together. Even when Don Thomé had arrived and she had been so entranced for a while, it had not worried him, nor had he ever made the slightest difference between Marie-Belle and the rest of the children. No, those years with Louis had been the good years, and it was only with his death that the fear had started.

When it happened, she could not believe it. They had been through so much together – the fever and cholera epidemics, floods and fire, childbirth and death, and he had never so much as fallen sick. He had always been there when she needed him. Then one day he had left the house, and the next thing she knew he had been brought home on a plank litter, the vital spark extinguished, struck down on the street as if by the hand of God. Dominic You had been walking by his side and had said he had dropped without a word or a sound. She had cried out then to the Christian God and to Vodun to give him back, but they had not heard. She had tried all manner of incantations and rites to raise his spirit, to bring at least part of him back, but it was to no avail; he was irrevocably gone. When François was born, three months after his father's death, she scanned his newborn features feverishly in the hope that the gods had relented and had given him back to her in this new form – but she soon knew that this was not so.

When she finally came to accept that the gods were not listening to her, something within her died, too, and her purposes strangely altered. It was then she knew who the real enemy was – Death was her enemy, and she could not, would not, face him. She would never face him, and if things went as she planned, she would never have to.

On the surface things went on as before, and she was on the crest of the wave, the wave that was New Orleans, which had been rising and building to greater power, greater riches, greater everything, for the past quarter-century; a wave she was rising with and for which she could see no ending, no limitation. She was Queen of the Voodoos; there was no power quite like hers; there was nothing she could not do if she so decided . . .

She came out of her reverie to see that Patty was now sitting bolt upright in the bed, staring at her with large, frightened eyes. 'Ah didn't break dem dishes,' she announced thickly. 'Dey jus' up an' jumped off dat ol' table lak de Debil hisself was in 'em. Boom, crash. All gone. Ah tell ya, Missus, Ah didn't put a finger on 'em; dey did it all by themselves. Ah jus' don' know what's goin' on 'round here.

53

Ah jus don' know – but it sho ain't good. We got a mean ol' Debil here, Ah reckon.'

'Now, Patty, lie down and go to sleep,' she soothed. 'I've told you and told you – this is *nothing* to do with you. You mustn't worry about it. It's just a little thing I can take care of, so don't you fret about it. We'll get new dishes in the morning, and if those break, we'll get other new dishes, but *none* of this is your fault and no one's going to blame you. Do you understand?'

The slave nodded her head vigorously and then cocked it to one side. 'Ain't ya goin' to bed, Missus? It's almost mornin'. Ah kin hear those cocks at it already out thar. No cause fo' ya to lose yo' sleep – ya lose sleep an' ya done get sick, an' den we'll all be in one heap o' trouble – an' nothin to help us then. We'd be as good as dead without ya, an' dat's de truth.'

She was beginning to work herself up again, so Marie said sternly, 'I said to lie down and be quiet and go back to sleep. When you do that, I'll go, but not before.' Patty glared at her wildly for a moment, then snuggled down, muttering softly to herself, and within a minute she was sleeping soundly.

Marie stretched wearily and, after covering Patty up, made her way slowly to bed. She was aware as she lay down in its downy softness of a deep burning within her, a restless, unquenched urge. She needed a man again, she thought sleepily, so she'd see about that on the morrow. Since Louis had gone it had just been a question of physical release; there had been no question of love. But the need was still there, a need easily met, for there were few men she had met who would not answer her summons. All she asked of them was the slaking of her need, and quietness – a dark flitting through the forbidden parlour into the sacrosanct confines of her bedroom, for she was anxious to screen this need, this activity, from her beloved Jean, who would not understand, and equally from her daughters, whose virtue was their chief asset in the society in which they had to make their way, and which therefore had to be guarded at all costs.

This thought brought her back to her starting point –

Marie-Belle. She knew already that the child was very different from her – she did not sense in her this need that was so constant in herself. There was coldness there, a constraint she had never known. She could not conceive of a life without men. What would Marie-Belle do about it? she wondered. What would she herself do about it? Finally, she drifted off into sleep, still worrying about the daughter she did not understand and of whom she was beginning to be a little afraid.

Chapter Six

The bangings, the rappings, the crashing of dishes and candlesticks had stopped, and peace had returned to the house on St Ann Street. It was not that the force was spent; it was merely that it had refocused in new directions, for Marie had suddenly found a new world that absorbed all her energies, all her interest.

The whole of her life had been spent in and circumscribed by the Vieux Carré; from Canal Street to the Esplanade, and from Basin Street to the wharves, there was not a street or an alley she did not know, but now she found she had known only the surface, and she was finding out what lay in back of those well-known façades, what lay behind the great double doors, the elegant iron railings, the graceful windows. And it was a new vision of the world that enchanted and delighted her.

As she walked beside the waddling hulk of old Bessie, carrying the tools of their trade – the curling irons, the rags, the henna rinses, the pomades, the shampoos and endless unguents the ladies of New Orleans demanded, all in a covered wicker basket – she no longer even thought about what an incongruous sight they made together; she was far too absorbed in what new wonder she was going to see next.

At first it was the settings that occupied her: the elegant, high-ceilinged rooms, their contents endlessly reflected in great gilded mirrors; the charming gardens, with their ordered, brilliant beauty and tinkling fountains; the million diamonds winking from the cut-glass chandeliers, imported all the way from France; the soft sparkle of silver; the opalescent glow of delicate Sèvres vases decorating the mantelpieces and marble-topped tables; the opulent outlines of the antique Louis XIV and Louis XV furniture; the more delicate and elegant lines of the First Empire; and, in some houses, heavily carved and ornate furniture of the new

France under the Bourgeois King, Louis-Philippe. Then there were the rich brocades, the shimmering damasks, the heavy silks in all colours of the rainbow, at the windows, shrouding tables, on the backs of the womenfolk; the Aubusson carpets soft to the foot; the muted colours of Gobelin tapestries, soft to the eye. It all aroused in her sensuous satisfaction, and a longing almost amounting to avarice. It was a new world that she coveted.

She had never in her life gone hungry, she had always had plenty of clothes, and a good bed to sleep in; she had never wanted for anything, but she did so now. She looked at her immediate surroundings with new eyes, and hated what she saw: the cluttered house, the plain furniture, the dusty, unkempt yard. For the first time she doubted her mother, and her mother's power. She became impatient and sharp-tongued, and critical of everything and everybody. This eventually resulted in a confrontation with her mother, who had gathered part of what the problem was from Marie-Philome, in whom, to some extent, Marie had confided her newfound longings.

'You suddenly seem not very happy with life,' she commented to her daughter.

'I had not realized before how poor we are,' Marie said sullenly.

'We're not poor.' Her mother's tone was mild. 'We have everything we need.'

'Compared to what other people have, we have nothing.'

'If you think keeping a household of fifteen housed, clothed, and fed is nothing, you should try it sometime,' Marie Laveau said dryly.

'Oh, not that,' the young Marie snapped crossly. 'I know we have enough. I mean we have nothing of value.'

'And you think it's because we can't?' her mother queried.

'Well, if we can, why don't we?' Marie challenged.

'You mean the chandeliers, the mirrors, the soft carpets, and all the rest? Somehow I can't see any of those lasting too long or fitting in too well here, can you?'

'That's just what I mean – this house is small and shabby,

57

and everything in it is the same; it's nothing. If we can have better, why don't we?'

'Probably because it means nothing to me,' her mother said sombrely. 'I was brought up in surroundings such as those that have so taken your eye, and, believe me, they don't make you one bit happier, one bit healthier – the outward show means very little. After all, you can only sleep in one bed, sit on one chair, eat off one table.'

'Well, maybe it didn't mean anything to you because you've had it,' Marie said sullenly. 'But I never have, and I think it would be wonderful to be surrounded by all those beautiful things. And the *people* in it are totally different, too; it's a different world.'

'You only think it is because you have not done what I have told you to do. Thus far you have not looked below the surface – you have not looked at the *people*. When you do, you may be surprised at what you find, and one day you will know that we had far more here than you ever guessed.' She paused. 'Still, what you say is true – you have never known these things. You have never been to the house on Rampart Street where I was born, have you? It stands untenanted at the moment, so we will go there one day soon. Some of the old things are still there. I have kept my mother's sitting room and her bedroom as they were. It might amuse you to see them.'

Marie had flushed at her words, since part of what her mother was saying was perfectly true. She had been so busy taking in her surroundings, looking at the clothes and the jewels, that she had scarcely paid any attention thus far to the people inside, and so she leaped at her mother's peace offering.

'Yes, that would be very nice. But, Mama, if you have such nice things, why don't you bring them here? I don't understand what you have against them.'

Her mother frowned and said coldly, 'I have nothing against them, or for them, either. Sometimes it is just not very wise to show all you have. It pleases me more that people with surroundings like that should say of me, "Poor Marie Laveau, how she has come down in the world and

58

what a hard time she must have of it," than that they should say of me, "That Marie Laveau, flaunting herself like that! Who does she think she is, trying to ape her betters? She must be shown her place." That way you would never get anything from them.'

'Then they *do* have all the power, don't they?' Marie murmured rebelliously. 'And everything that goes with it.'

'I've already told you that,' her mother snapped. 'But they don't have *all* of it – not by a long shot. It's time you listened to me, Marie, and used your eyes for something other than gaping at the obvious. You have so much to learn, so very much to learn, still.'

'I'll have all that myself one day.' Marie was continuing her own train of thought. 'I'd *like* to live like that.'

Marie Laveau looked at her with amused exasperation. 'All that, along with the diamonds in your tignon and the bells on your toes, I suppose! Well, maybe you will at that, maybe you will.'

Crouched over the smoke in the courtyard sometime later, she thought over the conversation. No one knew what she had; no one knew how much she was worth. She supposed that one day someone would have to know – Jean, perhaps, though he did not seem to have much of a head on him for business. It certainly could not be Marie-Belle. She thought of all the properties. Besides this house and the one on Rampart Street, there were many others: the house at Bayou St John outside the city called Maison Blanche; another on Bourbon Street; and several, darker in every sense of the word, along Gallatin Street, a street which her own children for reason enough were forbidden to enter. It was these that were the most profitable. There were, besides, the jewellery and the money in Valdoux's bank – she had almost lost track of exactly how much. Looking up at the plain outlines of the little house, she smiled slightly. She was sure now that Marie would never understand her affection for the place. It was not only that this had been her home with Louis, the home that many of the children had been born in; it was far more than that – it was one of her greatest triumphs . . .

Old Senator Ledoux had been a friend of her father's, a fact she would have held against him had he not been in such urgent, pleading trouble when he had sought her out.

'It's my son Gaston,' he had explained. 'The young fool is in trouble, serious trouble. A matter of assault. He is to be tried before Judge Cross next week – an Anglo judge, yet! And one who bears no love at all for our kind. Unless some miracle occurs, it will be the parish prison for him, and the disgrace will kill his mother. I've heard tell of your special powers, Marie, and if you can somehow work that miracle you may name whatever you like as your fee, and I will be your friend for life. I beg you to help me.'

It had seemed a true test of her powers, and she had accepted the test. It had not been easy. She had spent long hours in the cathedral and longer with the snake, and when court had gone into session, there had been something from her hand beneath the judge's chair, something equally in his water bottle, and something in the mind of several of the jurors. The combination had worked excellently, and to the surprise of all, Gaston Ledoux had been triumphantly acquitted.

Apart from the fervent blessings and protestations of friendship from the Ledoux family, she had accepted the free title to this house on St Ann Street and a quarter-share of their plantation's yield for that year. It had brought her five thousand dollars, now gaining interest along with the rest in the bank. So this house, too, was something uniquely her own, and right where she wanted it, in the very heart of her territory ...

The expedition to the house on Rampart Street took place the very next day, and, although it was just around the corner and a short three blocks in the direction of the Esplanade, it was not without significant incident.

As Marie and her mother turned the corner of St Ann into Rampart, they almost bumped into an elegantly dressed man with a long, strong-jawed face framed in long, silvery sideburns. Her mother would evidently have gone by, save that the man barred their path, doffing his tall beaver hat and saying in a rather high-pitched, cultured voice, *'Bon-*

jour, Marie. Comment vas-tu? Il y a longtemps que je te n'ai pas vu.'

Her mother stopped. *'Ah, bonjour, Monsieur Montal. Je vais très bien, merci. Et vous et votre famille?'*

'Très bien aussi.' He eyed the younger Marie curiously.

Marie Laveau said reluctantly, *'Ma fille, Marie.'* Marie dropped him a very small curtsy and eyed him back with equal curiosity.

'Another Marie, eh? And almost as pretty as her mother,' he said with a roguish gallantry that struck a peculiarly false note. 'Haven't I seen her in our house?'

'Possibly.' Her mother was noncommittal. 'She is serving an apprenticeship with Bessie, who, I believe, does the hair of Madame Montal and your daughters.'

'Ah, excellent, excellent! So she is following in your footsteps.'

'In some respects,' her mother agreed, and a heavy silence fell.

'Well, I must not keep you,' he said hurriedly, and, saluting them again, he went on his way.

'I've never seen him before,' the younger Marie said as they continued on their way. 'Who is he?'

'You probably weren't noticing – he's the head of the Montal family. Very rich. Money comes from cotton and indigo plantations upriver aways, but they have a big town house over on the corner of Toulouse and Bourbon streets where they spend most of their time. Madame Montal was a St Yves, and none of the St Yveses can be bear to be far from the New Orleans social scene. Her sister is the wife of Valdoux the banker.'

'Oh, I know now – the one with the lovely fountain and the pink marble fireplaces,' said Marie, enlightened.

'Well, I'm glad you noticed something, at least.' Her mother's tone was dry. 'He obviously already has his eye on you, so you'll have to watch out for him – and all the Montals, for that matter. They think the world – and particularly New Orleans – was created expressly for their benefit. A queer, proud family.'

They had reached their destination: a small house, its

shutters closed, snuggled up to the old ramparts on the north side of the street. Her mother said no more. She fitted a key into the green door, which swung open, revealing a small foyer. For a second she hesitated, then plunged in through the little archway to the left, signalling Marie to wait. There was a creaking of shutters and light filtered through the arch. After a few moments her mother reappeared and beckoned her in.

Marie let out an exclamation of delight as she passed through the archway into the sun-filled room where startled dust motes danced in the lightbeams. Her mother had hurriedly pulled off some of the dust covers, and delicate gilded furnishings of the First Empire period, upholstered in a pale jade-green, were revealed. They stood on a pale rose Aubusson carpet, and overhead an exquisite teardrop chandelier gleamed bravely through its thin coating of dust; twin lustres of the same design contributed their fainter gleams from the mantelpiece of pale grey marble.

'Oh, *Maman*, it's just beautiful!' Marie gasped, hurrying from one piece to another in ecstasy.

Her mother did not answer; in her mind's eyes she was watching Jacques Paris stalk about on the Aubusson carpet as he shouted accusations at her, his face contorted with frustrated passion. Her father looked at her from the fauteuil; he looked drawn and embarrassed. 'It's all yours, Marie. I will be living from now on up at the plantation.' And Louis was there, too, smiling faintly at her. 'If we have any more children, we'll have to start hanging them from the chandelier, my love.'

'I'll open the other shutters,' she said abruptly and hurried out.

For Marie the rest of the house was an anticlimax after the wonders of the drawing room. The furniture in the small dining room, though good, was much used, the carpet faded, the larger service rooms beyond equally so, and it was not until she reached the main bedroom over the drawing room that her interest revived. Here the carpet was a deep shade of blue and on it stood the massive dark four-poster bed, its *ciel-de-lit* ruched in heavy silk of the same shade of blue caught up by silver stars – even stripped of its coverings, it was still magnificent. 'What a wonderful bed!' she breathed. 'Oh, it's *all* so beautiful!'

'It's a Seignouret,' her mother said briefly. She was standing at the doorway and had not crossed the threshold. 'The best, nothing but the best,' her mother murmured, as if to herself. 'It had to be that way. My first five children were born in that bed, and my mother died in it.' There was pain in her voice.

'Oh, *Maman*, couldn't we . . .' Marie began to say. But her mother broke in roughly: 'No. I've already told you, no. Have you seen enough? There is nothing else.'

However, on the way out, she obviously relented a little. Before closing the shutters again in the drawing room, she went over to a small table on which rested a workbox executed in intricate marquetry. She stood looking down at it for a moment, then picked it up and offered it to Marie. 'Here,' she said. 'This you may have for your own, since you set such store in nice things.'

'Oh, *thank* you, *Maman*.' Marie examined it with delight. The red velvet interior housed a treasure trove of gilded scissors, thimbles, and other trinkets. 'Was it yours or your Mama's?'

'It was my grandmother's,' her mother answered, 'the first gift my grandfather ever gave her, so guard it well.'

'Oh, indeed, I will. Was she the one who came from overseas?'

'She came from Santo Domingo, after the French were chased out.'

'And before that?'

'And before that, who knows?' Her mother closed the shutters with a resounding clang, plunging them into instant darkness, from which her voice came muffled. 'It does not matter where she came from. After all, it is what she *was* that counts, isn't it? It is something that neither of us will ever escape from!'

Chapter Seven

'Bessie, will you get through with your fussing?' Madame Valdoux's tone was pettish. 'I declare, if I have to sit here one minute longer, I'll just faint dead away.'

Bessie patted another curl of the towering, elaborate hairdo into position and grunted placatingly. 'I find sitting still so trying,' Madame Valdoux complained. 'I swear I feel one of my terrible headaches coming on already.' She rolled an appealing eye towards her daughter Claire, who had already been done and was now sitting languidly viewing the proceedings. 'Claire, dear, would you get me my smelling salts? I declare, I heard your father come in several minutes ago, and you know how cross he gets when we're not ready and how upsetting I find that – my nerves just won't stand it.' Her voice had become almost a whine.

Emilie Valdoux revelled in ill health and bad nerves; they were her chief weapons in keeping her husband and family in line. For the most part, being of a generally amiable disposition, she got her way by a constant appeal to their sympathies for her various chronic conditions. If this failed, she had to resort to stronger measures, ranging from headaches through the vapours and hysterics to fainting fits; one of them generally worked. In this she was totally unlike her sister, Margot Montal, who imposed her will on her family with a mixture of cold withdrawal and icy disdain. As a consequence, each one of them despised the other, but their proud St Yves blood served to give them common cause against the rest of the world.

There had been St Yveses in New Orleans since the very first settlement, most of whom had done very well for themselves, carving out large portions of Louisiana for their own, and keeping it in the family by diligently intermarrying. The process, some whispered, had gone on too long; there was bad blood in the St Yveses.

But Emilie St Yves Valdoux, and particularly Margot St Yves Montal, would have none of it – good blood to good blood could only result in more and better, and they would point triumphantly to the large and flourishing family of their only brother, Gaston St Yves, to prove it. Margot St Yves had cemented her proud position by marrying into the equally venerable Montal family. Emilie could claim no such antiquity for the Valdouxs – a fact she was not above pointing out to her husband on occasion – but could counterbalance this by the fact that she had made the wealthier marriage of the two sisters. None the less, with the honour of the family firmly in mind, she was bent on marrying off one of her daughters to a Montal and her eldest son to a St Yves. That, she felt, would take care of things nicely – if only she could get her husband to see it that way.

'Oh, dear, there he is now!' she exclaimed as firm footsteps approached the door of her boudoir. 'Bessie, be done this very minute and get me out of this wrapper!' She plucked feverishly and ineffectively at the ties of the fine linen wrapper covering her gown as the big mulatto gave a last satisfied grunt and then leaned over and with a deft flick undid the wrapper. Madame Valdoux tottered to her feet, casting a last anguished glance at the mirror before the door opened to admit the master of the household.

Paul Valdoux was a dark-complected man of sombre, saturnine mien, with tight black curling hair, but the rest of his face was totally belied by a pair of very mild, hazel eyes, which were indeed the key to his whole character. He wove his way through the scented, cluttered room, kissed his daughter gingerly on the forehead, and bowed politely over his wife's hand. 'We'll be with you as soon as I have my fan and gloves,' Emilie announced triumphantly.

There was a brief bustle while Bessie found the required articles and Marie packed away the tools of their trade in the wicker basket, but it was not until the door was closed on their incongruously disparate shapes that anything further was said.

'Bessie has an assistant now, I see,' Paul Valdoux

observed, looking after them. 'Lovely little thing, isn't she? Face looks familiar, somehow.'

His wife, who had been taking a long, satisfied sniff at her smelling-salts bottle, opened her eyes and shot him a shrewd, appraising glance. 'Oh, do you think so?' she said. 'I wouldn't have said she was a bit like her mother. Not at all the same.'

'Her mother?' he queried patiently. It often took quite a while for the workings of his wife's mind to become apparent. 'Surely not old Bessie!'

'No, of course not, Marie Laveau's girl, another Marie – *most confusing*! She's learning the trade from Bessie, although so far I've yet to see her *do* anything!'

'Marie Laveau's daughter, a hairdresser?' he said in an amazed tone.

'Why shouldn't she be? It's a perfectly good metier. Her mother was also one,' Emilie responded a trifle acidly. She was about to add that not all mixed bloods were destined to be the mistresses of Creole men, but she recollected in time that a Creole lady was not supposed to know things like that.

'Oh, I'm just a bit surprised. The child looks so young, that's all,' Paul Valdoux murmured. Apart from Marie herself, he was probably the only person in New Orleans who knew the scope of her material empire, and knowing her of old, he wondered privately what she was up to. Aloud he said, 'Your hair looks lovely, my dear. You will put to shame all others at the reception. Shall we be on our way?'

His wife preened; her hair indeed was now her chief glory, being long and lustrous and of that lovely shade of deep red called *chataigne*. When young she had been very pretty, with a little rosebud mouth and white, white skin, which, now that her fortieth birthday was hard upon her, was crinkling alarmingly into a fine network of wrinkles over which she laboured with despair. The little rosebud mouth, which had so enchanted the young banker Valdoux, had in the course of long and constant complaint drooped peevishly at the corners and two long lines were now accentuating that droop. It drooped again. 'Not yet, Paul. There is something I must talk to you about, and we are still on the early side. Claire, dear, will you run and see that the carriage is ready and waiting for us?'

When her daughter had left the room, she said urgently, 'Now, Paul, I want you to talk to Vincent Montal tonight about Claire and Dominic.'

An expression of distaste crossed his face. 'Oh, really, Emilie! Claire is only sixteen. She's still just a child. I've told you time and time again that I am not in favour of discussing anything at this early stage with Vincent or *anyone*. Nor, as you know, am I at all easy in my mind about first cousins marrying. This is an obsession of yours – you have been thrusting Emile at your brother's child as if she were the only girl in the world for him, and *he* is only seventeen.'

'It is never too early to begin thinking of these things,' his wife said stubbornly. 'Let it go too late and you will find the young ones getting ridiculous ideas of their own, and then there is always *more* trouble. Dominic would be an excellent match and is a very amiable young man – the *only* amiable Montal,' she added thoughtfully. 'Besides, you know yourself how long these arrangements take. I, too, would not wish to see her wed before she is eighteen. That is a good age for marriage.'

'No. I will not even think of talking about it before Claire is seventeen.' Paul Valdoux was firm. 'And that goes for Valerie and Louise, not to mention Emile, Bayard, and Lamont. Matrimony is a serious business, Emilie, not a race to see who gets there first. I don't know why you are in such a hurry – your sister Margot is in no such rush to push St Regis and Dominic into marriage, I can assure you.'

'No one pushes St Regis into anything,' his wife said with a little shudder. 'He finds his own way! How twins like he and Dominic can be so unalike, I've no idea.' Then her face began to pucker. 'But if it is not soon,' she wailed, 'I may not live to see my grandchildren – you know how it is with me.'

'Nonsense, my dear,' Paul said sternly. 'And I warn you,

on this my mind cannot be altered, so let us speak no more of it.'

She dabbed at her eyes with a tiny square of cambric and shot him another calculating glance under its cover. His tightly pressed lips and the muscle twitch along his lean jaw told her it was no time to press the matter. 'As you wish,' she said with a final sob, 'as you wish.' But it was a retreat, not a surrender.

Another domestic drama was in progress in another part of the Valdoux household, a drama that was to have far-reaching consequences. Bessie had trundled off to the kitchen quarters to seek some refreshment after her labours, leaving Marie to her own devices. She chose to wander in the garden, which was at the height of its summer glory. She was walking towards the ornamental fountain which was surrounded by flowering shrubs and set against the back wall of the courtyard, when she was startled to hear a hopeless sobbing coming apparently from the middle of a hibiscus bush. She bent down to see a slim figure with a mass of tangled chestnut hair in an attitude of abject misery, cradling a small black dog in its arms. 'What on earth is the matter?' Marie demanded. 'And what are you doing there? Can I help you in any way?' A startled, dirt-steaked, and tear-stained face looked up at her and she recognized Valerie Valdoux, a girl of her own age and third eldest of the Valdoux brood.

'Who are you?' Valerie gasped between sobs.

'Marie Laveau, Bessie's assistant. What's the matter?'

Valerie burst into a fresh storm of sobbing. 'It's Fifi, my dog – she's been acting strangely all week long, and today I found she'd crawled under here, and, oh, I think she's dying.'

'What's wrong with her?' Marie cautiously crawled in beside her and bent over the dog, which opened one dull eye and whimpered softly. She felt its nose, which was hot and dry. 'Has she been injured in any way?'

'No,' Valerie sobbed, 'but she hasn't eaten for days and she's been sick. I think she may have been p-p-poisoned. I've prayed to St Geneviève and, oh, *so* many more, but it doesn't seem to be helping. And if anything happens to her,

I'll just lie down and die – I know I will.' In many ways Valerie was truly her mother's daughter.

'Now, don't take on so,' Marie soothed. Obviously, prompt action was called for, so she said with far more confidence than she felt, 'I'm sure I can fix the dog up in no time. I'll run right home and pick up some medicine and be right back.'

A faint gleam of hope came into Valerie's eyes. 'You mean you can make her better? Oh, if you do that it will be a miracle! You'll be the most wonderful person in the world!'

'Just stay right here,' Marie commanded, 'and I'll be back as soon as I can.'

She ran back to St Ann Street as fast as she could and burst in on her startled mother. 'An emergency at the Valdoux house!' she gasped out. 'Valerie Valdoux's dog is dying, poisoned, most likely. Quickly, what do we have I can give it?'

'Valerie Valdoux's *dog*!' her mother exclaimed incredulously.

'Yes, yes.' Marie was almost dancing up and down with impatience. 'She's in a terrible state about it, and I promised I'd save it. Quick – you must have *something*.'

Her mother's eyes narrowed. 'Well, it's not the usual run of things, but here ...' She opened up one of the many drawers and took out two small packets. 'See if you can get some of these into it.'

'And a gris-gris – there must be a gris-gris, too. I can do a lot with that,' Marie said eagerly.

Again her mother gave her a sharp glance and silently handed her a charm. 'Oh, thank you, *Maman*,' she called back over her shoulder, then raced out again.

With great difficulty the girls succeeded in getting some of the powders down the throat of the semi-comatose dog. Now Marie was sitting, holding it in her lap, willing as she had never willed before that the small black form should not die. Part of her mind was calling the ally, demanding his help; the other was fixed on the image of the dog frolicking happily among the bushes. 'It will be,' she willed. 'It will be.' With a shaky hand she tied the gris-gris to its collar.

After about an hour the dog stirred and looked up at its mistress. Its eyes were noticeably brighter, and to Marie the small body seemed not as fevered. 'I think,' she announced with pride, 'that it is on the mend. If you will take it into the house and wrap it up warmly and give it some more of the powders and get it to drink some water, it should be all right. I'll come back tomorrow morning to make sure.'

Valerie looked at her with awe. 'Oh, Marie,' she whispered, 'if this be so, and Fifi lives, I will be your faithful friend until I die, no matter what happens to either of us. This I do swear, as God is my witness!' And like her mother, she had a fine sense of the dramatic.

'Time enough to thank me if Fifi gets better,' Marie said with some unease.

The next day she hurried back to the Valdoux house as soon as she dared. She had some difficulty persuading the old Negro slave, who acted as butler, of the urgency of her errand, but after a muttered consultation with the slave who ministered to Valerie's needs, he reluctantly led her up the main staircase to the third floor, tapped on a white-painted door bordered in gold, and ushered Marie in.

The first thing that greeted her eyes was the small form of Fifi frisking about and wagging her tail. A second later Valerie hurled herself upon Marie and, kissing her on both cheeks, exclaimed, 'Marie, she's better – she's well again! Oh, Marie, my dear, you are a *wonder*! How *ever* did you do it? I just can't get over how clever you are. I think you're the most wonderful person in the whole wide world, and I'm so proud to have such a friend.'

Marie flushed, partly with pleasure, partly with relief. 'I just stopped by to see if she *was* all right,' she said awkwardly. Then, to cover her embarrassment, she added, 'What a lovely room this is, and you have it all to yourself, too. How marvellous!'

'Oh, is it?' Valerie looked around her with a surprised air. 'Yes, Claire and Louise and I have our own rooms, and Emile has his, being the eldest, but Bayard and Lamont share because we *always* seem to have people to stay, and this isn't a very big house.' Marie gave a little inward gasp. 'Do you have to share, Marie?'

Marie explained her home situation, and the conversation moved on to topics engrossing to all fourteen-year-old females. This pleasant *tête-à-tête* was interrupted by another tap at the door. Valerie made a little moue of exasperation at Marie and called out, 'Who is it?'

'It's I, Emile. May I come in?'

'Well, I have a friend here, but if it's important . . .'

'Yes, it is. I'd like to see you both.'

She shrugged in mock despair at Marie. 'Well, all right, then, come on in.'

A head of rather tight auburn curls – verging almost on the carroty – appeared around the door, followed by a medium-sized body on the stocky side. Emile Valdoux was a rather solemn young man. A stolid air of responsibility surrounded him like an aura; indeed, it was the keynote of his character. He had felt responsible from a very tender age – responsible by his birth for his mother's ill health, responsible to his father as the firstborn, for carrying on the name and banking tradition of the Valdouxs, responsible to see his brothers did not get into too much mischief, responsible to look after his sisters, responsible . . . sometimes he felt as if he were responsible for the whole world.

None of this was very apparent to Marie, who saw a not-too-memorable white face, for Emile had rather unfortunately inherited his mother's skin tone. His only good and noticeable features were the fine hazel eyes he had inherited from his father. After the introductions were made, both girls looked at him expectantly, but he seemed at a loss as to how to go about his mission of importance. Finally, after a nervous cough, he said, 'I have heard what a great service you have rendered my sister, Mademoiselle Laveau, with respect to her dog, of which we are all indeed very fond.' Valerie gave a conspiratorial wink to Marie, who could barely suppress a giggle. 'In view of this, I would be most honoured if you would accept this small token of appreciation for your services.' And he held out a small purse.

Valerie let out a small gasp and muttered, '*Ça, alors!*'

Marie looked at the purse and looked at him, a dull flush spreading over the high cheekbones, the black eyes beginning to smoulder. 'Monsieur Emile,' she said in a voice of ice, 'I was only too happy to use what little talent I have in the service of a friend. I did not do it with any thought of expecting or receiving anything for my services. I must therefore *respectfully* decline your offer, and bid you good day.'

Valerie flung her arms around Marie and said hotly, 'Oh, Marie, don't go! *Zut!* Emile, now see what you have done! You have upset Marie! Really, you go too far at times!'

Emile turned a brilliant pink. 'I didn't mean . . .' he stammered. 'I only wished to thank you . . . I . . . I would not insult you for the world.'

'Well, you have insulted both of us,' Valerie pouted. 'So, *go* before you say anything else to anger us.'

Totally routed, a nervous Emile backed first into, then out of, the door.

'Oh, Marie,' Valerie cried, 'please don't be angry! Emile is just *like* that. Already he thinks of himself as a banker, and all *they* think of is dollars and cents. Otherwise, he's very amiable, I assure you. So don't be cross with him or me.'

Marie's tension lifted and she gave a rueful laugh. 'I shouldn't have flared up like that. I'm sure he meant well. It's just . . . well, it doesn't matter . . . And, anyway, I have to go now, Valerie. My mother will probably be furious that I sneaked out alone, but I couldn't wait to see how Fifi was. I've lots of things to do, so I must go.'

'Then I'll see you out, so long as you promise to visit me again very soon,' Valerie said gaily.

She led the way downstairs, chattering all the way, until they got to the last bend of the staircase leading down into the foyer. Then she drew back and exclaimed with distaste, '*Tiens!* My Montal cousins! Probably here to see Emile. Let's wait until they're out of the way.'

Marie peered over the balustrade down on to the scene in the hallway, where two young men of identical height and build were giving their hats and canes to the butler. They were laughing uproariously about something as they turned towards one of the downstairs reception rooms. As they did so, Marie could see that although their features were twin images of one another, there were subtle differences that made the twin on the right come sharply into focus: a more definite swoop to the aquiline nose, a firmer line of the long Montal jaw, eyebrows that peaked in the middle to give the face a demonic slant. Finally, she found herself looking into a pair of cold amber eyes that reminded her of a great predatory cat. As their eyes met and clashed, the whole scene darkened around her and for a second she thought she was going to faint. The eyes passed over and beyond her to Valerie, then narrowed slightly, and she was aware the young man was bowing derisively in their direction.

'*Bonjour ma chère cousine,*' he called.

'*Bonjour,*' Valerie called back in an odd, flat voice.

They disappeared from view and Marie muttered, 'Who did you say they were?'

'They,' said Valerie, as she soberly made her way down the remaining stairs, 'are my twin cousins, St Regis and Dominic Montal.'

'And the one who spoke to you?' said Marie with an inward shiver.

'That was St Regis,' Valerie answered with an outward shiver.

Chapter Eight

Marie was feeling pleased with herself. She felt she had made a step forward, a significant breakthrough of some kind, though of what it consisted she was a little hazy. She chattered happily to her mother about the incident as she arranged things in the multi-drawered cabinets in her mother's room. 'What was in those powders, Mama? I should know for the future, since they really worked wonders.'

Her mother, who had been extremely withdrawn and silent all morning, did not reply at once. Then she said, in a strange, flat voice, 'I am not sure the powders were any part of it; one was for arsenic poisoning, the most common kind, since you find it in rat powder and it is easy to get, and the other was merely something to help the stomach – but both were meant for *humans.*' She put an odd emphasis on the last word.

'Oh, then it is possible that it was not the powders, but my power,' Marie said, still happily. 'I did concentrate very hard, so maybe I cured Fifi by that.' But she made no mention of the ally.

Her mother did not reply, but a few minutes later she said, again in an odd voice, 'Look at me, Márie.'

Marie turned and a scream bubbled to her lips. Her mother was spreadeagled in a curious position against the wall by the bed, but her feet dangled a couple of feet above the floor. As Marie watched with frightened, dilated eyes, her hand held at her mouth, her mother floated away from the wall and wafted towards her, a foot above the floor; when she was close to Marie, she came down to earth with a great gasp and stood there panting, her eyes wide and fixed.

'You talk of powers, and yet you still know nothing of such things,' she gasped. 'What you have just seen *looks* like a power, yet it is nothing of the kind – it is simply a physical thing brought about by control of the breathing and control of the mind. It is called levitation. It is something that can be *learned*, just as I learned to do it from our father, for there is nothing of that in the worship of Vodun. It is something you could learn, if you have the mind – it may even come easier to you than it did to me – but it is a fairly useless thing, after all. Sometimes I have used it in the water rites to impress my people – to them, to see someone appear to walk on water is of the highest magic, and yet it is nothing of the kind. I show it to you because I am concerned about you and the way things are developing. There is so much you have still to learn on the practical level before you even start to utilize your powers. You do not seem to realize how precious these are and how they have constantly to be conserved for the important things. However great they are, if they are used without judgment, you can be in trouble – serious trouble! And so far you have not shown much judgment.'

'I've been trying, Mama, really I have,' Marie said in a troubled voice. 'And I'm not sure that I understand you.'

'What I am saying is that it is not very wise to show people you have any power at all, and particularly on something as unimportant as a *dog*.'

'I made a friend,' Marie pointed out. 'The dog's life was very important to Valerie.'

Her mother sighed impatiently. 'A fourteen-year-old girl who probably will have forgotten all about that friendship by next week, but who doubtless will chatter about it in her own circle so that you will probably be deluged with requests to treat the ailments of every pet canary and kitten in New Orleans.'

'Well, why not?' Marie said stubbornly. 'If I can do it and it will help.'

'Because it is not *important*. Look, I've already told you the uncertain nature of the powers. You've seen it already in the consultations I've let you sit in on. There are some people who badly need help, who you'd *like* to help, and yet, however much you want to, whatever you do, you don't seem to be able to do anything. And yet there are other cases when you don't particularly care, or the problem does not seem a very important one, and yet the slightest thing you do helps. It is baffling and very wearing. One of the important things I have found is that you have to make people believe in *you*, and when they do that you have to make *them* believe that what they are after is possible, and when you have succeeded in doing *that*, it often is. It sounds simple, but it isn't. You have to make them believe in you by a combination of real power and things that *look* like real power, but, in effect, are purely matters either of observation or physical knowledge that other people do not have. Your father told me he could walk for two hundred miles without getting tired. He could slow his heartbeat so you'd think he was dead, or sit in the snow and be warm, or by a single glance of his eye paralyse a snake or a small animal. But there was no magic involved in any of these. I can hypnotize people so that they will do my will. I can make them sick if they displease me. But these, too, are physical powers and can be learned. And, believe me, if you fritter away your time and energy curing dogs, you'll never learn them.

'Anyway, there is one thing I have decided,' she went on in a calmer tone. 'I think it is too soon for you to be initiated this St John's Eve – you are not ready. We will do it next year if all goes well.'

'I'm sorry if I have failed you,' Marie said in a low voice.

'Oh, you haven't failed me, child. In fact, you've done very well in some areas, and I have been working you hard, but from now on I want you to keep your eyes and your wits around you in the outside world. If you do that, I'm sure all will be well. Now I am going to set for you your first task – a little contest between us, if you like to think of it that way. I want you to bring me some news here that I don't already know myself. And I also want you to tell me how I *get* my information without leaving the house. When you know that, you will know much.'

In the days, weeks, and months that followed, Marie entered enthusiastically into her mother's challenge, but found it was no easy one. No matter how dramatic and immediate the incident, no matter how she hurried to get home to the house on St Ann Street, it was only to be greeted by her mother, a slight smile on the sensuous mouth, saying, 'Ah, you are going to tell me that young Sablon has been challenged to a duel again.' Or: 'So Senator Bienville has had a stroke at last. He should not have taken such a young mistress.' Or: 'So the LeBlancs have been killed in a riverboat accident. They are distant kin of the St Yveses, I believe.'

It baffled and infuriated Marie. How *did* her mother do it? Did she read her own mind, or did part of her accompany Marie wherever she went? What was the key?

It was not until she was already past her fifteenth birthday that she found the answer.

Unusually for her, she had accompanied Bessie to the kitchen of one of the larger mansions on Royal Street, and so was there when one of the house slaves burst in with catastrophic news. The young wife of the eldest son of the house was being prematurely brought to bed because of a miscarriage and was in a bad way. There was an immediate outburst of exclamations, moans, sobs, and excited conjectures, and in the middle of all this, Marie was startled to see the cook walk calmly over to the open window by the sink and, as she busied herself with her pots and pans, start to sing in a loud and penetrating voice.

Shocked by this strange behaviour, Marie listened to the words of an old melody, and found she was listening to an account of the current event mixed in with the original lyrics. Suddenly all was clear to her. Without further ado, she hurried out through the courtyard into the narrow alleyway that ran behind the house, just in time to hear the refrain taken up by a slave in the next yard who was beating a carpet. She hitched up her skirts and ran as fast as she could back home, and, bursting into the front parlour, she gasped out to her mother, 'I know how it's done! And I think I've beaten the message chain! Young Madame Garonne is prematurely brought to bed, and you may be being sent for.'

Her mother smiled faintly. 'At last!' And they could hear the faint, reedy voice of Patty lifting in the message song. 'So now you know. When I said I knew what was going on in every household of consequence in New Orleans, it was no empty boast. It is a vast network, set up over the years and constantly renewed, which gets information to me faster than a person can run. Now a lot of things, other than that, should be clear to you.

'I have often seen you impatient when I have taken time to give a gris-gris or a hex, or advice and help of some sort to a slave who apparently has given me nothing in return. I have read in your mind that you feel it is I who waste my time on such matters. As you can see, there is probably nothing that I do that is more important, because much of what I accomplish otherwise is based on the goodwill of such people. You have set your sights and your longings on the drawing rooms, but you won't find an easy way to power in them; rather, look to the slave quarters and the kitchens, for they will offer you an easier route to power.'

A heavy pounding on the outer door interrupted her and she opened it to find a Garonne slave, who gasped out, 'Please come! The mistress is brought to bed! Monsieur Pierre begs ya to come an' help.'

Marie Laveau raised her hand and was silent for a moment, as if listening to something. Then she said, 'I can do nothing. Return to your house. Your mistress is already dead and past my help.' She turned slowly to her daughter. 'That,' she said, 'was not in the message – but, all the same, she died five minutes ago from loss of blood.'

As Marie explored the ramifications of her mother's empire, not only in the Vieux Carré but also in the fashionable Faubourg St Mary, whence it had spread, her respect and admiration for her grew. Some blacks actively loved her, most stood in awe of her, some were very afraid of her, but all did not hesitate to obey her. She also came to understand how white members of a household that had somehow incurred her mother's displeasure could be made to suffer for it in a thousand different ways.

However, much as she was impressed by her mother, she had long realized that she was not infallible. She had been quite wrong, for instance, about Valerie Valdoux, who had remained Marie's firm friend. Both knew that there were bounds to this friendship, but within these bounds they had become very close, and in her frequent visits to the Valdoux house on Royal Street, Marie had, through Valerie, got to know the other members of the household: Bayard, her younger brother, who was a real hellion and always up to some devilment; Lamont, a born follower and more docile than his brother, though always in some kind of trouble because of him; Claire, who had inherited her father's amiable disposition, but who was inclined to be lazy and who found the more volatile Valerie something of a trial; Louise, who was silent and somewhat sickly; and, finally, the stolid Emile, with whom Marie always felt a certain reserve, but whose good qualities she gradually came to appreciate.

From Valerie, she heard all the gossip of the Valdoux family and its allied houses, and of how there was a constant battle going on between her mother and father over the marriage arrangements for Claire and Emile; how her mother wanted her niece, Marie St Yves, to be Emile's bride, and wanted Dominic Montal for Claire. 'And what do they think about it?' Marie asked.

'Oh, Claire is so lazy I don't suppose she cares *who* she marries, as long as she doesn't have to do anything about it,' Valerie said hotly. '*I* certainly will when my time comes. As for Emile, well, if it's what Papa wants, naturally he'll do it. He's like that.

'However, I don't think *Maman* is going to get her way all that easily – at least as far as Dominic goes. He does what St Regis does, and I can't see St Regis settling down at *all* unless he gets exactly who and what he wants. He's like that!' she added, using her favourite phrase of the moment.

'And who do you think that will be?' Marie said. She was intrigued by what she had seen and heard of the Montal twin.

A worried look crossed Valerie's face. 'Well, I can tell you one thing – it won't be *me*. I wouldn't have St Regis if he were the last man in the world. So if he or *Maman* get any crazy notions about that . . .' She fell silent, then burst out, 'I hate St Regis. I always have and I always will.'

'But why?'

'Because he poisoned my dog, that's why,' Valerie hissed.

'Oh, you must be mistaken!' Marie cried. 'Why should he have done a horrid thing like that?'

But Valerie blushed, tossed her curls, pressed her lips tightly together, and would not say another word.

Through Valerie she also got to know the Montals better, though they were not a family easy to get close to. It was generally accepted that, while it was Vincent Montal who held the pursestrings, it was the redoubtable Margot who ruled the roost. Besides the twins, there were three other Montals, all girls: Anne, who was cold and imperious like her mother; Yolande, who was extremely pious and withdrawn; and the youngest, Geneviève, who, as if to compensate for her sisters' lack of emotion, was extremely emotional and overly affectionate.

'Really, there are times I find Geneviève very trying,' confessed Valerie. 'It's not that I don't like affection. I mean, I'm very much that way myself, but that child *can't* get enough of it. When she's around she is always kissing and hugging you until you can hardly breathe. And with the boys! Well, she's incredible!'

Marie was to see a sample of this behaviour one day when the youngest Montal had been brought over to play with Louise. Emile happened to be passing by as Geneviève entered the foyer and she flung herself at him with a delighted squeal. He laughed and picked her up and she immediately flung her arms around his neck, clinging tightly to him and smothering him with moist kisses. He submitted to this for a time and then tried to pry her away, saying good-naturedly, 'All right, *ma petite cousine*, that's all for now. I must go.' But she squealed and protested and clung even tighter until he was literally obliged to use force to put her down. As she turned away from him, Marie caught a glimpse of her face, which was flushed, the eyes almost glazed, and the little pink mouth was quivering and moist. It sent a queer thrill through Marie, as if she had glimpsed something exposed that was vaguely unpleasant, and should be hidden.

When she related this incident to her mother, the latter's reaction was curious and interested. 'Hmm, trouble in store for the Montals,' she observed.

80

'In what way?' Marie asked. 'I don't really understand it.'

'No, I don't suppose you do.' Her mother's tone was dry. 'But you will someday. It is nothing to concern yourself with at the moment.'

Once, Marie saw Vincent Montal with his daughter, and this, too, left an indelible impression. It was known that outside the intimidating orbit of his wife and the Montal household, Vincent was very much a man about town. He had a white mistress he kept in one of the newer parts of the city, was a frequent visitor to the more expensive bordellos, and was rumoured on occasion even to frequent the lowlier establishments on Gallatin Street. It was also rumoured that on his plantation upriver, which his wife never visited, there was a fine crop of mulatto children. And he was known to be a ready buyer for any nubile female who was offered for sale on the slave block of the St Louis Hotel. At home his relations with his children were extremely correct and formal in the old manner – with the exception of Geneviève, of whom he was clearly the most fond.

One day, when Marie was assisting Bessie dress Madame Montal's hair for a ball, and Geneviève was in the boudoir watching the proceedings, Vincent Montal entered. He bent down to kiss his daughter on the forehead and was immediately seized by the limpet-like arms, as Geneviève repeated the performance Marie had already seen with Emile. Vincent Montal submitted to the onslaught of kisses and hugs good-humouredly for a while, but when they showed no signs of abating, a look, almost of apprehension, crossed his face, and he tore the child's arms from around his neck and said roughly, 'That's enough, Geneviève. You simply must learn to control yourself. You are getting to be a big girl now.'

The child looked at him with glazed eyes for a second, then burst into a flood of tears and rushed from the room.

'Really, Vincent,' came the cool, controlled drawl of his wife from the dressing table. 'Do you *have* to create such scenes? One minute you encourage the child in her excesses, and the next you are stern with her. No wonder she is becoming so difficult!'

The relating of this bit of news to her mother brought a reaction that surprised Marie. '*Pauvre petite*,' she had sighed. 'I feel for her. I fear that in her ambience she is going to find life very difficult and very unhappy, indeed.'

Chapter Nine

It was the eve of St John's Eve and Marie was nervous, very nervous, for this night she would be initiated, the first step towards the great ceremony on the morrow. For the past month she had withdrawn from the normal world, and had remained closeted with her mother, who had drilled and re-drilled her in the detailed knowledge of the cult, which was required before she could be a *hunsikanzo* – an initiate. Only after that was done could she become a *Mambo*, a full Voodoo priestess.

Earlier in the day, as the first part of the ritual, she had rolled naked upon the sacred drums to be used at the ceremony, drums which were but newly arrived from Africa, where they had been sent to be 'renewed' – the sun of Africa giving them new strength, her mother had said. Indeed, she had felt a very distinct vibration when she had touched them. Now they stood ranged along the back wall of the front parlour, as she sat clad in a simple white cotton shift, a white tignon binding her hair. Across the room was her mother, who sat in the great armchair of carved teak. Both of them waited in silence.

The door opened to reveal Crocodile, who came in with another Negro whom she recognized from the Calinda ceremony as Hungan Thomas, a mulatto woman whom she had never set eyes on before but who her mother introduced as Mama Antoine, and a priestess. They were all clothed in white.

While the introductions were being made, Crocodile put on a great cape of black and white Colobus monkey skins that looked very bizarre over his everyday clothing but which nevertheless bestowed on him a sudden and unac-customed dignity. He then seated himself at her mother's right hand, facing her. *Hungan* Thomas sat beside him, and Mama Antoine was to her mother's left. Then began the questioning, in which her mother, for obvious reasons, took no part.

After what seemed a small eternity to Marie, the questions ran out and they fell silent, looking expectantly at Crocodile, who gave a satisfied nod and said, 'This child of Vodun is ready.' He got up and lighted a small candle from the tapers that were already lighted in the four corners of the room, and he stood in front of Marie, the candle in his left hand, a small phial in his right. In a deep and solemn voice, he intoned, 'Do you swear to venerate the powers of mysteries of the Great God, and do you equally swear to keep its secrets and to obey the dictates of its servants?'

'I swear,' Marie whispered.

His right hand resting lightly on top of her tignon, he bent slightly and put the back of his left hand, with the candle, against the left side of her head. 'Now through the power of Vodun in me, I bind your Powers to you and pronounce you a *hunsi-bocal*, a child full of wisdom.'

He lifted the hand holding the phial from her tignon and held it up. 'By the sacred water, by the water where the power is born, and by the Blood of Sacrifice I baptize you and pronounce you a servant of Vodun.' He upended the phial and the pink, thick liquid trickled slowly down her face and she had to fight the urge to brush it away.

'Now you are a *hunsikanzo*,' he said, then stepped back.

For the first time her mother stirred in the deep chair and rose to her feet. She picked up a gourd covered by a loose lacework of beads and attached to a wooden handle from which long, coloured streamers hung. She approached Marie, rattling it softly, then held it out to her. 'Receive this *asson* to be your own, and with it the forces of the East, the hidden forces of the ancestor stars, which bring the knowledge of what has been.' Marie took it in her right hand, and her mother did a curious jigging dancestep back to her chair and picked up a clumsy-looking metal bell which stood on the small table beside it. With the same jigging step she returned, sounding the metal clapper very softly. 'Receive this *ogan* to be your own,' she repeated, 'and with it the forces of

84

the West, the hidden stars of the future, which bring the knowledge of what will be.' For a second her eyes met Marie's, who was suddenly terrified by what she saw in their depths. Then it was as if a veil was drawn across and she saw no more, as her mother went on: 'Let your *ogan* sound the call to the drums; let it establish the magic circle of sound; let it lead them to the beat of power.'

Marie took the *ogan* in her left hand and gave it a tentative shake. The bell clanged with startling loudness in the confines of the room, and she was shocked when the drums against the wall gave out a soft, deep answering reverberation.

'She gives homage to the *loa* and they answer,' her mother proclaimed, throwing her arms up with a sudden violent gesture that set Marie's heart pounding. 'The *vada* is finished; the royal rite of the sun and of the snake is ended.'

She looked down at Marie and said in her normal voice, 'There, it is finished. Tomorrow we will have the *petro* out at the lake, and in that rite your magic powers will be confirmed – you will be a Mambo.' She turned to the others and said, 'Crocodile, would you pour the wine? And there are some sweet, wild-honey cakes on the table there if you'd care for them.'

This snap of the powerful tension that had been building throughout the ceremony, and the sudden return to normalcy, set Marie's mind reeling. While the others started to chat about everyday things, she accepted a glass of wine and sipped it, but she did so in silence. There was a terrible feeling of depression and anticlimax inside her. She was grateful when, after a few minutes of this, her mother said, 'I should run along to bed now, Marie. It's going to be a wearing day for you tomorrow, and we all have some details of the ceremony to discuss.'

Before she sought her bed, she stole for a few minutes into the warm humidity of the June night and looked up at the stars blinking in a black-velvet sky. She had just been given the mystical power they contained, and yet she was not sure that she felt anything different at all. All she was sure of was that again she had this strange sensation of being torn in two, a sudden sense of incompleteness.

The order of going the next evening was somewhat different from what she had experienced on the only other occasion she had attended the rites. This time the gig took them only as far as Bayou St John, where they boarded a large skiff and were rowed up the quiet inlet towards the lake. Since this was to be a water ceremony, her mother had explained that the skiff was necessary for some of the proceedings, and particularly for one feature that she had had in mind. The great flat cart, with its usual load, was to go on by road and meet them at the rendezvous point at the lake's edge. In a low voice her mother went over with her once again the main details of the ceremony, then fell silent.

Marie, tense and wondrous, found the quiet gliding very peaceful as they slid between the banks of dense vegetation draped in veils of Spanish moss, moss which reached out long grey-green arms towards the deeper green of the water. Only the occasional shack at the water's edge, and sometimes a larger, more solid house, broke the luxuriance of the scene – always with an air of alien intrusion and a melancholy solitude.

They were not alone on the bayou; other boats passed them, obviously bent towards the same destination; some had white oarsmen who generally called out a cheerful greeting to them, and others were full of blacks who passed them with downcast eyes in respectful silence. The bayou's banks receded, the smell of marshlands became more intense, and finally the fresh breeze of the great lake was in their faces and they shot out on its ample, barren bosom. It was completely dark now. The moon, which would be full, had not yet risen, but the sky along the lake's edge was rosy and shimmering from the multitude of fires that burned along it. The black, capering figures outlined against the flames put Marie in mind of sundry paintings of similar scenes the nuns at the convent had been apt to show to underline their remarks on Hell and its dangers. She realized, ruefully, it was not a very apt thought to have at this particular moment.

As the skiff approached the shore, the white-clad regal figure of her mother was recognized, and some in the crowd began shouting her name and cheering, and presently a dense throng was lined up awaiting the beaching. Marie Laveau appeared to brace herself as the skiff touched shore, and she was met by a forest of outstretched hands. She got out, Marie following hard upon her heels, and the rest of the boat party, numbering some half a dozen, filed slowly after them bearing various things to be used at the rite. Her mother raised her hands for silence, and when it was quiet enough to make herself heard, she started to speak slowly and clearly about the significance of the great rite. Marie was intrigued by the fact that she was speaking in 'Gumbo' French, the patois of the common people, quite unlike her normal French, which was almost, though not quite, as elegant as that spoken by the Montal and Valdoux households. The thick patois seemed to come from an entirely different person.

Suddenly her mother raised her voice in song: '*Saiya ma coupê ca*,' she trilled.

Again she raised her hands for silence, and pointed imperiously to a spot at the very edge of the lake. 'There will the sacred fire burn,' she commanded. 'Bring from each bonfire a brand, and as the brand is given, a wish may be made. May Vodun grant it!'

In a matter of a few minutes, a large bonfire was roaring away on the designated spot. A great iron cauldron, which had been brought on the boat, was carefully lifted on to the blazing pile by two hungans, while another poured in water from a cask. Crocodile, in his cape of monkey skins, approached it, lifted his two hands, filled with salt, towards the stars, said something in a tongue Marie did not understand, and flung the salt into the pot. Now it was her turn. She approached the cauldron holding a box containing black pepper and other spices. Nervously, she trilled the 'offering' song and poured the contents into the pot.

A box was brought up, and out of it was taken a wriggling

black snake. A machete flashed and the snake lay in three parts, still twitching. Her mother picked up the portion with the head and flung it in, Crocodile, the middle section, and Marie, with a little twinge of distaste, the tail. The crowd once more took up the chant: *Ma'mselle Marie chauffe ça.'* A black cat was brought into the fire's orbit, and with a single stroke her mother cut its throat and flung it, too, into the by-now boiling pot. *'La Reine Marie chauffe ça,'* the chant continued. A black rooster, its feet and head tied together, was lifted from a crate, and this was put in the pot alive. *'La Reine Marie chauffe ça!'* the crowd shouted.

Crocodile handed over a pouch full of various coloured powders. Marie Laveau held it up to the crowd. 'For the love of God and man,' she chanted, 'join your hands and circle slowly around the pot.' A human chain was formed and started to circle in a slow shuffling dance as she poured, little by little, the powders into the seething pot. As she did so, the moon, as if answering a cue, rose large and yellow over the horizon, flooding the scene with a pale light.

Marie Laveau started to sing an oracle song that continued for several verses before the crowd answered in chorus: *'C'est l'amour, c'est l'amour, oui, Maman, c'est l'amour!'* ('It is love, it is love, yes, Mother, it is love.')

'Now,' she called, 'is the time for purification. Now do we greet the great spirits of the Waters. Take off your clothes and everybody into the lake.' She tore off her own shift.

After a moment's hesitation, Marie followed suit and plunged rapidly into the sheltering waters that struck cold but silky-smooth on her heated skin. The whole lake edge was now black with bobbing heads, accompanied by much laughter, squealing, and splashing. Marie paddled around for some time until she began to feel chilled. Then she climbed back into the boat, as her mother had instructed, and wrapped herself up in a blanket. Other people left the water, making for the silent drums and touching them with reverence.

When the crowd in the water had noticeably thinned, the drums started with a soft, insistent beat, the fires were renewed and blazed skywards again, and the dancing began.

Her mother had instructed Marie not to take part in this, so she amused herself by trying to count the crowd and sort out its constituents. Since most of the dancers had not bothered to dress and were completely naked as they danced around the fires, this was a fairly easy task. The majority of the crowd, which must have numbered more than four hundred, was black or shades of coloured. However, Marie could also make out a goodly number of white bodies, particularly white female bodies, and she estimated there must be between fifty or sixty whites there, most of them women. This fact would have surprised her a year ago; now, after seeing what went on in some Creole households, she was not in the least bit amazed.

The tempo and the dancing increased. Crocodile, who had thrown on his monkey-skin cape again, climbed into the skiff beside her and said briefly, 'I'm going to row you farther out and anchor. Your mother says to start in on your meditation for the *petro*. You're to have no part in the rest of this to the end.' He got back into a little dinghy he had towed with them and pulled away.

Three young men armed with conch shells had ranged themselves in front of her mother, whose naked, full-bodied figure could be seen clearly outlined against the leaping flames. The drums stopped suddenly and the conch horns rang out with their queer bleating cry. Quietness came and Marie Laveau started to talk to the crowd, but Marie was too far away to hear most of what she said. At the end she raised her voice and sang out, 'Now is the time for play – now is the time for love, my little ones – love in honour of Vodun, and when the conch sounds again we will eat and drink. Be happy, my little ones.' Soon couples were running off hand in hand into the darkness, as Marie had seen before.

She tried to close her mind to what was going on as the drums once more took up a soft, sensuous rhythm. She wanted to compose herself for the task at hand. She had been practising levitation for months now, under her mother's direction, and had become quite good at it in the confines of her home. But it was quite a different matter to

89

attempt it here before this multitude on the uncertain bosom of the lake.

'You are very young to become a Mambo,' her mother had said. 'And it is important that they accept you from the first – the *loa* may possess you and all will be well, but if they do not and nothing happens, there will be much muttering that you have only been made a Mambo because of me, and that will be bad for you. So at the end we will do this thing together, so that they may see you have the same powers as I. We will float from the boat to the land, and then, even if the *loa* do not come, all will be well.'

Again the conch shells were sounded and the crowd settled down to the ritual feast, with some eating and a lot of drinking. A young woman brought Marie some jambalaya, but she was so keyed up that after a couple of mouthfuls she began to feel sick, so she dumped the rest over the side as an offering to the water spirits.

Back on land the conches sang again and a hush fell on the crowd, which started to press in upon the main bonfire. They took up the same chorus of '*La Mambo Marie chauffe ça*' until four very large Negroes hurled barrels of water upon the dying blaze, and with sheets of steam the fire under the cauldron sizzled out. The black men lifted it off the dead embers and slowly decanted its contents into a large ornamental wooden cask.

'For those in dire need and for the next year,' her mother proclaimed in a loud, clear voice. Then she pointed with a dramatic hand. 'The moon wanes and day is almost here, but before we end these sacred rites a new Mambo is to be presented to you. Her name . . . her name is Marie Laveau!' A whisper of surprise went through the crowd. 'I go and I will come. Follow me into the water, those who wish to see!' With a few quick strokes, she had reached the skiff and had climbed over the side, her body glistening rosily with the water, and Marie, who had been completely absorbed by the proceedings, realized that another skiff now lay behind them on the lake, filled with torches that outlined them.

'Are you ready?' her mother demanded.

Marie nodded dumbly.

'Then hold my hand and concentrate,' her mother ordered. With all her consciousness pinpointed towards one end, Marie faced the densely packed shore. Slowly she felt herself rise and a wild elation flooded her. She was doing it! A low moan went up from the crowd, and she felt her mother's hand propelling her forward. They floated gently and silently over the surface of the lake towards the shore. When they were almost upon the first row of people, who were actually standing in the water, a woman suddenly screamed and in an instant all was pandemonium. The crowd turned in panic and started to run.

Marie, her concentration broken, felt herself dropping and then was pulled down by her mother, who also had fallen sideways. They ended up sitting in a foot of water, looking horror-stricken at the crowd, now streaming away into the darkness, leaving darker mounds of broken bodies behind.

'Quick!' her mother whispered. 'Back to the boat and we'll get dressed! Let's hope Crocodile has kept his wits about him!'

Dazedly, Marie did as she was told, and was still hunting for one of her shoes when the skiff once more jolted a-ground. She looked up to see Crocodile hurrying towards them. 'How bad is it?' her mother demanded worriedly.

'Bad enough!' His tone was grim. 'Though no one is dead. About a dozen with broken legs or arms – all trampled. They are being looked after, but there'll be hell to pay tomorrow in New Orleans – four of them were house slaves. The one I'm worried about is Bessie. You'd better have a look at her.'

The huge bulk of Bessie came into view, being supported with difficulty by three young men. Somehow they managed to get her into the boat, where she lay gasping and wheezing.

'We'll take her to Maison Blanche by boat,' Marie Laveau said after a quick look at her. 'It'll be faster and less hard on her than the cart. We'll stay the night there and I'll see what I can do.'

They set off rapidly in silence as the Voodoo Queen crouched over the old woman. Suddenly Bessie struggled up into a sitting position, a stricken look on her face. 'Oh, Ah feel powerful bad, Marie,' she choked out, 'powerful bad.' An agonized look came over the placid face, a hand clutched at the massive bosom, and she let out a curious mewing sound like a small kitten. Then she slumped over sideways, her head banging against the side of the boat.

Marie Laveau let out an exclamation and bent over her, listening for a heartbeat. Finally, she straightened. 'She's gone,' she announced in a flat tone. 'There was nothing I could do.' They had stopped the boat and she got slowly to her feet. 'Poor Bessie,' she said softly, 'she never got to have her stall in the market, after all – and it was such a little thing to ask.'

Then, in a harder voice, she said to Marie, 'And it looks as if you have just become the heir to a full-fledged hair-dressing business. Your apprenticeship is over now, in every sense of the word – you're on your own.'

Chapter Ten

Bessie's death had been a great shock to Marie, and other shocks were to follow in its wake. Although she had been fond of the old mulatto and had learned much from her, she had never realized what a buffer Bessie had been between her and the more unpleasant side of her new world. She was soon to find out.

Not that she had any trouble in the streets as she now walked them alone, her covered wicker basket on her arm. Word had gone around about the events out at the lake, and there were few souls in New Orleans – black or coloured – who dared accost a Mambo of such demonstrated powers. With the Creoles, however, it was quite another matter; almost overnight their attitude towards her had undergone a palpable change and she learned what it was to be 'put in her place'.

Their complaints about her hairdressing skills she could understand. Although she was good with her hands, she could not expect, or be expected, to emulate the expertise that old Bessie had developed over many years. But their hostility went far beyond this and manifested itself in a thousand different ways.

With the more amiable ones it showed in little ways, such as: 'Why don't you go to the kitchen and ask the cook for a drink, Marie? It's very warm today.' Or there was a calling-back after she was all packed up and halfway through the door, to be awarded a five-or ten-cent tip with a magnanimous, 'There, that's for all the trouble you have taken!'

With many it was worse, much worse. There was the oft-used 'missing jewellery' ruse. She would be packing up, almost ready to go, when the lady of the house would suddenly exclaim, 'Oh! Now where *is* that ring? (or brooch, or necklace.) I swear I had it right on this table!' There would be a feverish hunt, and, if she made a move to go, there came a sharp: 'You'd better wait here, Marie. I've simply *got* to find it. Perhaps if you had a look . . .?'

She soon learned that this was not the thing to do, for when the ring or whatever was found, there would be a sly, 'Oh, I'm so glad you found it by yourself, Marie. I do so *despise* unpleasantness of any kind.' So, mostly, she would just stand silent until the player tired of the cat-and-mouse game saying, 'How did it get there, I wonder?'

Sometimes the game would last a long time, making her late for her next appointment, with the certainty of more unpleasantness. Sometimes they would insist on going through her basket, finding nothing, but disarranging everything. There was never an apology. 'You can never be too careful,' they would say. And: 'It's for *your* protection, as well, you understand.' At other times there would be a catechism of questions – most of them highly personal – with a uniform phrase scattered throughout: 'Now, what do your people do about that, Marie?' As if she belonged to a strange and alien species.

And in a few instances, failing to bend or break her in any way, she would be dismissed on the most trifling of excuses and the doors of that particular house became closed against her.

'What *is* it with them?' she fumed to her mother. 'There is no satisfying them anymore. If I didn't know better, I'd think I'd been hexed. What should I do?'

Her mother smiled grimly and shrugged. 'I told you it would come. That it has not come sooner is simply because they did not really see you before; you were just there in the background. Now they do, and they know you for what you are to them – a dangerous threat. If you don't believe me, just look in the mirror.'

Marie had indeed changed. Now just past sixteen, she had grown to her full height, a tall and willowy five feet, seven inches, taller than her mother by a full inch. She was deep-bosomed and slim-hipped. Her face had fined down and accented the fine bone structure: the high cheekbones, the slim aquiline nose, and the soft, delicate mouth. Her tignon, binding her wavy, lustrous hair, gave her the look of an Egyptian goddess, and she carried herself like a queen.

'You make the small, petite women look insignificant and faded, and those of more generous build, dumpy and frowsy,' her mother said. 'You take from them practically the only thing they have. So can you blame them for making things difficult for you, for fighting you with the only weapons they have?

'You've got to understand them for what they are – and they are what Creole men have made them. Creole men are peacocks living in a fantasy world of their own making, in which they must strut and preen and be admired. From their wives they demand four things: purity, beauty, fertility, and unobtrusiveness. For wit, for excitement, for stimulation, even for companionship, they look not to them, but to us. And, as you well know, they do not look in vain. It follows that unless a Creole woman is completely stupid – and few of them are – she has very little to be happy about. True, she is decked out in fine clothes and jewellery, lives in a fine house, and has countless slaves and servants to do her bidding. But in reality she has no more freedom than those selfsame slaves – she's a possession.

'The Creole women have little power and few weapons. As long as their beauty lasts, they may hold their husbands, but this, as you know, is rare, for you can't hold a man with skill at needlepoint or a light touch on the harpsichord. Many of them tyrannize their families in a variety of ways, as you have seen. This is one of the few areas in which their husbands do not dare, or do not care, to cross them. But children grow, and children leave, and so it is often a very empty victory. So the majority of them end up praying on their knees in the cathedral to a cold God for surcease in the hereafter, with colder Death in their hearts. If they have other, more earthly needs' – she paused and pressed her lips together tightly – 'well, God help them! Why do you suppose you see some of them at the rites?'

'What you say may well be true, but what do I *do* about it?' Marie was too full of her own troubles to be concerned about theirs.

'Show them you're no threat; show them you're on their side. Tell their fortunes, listen to their troubles, flatter them – use your powers if you have to. There are some you'll never get through to, but with most of them there is a way – it's up to you to find it.'

But it was not that easy, for if Marie was having trouble enough with Creole women, she was finding even more with Creole men. It ranged all the way from masters of the house who would lie in wait to suggest everything from a midnight rendezvous to a little apartment of her own somewhere if——, to younger sons of the house who would lurk in dark corners to try for a quick grab, a kiss, or a pinch. She became more expert than a master swordsman at the art of parry and thrust, and had even used a long hatpin to full effect on sundry more desperate occasions. This, she told herself grimly as her sixteenth year waxed and waned, could not possibly go on much longer; something had to change, but she was still undecided in what direction this change should be.

In all this hurly-burly, two young men – one black, one white – fell genuinely and hopelessly in love with her. They were both aware that it was hopeless for quite obvious reasons, and they guarded their secret in their hearts, from the world, and from her. Not that if Marie had known it would have made any difference to her – she was too obsessed by her own problems – but the twin event was to have far-reaching consequences.

Her mother, while sympathetic to her additional problems, was too busy with domestic affairs to give much heed to her, for in the house on St Ann Street and in its inhabitants, equally great changes were taking place.

Marie-Philome had been presented at a quadroon ball, and an 'arrangement' had arisen out of it with a widower on the young side of middle-age, of impeccable lineage but somewhat reduced circumstances, which saw Marie-Philome installed in a house of her own on South Rampart. Marie had protested violently when she had first heard of it, thinking that it must be entirely her mother's idea, but she was considerably surprised to find that it was Marie-Philome's idea from start to finish. 'It is a most suitable arrangement,' her mother had observed. 'He is a man who is not thinking of remarrying, and Marie-Philome is extremely fond of him, so that it may well last for their lifetimes. She is very much like my mother in both looks and disposition, and I think she will be very happy.' As indeed she seemed to be.

With Celeste, who also was no longer under the parental roof, it was another matter. As time had passed and her sisters had bloomed, she had become swarthier and even more waspish of tongue and disposition. When the amiable Marguerite, now in Natchez, had volunteered not only to find her an apprenticeship at a milliner's but also to take her into her own home until she was established, her mother had accepted with relieved alacrity, though Celeste had fought the move every inch of the way and had gone off complaining about her unhappy lot. Her going was a great relief to Marie, who felt she had quite enough hostility to contend with in the outside world without having to face it at home, as well.

Celeste's was not the only departure, and the other was not at all to Marie Laveau's liking, since it upset one of her cherished plans. Daumeny had decided not to go with Jean into the iron-working business. Now twenty, he had grown into a large rebellious, rather reckless young man who had made it increasingly clear that he found the home atmosphere irksome. Marie had heard, on her hairdressing rounds, that he had been seeing an Anglo white girl of poor class. She had not passed this information on to her mother, thinking it would worry her to no purpose. But when Daumeny announced that he wanted no part in a family business and, further, that he was determined to seek his fortunes somewhere other than New Orleans, she was sure that the girl figured in his decision. Consequently, she was not surprised when, shortly after Daumeny's dramatic announcement, he moved out of the house and left New Orleans with the girl. The letter he wrote to his mother said, in short order, that he was off to seek his fortunes in the iron foundries of the North, that he was going to marry the girl, and that he would never return to the hidebound society of New Orleans.

His mother was furious. Not that she had ever paid much attention to him, coming as he did between her beloved Jean and the easy-going beauty of Marie-Philome – but that he dared to thwart her wishes aroused her venomous wrath. Marie watched with misgivings, not only for the young couple who she fondly hoped were beyond the range of her mother's powers, but also for herself should she at some future time incur that same anger.

Still, there were some compensations. The little house was emptying rapidly. Marie shared only with Amelie and Marie-Jeanne. And, as the eldest girl left, she had considerable say in what went on. Likewise, Jean, who showed no signs of wishing his independence, now shared only with Charles-Louis – also slated to learn the iron-working business – and young François.

However, another great shock was to come to Marie at home. She had become so used to coming and going in her mother's chambers during her Voodoo apprenticeship that she no longer felt any qualms about entering them. Consequently, having learned a prize bit of gossip on the way home one evening, she hastened to pass it on to her mother. Running through the front parlour, she burst into her mother's bedroom and then stopped in shock. Marie Laveau was sprawled naked on the bed in the middle of making love to a black man – and the black man was Christophe, the house man. Marie stood rooted in appalled silence until her mother said sharply, 'Get out, Marie! You've no business in here!' And she fled.

She spent a wretched night wondering what on earth she would say to her mother on the morrow, or what her mother *could* say to her. She need not have been so concerned; Marie Laveau was very cool and calm about the incident.

'So now you know,' she remarked serenely. 'It's probably time you did ... time you realized something you will not have learned about in your scented boudoirs. It is not only men who have needs that must be satisfied; women have exactly the same needs and exactly the same right to be satisfied. I am a free agent, and if I feel like making love to someone who wants me, there is absolutely no reason why I shouldn't. I like it. I always have, and I expect I always will. Maybe you are the same, maybe you aren't, but remember, it is just as natural as eating or breathing – regardless of what the nuns may have told you and whatever you may have heard from your Creole customers. I suppose you were surprised last night, because the young never seem to realize that those older than themselves have any of the same needs, but people don't change that much with age. You'll soon find that out. However, in the future, you might remember to knock before entering my bedroom – it will save you further shocks.'

'Oh, certainly, Mama. I'm really very sorry. I just didn't think,' Marie muttered with considerable embarrassment.

'And one other thing,' her mother added. 'Don't speak of this to any of the others, particularly Jean. He wouldn't understand probably anymore than you do, and it's none of your business, anyway.'

'I wouldn't dream of it, Mama,' Marie agreed with fervour.

Her mother's lack of embarrassment was more than made up for by Christophe's acute case of it. For months he could not look Marie in the eye, and went about with his head hanging down and a look of abject misery on his face. She felt extremely sorry for him, but she could think of no way to ease the situation, so she left it to time to heal his trampled feelings.

This whole business, plus her mounting frustration with her work, made her increasingly anxious for a change in her own life. She began to spend a lot of time with Marie-Philome and to contrast her sister's happiness and ease of life with her own meagre existence and its tribulations. It helped her to decide.

But what clinched it was a particularly nasty and frightening incident in the Montal household. She had gone to fix the hair of Anne and Yolande for a Carnival ball. They had both been extremely fussy and exacting, as usual, so it was already late when she had finished to their satisfaction. She was making her way out of the back courtyard – since tradespeople were forbidden to exit by the front portal in the Montal household – when, on passing the steps to the *garçonnière*, she found her way blocked by the tall figure of St Regis Montal. She stepped aside to pass him; he stepped in front of her; she went the other way; he did, too.

She stopped, her heart beating uncomfortably fast, and said placatingly, *'M'sieu*, please excuse me, but I am very late. I must get home.'

He still said nothing, but she could smell the reek of absinthe on him. She dropped her heavy basket and tried to rush past him, but he caught hold of her, pinning her arms to her sides, and said in a thick voice, 'Not yet, *ma jolie petite*! Let's have some fun first. I haven't been inside one of your sort for a while, and I have a fancy for it tonight.'

She opened her mouth to scream, but he clamped one hand over it lightning-fast, and with the other hand he gripped both her slim wrists and twisted her arms cruelly behind her. Then he began to force her up the wrought-iron stairs. She caught the glimpse of a frightened black face peering out of the slave quarters, but knew she could expect no help from that quarter; the Montal slaves were all too cowed. Summoning up all her strength, she threw herself back against him, despite the pain in her arms, then bit the confining hand as hard as she could. As he reeled off balance, she screamed at the top of her voice. St Regis gave her a vicious cuff on the side of the head and dragged her up the remaining stairs, but a door in the *garçonnière* flew open and Dominic Montal and Emile Valdoux appeared, both clad in evening clothes and evidently waiting to escort the Montal sisters to the ball.

'What's happening?' Dominic Montal said uncertainly.

But Emile, who had stopped transfixed for a second, brushed past him, his pale face convulsed, his whole body bristling with anger. 'What the hell do you think you are doing?' he roared at St Regis. 'Let her go!'

'I'm going to teach this hellcat a lesson in manners she

100

won't forget!' St Regis snarled with a curse, aiming another cuff at the wildly struggling Marie.

'If you don't let her go this instant, I'll have the gizzard out of you by morning!' Emile yelled.

'Go to hell!' St Regis sneered. And, kicking his own door open, he went to push Marie inside. Emile launched himself at his tall cousin like an enraged bull, and St Regis went down under the sudden onslaught, allowing Marie to spring free.

The commotion had brought a small knot of curious slaves out of their quarters, and now they stood in silence with fearful, upturned faces, anxiously watching the fracas on the narrow veranda.

Marie stood poised for flight on the top of the stairway, torn between her desire for escape and her anxiety for the smaller Emile at the hands of his vicious cousin. One glance told her that Emile, helped by the narrow confines of the veranda, was doing all right for himself. In fact, he was sitting on St Regis's chest and flailing away at his face with both fists, his own face glazed with fury.

An imp of devilment possessed her. 'Don't kill him, my dear Emile,' she said in a high, clear voice. 'He really isn't worth it.'

Suddenly one of the long French windows in the main house was flung open, and the cold, imperious voice of Margot Montal floated into the courtyard. 'What's all this commotion?'

Dominic hastily stepped in front of the struggling forms on the veranda and called back, 'Nothing, Mama – just St Regis and Emile playing the fool.'

'Well, tell them to stop at once, and both of you get in here. Your sisters are ready to leave now.' The windows closed with a definitive click.

Dominic dragged Emile off his brother, and St Regis staggered to his feet, blood oozing from his nose and from a cut on his lip. He gave a short ugly laugh as he gazed down at the smaller man, 'And what do you think that proved, my prissy, pompous cousin – that you're the better man? If you think that will get you what I was taking, I can tell you now, she'd never touch you in a million years.' And he went into his room, slamming the door behind him.

'He's just had a drop too much. He didn't know what he was doing,' Dominic muttered defesively. Emile ignored him and went over to Marie, who was leaning on the veranda rail weak with relief. 'Are you all right?' he asked anxiously. 'Did he hurt you?'

She gave him a grateful smile. 'No, I'm all right – thanks to you!'

He helped her tenderly down the steps, and took her basket, which the slaves had righted and refilled with her scattered tools. 'I'll see you home,' he said.

'Oh, there's no need,' she whispered, conscious of the curious stares about her. 'I don't want to make any trouble for you, Emile. You'd better go with Dominic, or Madam Montal will be angry.' Impulsively, she kissed him on the cheek.'But I can never thank you enough for this, Emile. I'll never forget it.' And fled out the back gate.

'Nor I,' he murmured, looking dazedly after her.

The incident made up her mind for her. Just before her seventeenth birthday, she tackled her mother. 'Mama,' she said with determination, 'I have come to a decision. I wish to take a lover, and so, if it's all right with you, I'd like to be presented at the next quadroon ball.'

Chapter Eleven

Her mother's reaction had been strange, partly relief and partly some other emotion which Marie had been hard put to define, but it seemed to be apprehension. 'You have thought well about this?' she had demanded. 'I had no idea you were even thinking along these lines. You still have a lot of work ahead, you know. I'm not at all sure it is wise.'

'Oh, indeed, I have thought about it,' Marie said with vehemence. 'And I wish you'd hear me out, because then I think you'll agree. To be frank, Mama, I have done what you wished – I have become a Mambo, and I have learned to be a hairdresser – but I am not too happy as a result. You say you want me to follow in your footsteps and become a Queen. *Bon*, I am prepared to do that – but that will not be for many, many years. I know how your business is run, I know how your organization works, I know how the ceremonies are organized – but, for what? I shall not actually get to *run* anything for perhaps twenty or thirty years, so I do not see what all the rush was *about*!' She paused expectantly, but her mother said nothing, so she went on. 'I should hate to think I will be doing what I have been for the past couple of years the rest of my life. You have said my aim is to get at the Creole men and their power through their women, but it strikes me that if the women feel I am such a threat now it would be better if I had the protection of a lover. Then they would know I would not be after *their* menfolk, and I'd have a lot better chance of gaining their confidence.'

Marie Laveau nodded. 'Go on.'

'I don't want to get *married*,' Marie went on with decision. 'I don't think I'd like that, but a *petit arrangement* such as Marie-Philome has would suit me very well.'

'You're not Marie-Philome!' her mother interjected.

'Oh, I know *that*, but I do like nice things, just as she does.

I like beautiful clothes, I like money, I'd love a nice house – and I'm not going to get *any* of those doing what I am now. I know these things don't mean anything to you, but they do to me, and all these a lover would provide.' She paused, hopeful for some reaction.

'Do you have a particular one in mind, or will just anyone do?' Marie Laveau asked, a slight sneer in her voice.

To her surprise, her daughter nodded vigorously. 'Yes, I have. A very particular one and – oh, Mama! – he's just beautiful! I know you'll think so, too.'

Her mother tried not to appear as astonished as she actually felt. 'You mean you have him all picked out? Who is he, and how does he feel about it?'

'It's Etienne LeBlanc.' Seeing the name meant nothing to her mother, Marie rushed on: 'Don't you remember? His parents were killed in a steamboat explosion upriver a couple of years back. He's some kin to the St Yveses, though I've never figured out quite how. Anyway, he's the eldest. There's a younger brother and two sisters, and they're *terribly* rich, and it's all theirs right now! They've been living on one of their plantations until recently, but about three months ago they came to live with an uncle and aunt who have a big place over on Royal. The eldest sister, Marie-Thérèse, is husband-hunting. Valerie doesn't like her much because she is terribly cold and snobbish, but she shouldn't have much trouble finding a husband – she has a simply *huge* dowry. Then comes Etienne, who is just the most handsome thing you've ever seen, and *so* debonair! His brother Justin isn't half as good looking, but he's such fun. Valerie likes him a lot. And she says the younger sister, Clarisse, is sweet, too, though she hasn't been here much – she's still just a child and lives up at their big plantation, Castle Blanche. But, anyway, the three here are just too wild and wonderful for words! They are taking New Orleans by storm!'

'And how did you happen to meet this paragon?' Marie Laveau asked with foreboding.

Marie blushed and looked down. 'Well, I haven't actually *met* him,' she confessed. 'In fact, I've rather avoided him.

But I've seen him at the Valdoux's, and Valerie has told me *all* about him.'

'Then how on earth do you know that any of this is even possible?' Her mother was vexed. 'Really, Marie, I never thought you could be so scatter-brained. For all you know, an affair might be the last thing the young man has in mind – his marriage might be being arranged right now. Even if this isn't so, what makes you think you'd be to his taste?'

Marie fixed her gaze upon her mother. 'That will be taken care of. All I want you to do is to take care of the practical arrangements – to see that our meeting is brought about in the usual way. I will see to the rest. I *will* be to his taste.'

They looked at one another in silence for a moment. Then Marie Laveau said briefly, 'I see. Well, in that case, if you are set on this, I will see to it. But I must warn you it might not be as easy or as idyllic as you seem to imagine. You have never had to cater to a man's needs and whimsies; the time may come when you regret this step.'

Marie was cool. 'This is something I would have to find out sometime, isn't it? And as far as I'm concerned, the sooner, the better.'

'*Bon*. Then I must get started at once. The end of Carnival is quite near, and I presume you do not wish to wait until next October. There is much to be done,' her mother said with decision. 'There are our places in the hall to be reserved, gowns to be made, invitations to be sent. In fact, I don't know how we are going to manage it all in the time available.'

They did it, of course, though afterwards Marie was to recall that never had she been through a more hectic time. When Marie-Philome had made her debut, Marie had been so engrossed in her own life she had paid little attention to what went on, a fact she now bitterly regretted as she whirled from fittings at the dressmaker's, to rehearsals in the hall of the Orleans Theater, where the ball was to be held, to dancing lessons, and to sessions with an old friend of her mother's who managed the balls and who drilled her on etiquette and other, more intimate, matters, which Marie mentally labelled as 'tactics'.

'Remember,' the old woman admonished her, 'that if you have your eye on someone already, you will have to discourage the others – and there will be many others, my dear – and discourage them without giving the slightest offence. You have no idea how touchy Creole men are on these occasions, and you certainly don't want your "coming-out" marred by a duel! There are rules to be observed in this. If a man asks you to dance, you must grant him at least one. If he persists, then you may decline the next. If he still persists, plead a headache and absent yourself in the withdrawing room for a while. If, after that, he still persists – but few will, because most of them know the rules as well as we do – then you will have to signal to your chaperone – in this case, your mother – and leave her to deal with it.'

'I'd no idea it was so complicated,' Marie confessed.

'Life tends to be complicated – particularly ours,' the old woman assured her with a wry smile. 'But come, there is still much to do . . .!'

At the rehearsals Marie was surprised to run into her childhood friend, Jacqueline Delambe, of whom she had seen very little since leaving the Mount Carmel convent. At the sight of her, Marie's heart sank slightly. Jacqueline had always been lovely to look at, but now there was only one word to describe her – gorgeous! Her skin was the colour and texture of camellias; her eyes were a light shade of violet, framed between the longest, silkiest lashes Marie had ever seen; her generous mouth was a deep rose-pink; and her lustrous blue-black hair framed her face and shoulders in deep, soft waves. There was about her an air of gentle sensuousness that enveloped her like an aura. Marie felt pallid, insignificant, and gauche by the side of her.

After the first wild rush of greetings and exchange of gossip, she began diplomatically to find out what this formidable opposition had in mind. 'What a coincidence!' she gushed. 'I never expected to find you here. I thought you were still at Mount Carmel.'

'Oh, I have been until now.' Jacqueline blushed. 'This is my mother's idea – just a matter of form, really, because I'm not ... well ... you know ... my future is already more or less arranged.'

This was a relief to Marie, but her curiosity was piqued. 'Who's the lucky man? Can you tell me?' she whispered.

Again Jacqueline blushed. 'Yes, I don't mind telling you – it's Dominic Montal.'

Marie gasped. 'But surely ...' she started to say, then bit back her words.

'What is it, Marie? Don't tell me he is the one *you* want!' Jacqueline exclaimed.

'No, of course not,' Marie said hurriedly. She was torn by indecision. 'It's just that ... well, as you know, I've been working as a hairdresser and have been much in the Montal household, and there has been some talk lately of Dominic's future ...'

'Oh, you mean about him and Claire Valdoux?' Jacqueline broke in.

'You know about it? They say the marriage is nearly arranged.'

'Yes, I've known all along. Dominic told me,' Jacqueline said serenely, 'but it is just a marriage of convenience. You understand? Dominic loves me and I him. He merely marries to please the family.'

'But when he does marry, which may be quite soon,' Marie protested, 'what then?'

'It will make no difference to *us*,' Jacqueline assured her.

Marie was flabbergasted and her curiosity was still far from satisfied. 'How did you meet him?' she asked.

'In church.' Jacqueline gazed at her with wide, limpid eyes. 'It was love at first sight – *so* romantic! And how about you, Marie?'

'Well since my future is not yet certain, I'd rather not say. But, believe me, when it is, I'll come to you first.'

Somehow, out of all the chaos and hurly-burly, order came eventually, and Marie found herself on the night of the ball, gowned, bejewelled, and more nervous than she had ever been. She paced up and down in her mother's bedroom like a caged lion, while Marie Laveau put the last touches to her own elaborate toilette.

Marie's dress was of heavy cream silk, cut low off the shoulders and with a very full bell skirt that accented her slim waist. The skirt was caught up in deep flounces at the hem with turquoise and silver paillettes in the form of squash blossoms, and to accent this she was wearing a heavy necklet of turquoise and silver squash blossoms, which her mother had presented to her, informing her that this was Navaho Indian work.

Marie Laveau was wearing a deep burgundy satin gown, with a turban to match, which accented the creaminess of her skin. Around her neck she was wearing a choker of deep red garnets and gold, which made her look like some barbaric goddess. By and large, Marie decided, they made a striking pair.

They arrived at the ballroom, which was in a wing of the Orleans Theater, just after nine o'clock, and were ushered up on to a crimson-carpeted dais, where the 'debutantes' and their chaperones, who were also the patrons of the ball, were to sit. Marie Laveau seated herself regally in the central chair, and Marie took the little gilt chair to her right. Also on the dais were several other mothers and their daughters whom she knew slightly, and there was Madame Delambe with Jacqueline, dressed in heliotrope silk, which deepened her incredible eyes to pure violet. Marie breathed a little sigh of thankfulness that she was not in active competition with her beautiful friend.

Arranged along two sides of the long room were banquettes on which sat the rest of the chaperones and their charges, elegantly gowned in a kaleidoscope of colours and all fanning themselves languidly. The privileged few on the dais were saved this labour, since overhead a punkah – after the style of those used in India, and operated by a popeyed piccaninny – wafted a gentle breeze for them. There was the scent of banked flowers and mingled perfumes. Soft music drifted from a discreetly hidden orchestra. From another room came the faint clink of glasses and the discreet pop of wine bottles being opened. The floor of cypress wood

– purportedly the best dancing floor in the city – gleamed under a fresh coat of wax. Even the moon was co-operating, shining full through the open French windows at the balcony overlooking Orleans Street.

Jacqueline leaned over to Marie, her eyes sparkling with delight. 'Isn't it *romantic*!' she breathed. 'Oh, I'm so glad *Maman* insisted on this!'

Marie managed a weak smile and a nod in return. Although she appreciated the setting, she was beginning to feel remarkably like a spider sitting in the middle of its web – but where were the flies? She began to get nervous all over again.

'For goodness sake, stop *fidgeting*,' her mother hissed in her ear. 'You're hopping around like a befuddled flea. Compose yourself. The guests are starting to arrive.'

Marie looked hopefully towards the grand staircase at the rear of the ballroom, where small knots of male heads could be seen slowly ascending into view – but the one she was looking for was not among them. She offered up a silent prayer to Erzulie, the Voodoo Goddess of Love, and then, to be on the safe side, one to the Virgin Mary. Her mother let out a little satisfied exclamation, and Marie looked up to see a familiar face. Emile Valdoux was advancing towards them, flanked by the Montal twins, and behind him – her heart skipped a beat – was the tall, elegant figure of Etienne LeBlanc, his younger brother Justin by his side.

'There he is, behind Emile,' she whispered.

Her mother gave a light sigh. '*Ah, oui, il est vraiment beau.*'

As Emile Valdoux bent over her mother's hand, Marie noticed how animated he seemed. His normally pale cheeks were flushed, and his mild eyes were bright and sparkling.

He's been drinking – the thought flashed through her mind as he passed on to her.

'You're looking very lovely tonight, Marie.' He smiled as he bent over her hand. 'When you are free, may I have the honour of the first dance?'

'Oh ... er ... why, thank you, Emile .. Yes ... later,' she muttered absently, her eyes fixed on Etienne. She braced herself for the first contact and projected every particle of magnetism in her towards him. *Oh, Erzulie, help me now!* she said silently. As he took her hand and muttered the usual polite phrases of the newly introduced, his chestnut eyes, which were almost identical in colour to his chestnut hair, widened slightly and he gave her another more searching glance; for a second his hand tightened and lingered on hers, and then he moved on.

St Regis was before her now. 'And how's our pretty little hairdresser this evening?' he drawled, but she was thankful to see that those disturbing amber eyes were not fixed on her at all but on Jacqueline.

The parade continued. The room was rapidly filling up now, and the dancing had started, the music taking on a louder, livelier beat. And when the cascade of guests had subsided to a trickle, Emile appeared before her to claim his dance.

She had been instructed that she should always leave the conversational opening gambit to her partners; but, feeling she knew Emile too well to follow this admonition, she said, as he gingerly swept her into a dance, 'I was really surprised to see you here.'

His step faltered and he looked at her in amazement. 'Why should you be surprised? Didn't you know I would come?'

'I wouldn't have thought this sort of thing was to your fancy at all – a respectable banking man like you,' she teased gently.

'Well, normally I don't go dancing much. But this is a special occasion, isn't it?' he parried. 'And these are the gayest balls in town, after all. So, why not?' He was trying to be animated and it sat rather oddly on his stolid, sober figure.

Etienne danced by, a very small, saffron-coloured girl in his arms, and she missed a lot of what Emile was saying as she followed them rather anxiously with her eyes. To her relief, they did not seem to have much to say to one another. Jacqueline danced by in the arms of Dominic, an expression of rapture on her face.

The dance ended and Emile immediately said, 'How about another?'

'Oh, not now, Emile,' she murmured absently.

His face fell. 'How about some refreshments, then?'

'No, thank you.'

'Well, perhaps a little later?'

'Perhaps.'

Looking rather crestfallen, he led her back to her chair. He glanced unhappily at her mother and then at her. 'Well, thank you,' he said stiffly and withdrew.

Her heart rose as the tall figure of Etienne approached. 'May I have the honour?' he inquired politely.

Again summoning all her resources, she gave him an upwards sweeping glance and a slight smile. 'Indeed,' she murmured and gave him her hand. His eyes widened again and without a further word he took her in his arms and swept into the dance.

This time she left the opening to him and for a few moments they danced in silence, to a beat which she recognized as a very modified form of the Calinda. Unlike Emile, who danced correctly and methodically, Etienne was a natural dancer, with much verve and grace, expertly guiding her on the crowded floor.

'I've just come from another ball,' he observed finally. 'An extremely dull affair with three girls to every man, and apparently three mamas to every girl.'

'Oh? I hope you are not finding *this* dull,' she murmured.

'No. This is much more to my taste.' He glanced down at her. 'Here there seem to be three men for every girl – I like competition.'

'Indeed! I am not sure you will find any worthy of you.'

His arm around her waist tightened slightly. 'You dance extremely well.'

'Thank you. I might say the same about you.'

'You're tall for a girl.'

'As you are tall for a man,' she retorted.

He smiled at her suddenly, revealing brilliant white teeth under his silky moustache. 'So you think we make a handsome pair?' he demanded.

'Quite the most handsome in the ballroom,' she assured him solemnly. 'See how enviously they regard us! They may even want to make a statue of us to commemorate this moment in marble.'

He threw back his head and laughed. 'At the other ball a girl told me she could see no one else in the room because she was drowning in the divine pools that were in my eyes. I can see you are having no such trouble. Would you not care to drown in my divine pools?' He gazed at her steadily.

'Oh, la!' she exclaimed in mock vexation. 'That would be too difficult, since I was just going to invite you to drown in mine!'

He laughed again, twin spots of colour appearing on his clear cheeks. '*Touché, ma belle.* I was beginning to think that I had seen all New Orleans had to offer and that it was not so special, after all. Now I can see I was wrong, quite wrong.'

The music stopped and Marie tensed for the next crucial moment. He hesitated for a second. Then: 'Would you perhaps care for a glass of wine?'

'If you think our public can do without us for a while, that would be delightful,' she murmured.

After that there was only Etienne. They laughed, they danced, they dined, they strolled, gazing into one another's eyes as the ball and the ballroom and the dancers receded farther and farther from them. Once St Regis tried to claim her for a dance and she contrived to shrink slightly against Etienne at his approach. Etienne had been smooth, but icy cold.

'Ah, my dear kinsman, how unfortunate, but I have already extracted a promise for this next dance from the young lady. It is a particular favourite of mine.'

When St Regis had bowed sardonically and withdrawn, Etienne said, 'That does not displease you, I take it? You do not care for St Regis?'

She shook her head. 'We do not seem very compatible.'

'Ah, yes, to be compatible with St Regis is not easy,' he replied tightly.

Earlier in the evening she had noticed Emile standing by

himself in the shadow of a potted palm, an unhappy, perplexed expression on his face. But when she next looked for him, he was nowhere to be seen and she felt a pang of guilt.

Occasionally, for form's sake, Etienne would return her to her mother, who sat narrowly viewing the proceedings, a slight enigmatic smile on her handsome face, but then he would stand guard over her chair as he exchanged polite pleasantries with the chaperones on the platform.

As the night drew on and the dancers began to thin out, he suggested a stroll in the garden. They descended the grand staircase and went out into the courtyard, where a few couples were sitting at the tables set out in the shade of the flowering trees and shrubs. It was cool and faintly scented, lit palely by the dying moon and a few flickering candles. 'The end of Carnival is near,' Etienne observed solemnly. 'Will you be attending the rest of the balls here?'

'Mardi Gras is only ten days away,' she replied. 'But until then I will be here.'

'I, also,' he said. Then, after a moment of silence: 'If that pleases you.'

'That would please me very much,' she murmured softly.

'You permit?' he took her hand and, raising it to his lips, kissed it softly, the fine hairs of his moustache tickling it and sending a little shiver of delight up her spine.

Her hand tightened on his and she drew him gently towards her. 'No,' she whispered, 'not like that – like this!' Softly their lips came together, his arms tightening around her as he kissed her lingeringly. With a sigh he stepped back, still holding her hands, and looked down at her.

'Till tomorrow, *chérie*,' he whispered. 'And for me until then will seem an eternity.'

Chapter Twelve

The Carnival of 1847 was now but a pleasant memory, and the city of New Orleans lay dormant, waiting for Eastertide and resurrection. But for Marie new life was already beginning, and the second half of a long-thought-about plan was coming to fruition.

It had been easy with Etienne, almost too easy. They had seen one another every day for the remaining days of Carnival, and on Mardi Gras, among all the frantic merry-making, he had told her he loved her, had asked if she were willing ... if he might talk to her mother ... in fact, everything that should be said and done on such occasions.

This accomplished, it was time to tackle her mother on the other new project. '*Maman*,' she said, 'Etienne wants to give me a place of my own on Rampart Street, and I already have one very much in mind, one that I think may be pleasing and profitable to us all – *your* house and its contents.'

'Oh,' said Marie Laveau with a strange smile. 'So not only do you want a new life, but you also want what is mine in the bargain.'

'No, *Maman*, it's not like that at all,' Marie said uncomfortably. 'It is just that ... well ... it is quite evident to me that you do not care for the house, yet you feel tied to it. Half the time it stands untenanted. I care for it and would care for what is in it – always. You could sell it to Etienne for a good price. He does not care a fig about money, and to him it would be a mere bagatelle. But to me it would mean a great deal, and, in a sense, the property would still be in the family.'

'That is true enough,' Marie Laveau said slowly, again with the same strange smile. 'In a sense it would be like selling it to myself.' Something seemed to be amusing her enormously. 'Well, if your handsome young gallant wants to talk to me about it, I am agreeable.'

Etienne was almost as enthusiastic about the house as Marie. But, to her surprise, he showed an almost feminine fastidiousness about its shabbier parts and decreed that it should be redecorated and that he woulld seek suitable re-furnishings for all but the drawing room and main bedroom from his plantation upstate; further, he would go up there himself to supervise the packing and transport. He also in-formed Marie that he would bring two of his house slaves down to cater to their needs, since they knew his ways and it would spare her the trouble of breaking in a new pair of slaves. Since breaking in anybody was the last thing Marie wished to do, she was pleased by his thoughtfulness, but a little surprised, also, that a young man so deeply in love as he professed to be should be so taken up with the thought of his own creature comforts.

No sooner had he left town than Marie received an urgent summons from Valerie Valdoux, and when she answered it, it was with a certain heaviness of heart. Her new life would bring her much gain, but also some losses, and Valerie would perforce have to be one of the losses, since there could be little or no communication between an aristocratic young lady on Royal Street and an inhabitant of one of the little houses on Rampart. She was extremely fond of Valerie, as she knew Valerie was of her, and it grieved her to think that she would have to give her pain and that their ways would have to part. She had hoped to be able to break the news as gently as possible herself, but one look at Valerie's woebegone face told her that this was already too late.

'Is it true what I've heard – that Etienne is setting you up on Rampart?' Valerie blurted out as soon as they were closeted alone.

'Where did you hear that?' Marie temporized.

'Oh, everyone has been behaving so queer and strange lately, and you haven't been around to visit for so long – I just *knew* something was up, I finally got it out of Justin; he's the only one around here who'll tell you *anything*. Why, Marie, *why* must you do this thing?'

Silently cursing Justin LeBlanc, Marie said, 'Etienne and I are in love. What else can we do?'

'But you know what this will mean,' Valerie went on, wrapped up in her own grievance. 'We'll not be able to be friends anymore. I won't even be able to speak to you. I don't know how I'll survive. Everyone is changing so, everyone is leaving – my whole world is falling apart.' She burst into tears.

'Now, now, Valerie, it's not that bad,' Marie soothed. 'You made your own debut this year, and from now on you'll be so snowed under with beaux and parties and things that you'll hardly have time to miss me. And we can meet sometimes – say, at church.'

'But it won't be the same,' Valerie wailed. 'Nothing is the same, and I'm so miserable. You've no idea what things have been like around here lately. Mama's been impossible; she's been so upset because the Montals are doing nothing about Claire and Dominic. And Papa's been upset because he thinks the LeBlancs have been a bad influence on Bayard and Lamont – though it's not *their* fault,' she added obscurely. 'And now he's even more upset because Emile came to him on the first day of Lent and said he'd decided he'd marry Marie St Yves, and he'd just as soon the arrangements were made as quickly as possible so they could get married at Easter.'

'Emile!' Marie said in astonishment.

'Oh, *yes*! I told you everything is topsy-turvy. I'm sure he's just doing it to please Mama and calm her down. He scarcely knows Marie, even if she is his first cousin. Papa thinks so, too, and he tried to talk him out of it, but Emile was absolutely adamant. I just don't know what's got into him. And, oh! even if he is a bit stuffy, I *am* going to miss him so.' She burst into renewed sobs

'Well, he won't be going very far, will he?' She was still trying to be soothing, though the news had surprised her.

'The plan is to take a long honeymoon trip to Europe and for him to study banking methods over there. Then when they come back they'll have a new house over in the Garden District – on St Charles, I think; they're buying it with her dowry. With Emile getting married, Claire's going to have

116

to do something soon about Dominic. It's not as if she doesn't like him; I know she does. Oh! If only she were less supine! Some other woman will make off with him if she doesn't watch out.'

Feeling like a traitor, Marie said noncommittally, 'Well, as you've always said, he probably won't do anything before St Regis does.'

'But that's just it!' Valerie suddenly cheered up. 'It looks as if St Regis *is* thinking of marriage. Not to me, thank *le bon Dieu*! To Marie-Thérèse LeBlanc – of all people. I think Tante Montal has been pushing it because she likes Marie-Thérèse – birds of a feather, *I'd* say. Marie-Thérèse is as cold as a fish, the only LeBlanc I *don't* like. St Regis actually seems interested, though whether it's in her or in that huge dowry of hers, I wouldn't know. Anyway, as you can see, everything is changed and everything is so trying, and if it weren't for Justin, I don't know what I'd do,' she finished breathlessly.

Marie shot a shrewd glance at her friend. '*Eh, bien.* So it's like that, is it? We may be sisters-in-law *à la main gauche*, after all.'

Valerie blushed. 'It's nothing definite, but I do like him, even if he isn't as handsome and as dashing as Etienne,' she murmured. 'But perhaps one day . . . I'm in no hurry, and of course it is out of the question until Claire marries.' Her face began to pucker again, 'And that's another thing, Marie. What if Etienne decides to get *married*? What will happen to you then?'

Marie shrugged. 'If and when that happens, we'll just have to see, that's all. For now there is no question of that.'

'Perhaps, but you just don't *know*. Oh, the LeBlancs are so lucky! They've no one to tell them what to do or how to behave or anything. Mustn't that be wonderful, Marie?'

'I don't know,' Marie said, 'but I imagine I'll soon find out.'

There were more tears and lamentations before she could extricate herself from Valerie, and she did so only by the firm promise that they would see as much of one another as possible between then and her actual move to Rampart Street.

'Oh, I am going to miss you so!' Valerie sobbed.

'And I you, my dear, and I you,' Marie sighed.

But if she was to lose one friend, she had also regained an old one. Now, as she passed between St Ann Street and her house on Rampart – for the deed was signed and sealed to her – she would frequently run into Jacqueline, who was bent on much the same business to a house, but three doors removed from Marie-Philome's, on South Rampart. Jacqueline was so happy and so radiant with happiness that Marie found their meetings a source of happiness herself. The rosy cloud that surrounded Jacqueline lapped over and encompassed her and she caught herself thinking the same rosy, romantic thoughts as her friend and longing for Etienne's return.

Their reunion was correspondingly rapturous, and when the sighs, the kisses, and the protestations of undying love were done, he said with another heavy sigh, 'Alas, my sweetest love! I fear it will take at least ten days for the things from Castle Blanche to arrive and for the house to be finished. How will I survive so long without you?'

Marie withdrew a little. 'Then why should we wait, Etienne? Why not sooner?'

He looked puzzled. 'But I have just said, my sweet, the house will not be prepared.'

'Is that the only house in New Orleans?' she demanded. 'Is there not somewhere else we could meet?'

'You mean you would be willing . . .? Before . . .?'

'Why not?' she said with determination. 'We love each other; we want to be together. That is certain, no? Why should a few bits of furniture stand in our way?'

'But . . . it is totally against the custom,' he stammered. 'Your mother, she would never allow . . . we couldn't.'

'My mother need never know. Why must we be like everyone else?' she said eagerly. 'Did you not tell me you were in the *garçonnière* of your uncle's house? And is there not a wicket gate and a private entrance to the courtyard? You don't share apartments with Justin, do you?'

118

'Well . . . er . . . no.'

'Then why could I not come to you there? Next Saturday my mother will be away from the house all night. The others will think I have gone with her, as I usually do. She leaves the house around ten. I could be with you a little later. It is only, after all, a few blocks away. The wicket is on Bienville, no?'

'Yes,' he replied hesitantly.

'So leave it open for me and meet me inside. It will be something all our own, something the world will never know about – just *us*. Won't that be exciting and romantic, my love?'

He still looked confused at this daring departure from the Creole way, but he gave a little shaky laugh and took her in his arms, pressing a hot, flushed cheek to hers. 'This is something I did not expect. *Vraiment*, Marie, you take my breath away. Why not, indeed! What are the stupid rules for, but to be broken! But surely there is no other woman in the whole of New Orleans such as you!'

In that, he was undoubtedly quite right, Marie reflected a trifle smugly, as she nestled against him.

Saturday dawned and dragged, and Marie waited with ill-concealed impatience for the night. Her mother had asked her if she were going to the rites at the lake, but she had not been at all concerned when she had declined on the grounds that she would be going to High Mass at the cathedral with Etienne on the morrow and would prefer not to be over-tired.

When the gig had rattled off, she had taken a purple-hooded cloak from her mother's closet and had let herself out of the right parlour entrance. She hurried through the darkened streets, which because of the season were largely deserted, and the few late wayfarers she met, recognizing the cloak, kept at a respectful distance.

The night was a moonless one and cloudy. The dampness was like a cold hand stealing up from the river. There were lights still showing in the house on the corner of Royal and Bienville, as she passed, and she wondered with a thudding heart what she should do if Etienne had been detained by company and was not at the wicket to meet her. Her questing hand struck the wood of the gate and it yielded to her touch. Then she was in the hushed garden, and the tall, shadowy figure of her lover appeared out of the gloom.

Etienne gathered her in his arms and kissed her hungrily. 'Not a word,' he whispered. 'There are many still awake in the house.' And he led her by the hand to the dim outline of the *garçonnière* strung out behind the main house. Silently they passed up the private stairway from the garden, and it was not until they had reached the safety of a small tapestry-hung chamber, its heavy curtains closely drawn, that the silence was broken.

'*Eh, bien!*' Etienne exploded with relief. 'Here we are, my darling!' He was flushed, the dark chestnut eyes bright with excitement and desire. Under a crimson-padded *robe-de-chambre*, she saw he was wearing just an open-necked frilled shirt and a pair of dark green nankeen trousers. Suddenly she felt an urge to giggle.

She looked around her. It was a dark and starkly masculine room dominated by the large mahogany bed. There was a shaving stand, a huge armoire with a chest of drawers to match, a table on which gleamed a wine decanter and some glasses, and a bedside table on which stood a five-branched candelabra, providing the room's only light. The room smelled of pomade, leather, and shaving soap. Up to now she had always felt in control of any situation in which they had been together, but in this very masculine atmosphere she felt that the balance had tipped. It was he who was very much in command at that moment. She experienced a slight twinge of misgiving.

He deftly removed her cloak and stood looking down at her. 'You are a little nervous?' She nodded. 'No, no need to be nervous, *chérie*. It is the first time, of course? But have no fear. I will be very gentle.' He smiled at her, and with an ease that spoke of considerable practice, he began to undress her.

When she was naked he sank to his knees and drew her to

him, pressing his blazing cheeks against her stomach and covering it with kisses. 'Ah, my copper goddess,' he murmured, 'you are as beautiful as I dreamed you would be.' His mouth moved downwards, and when it reached her mound, his tongue searched expertly into its cleft. The hairs on the back of Marie's neck rose and she closed her eyes. His mouth moved up again, this time seeking the nipples of her firm, large breasts, which under his insisting lips swelled and rose to meet his touch.

'You must not be afraid,' he murmured again. And, picking her up, he deposited her lightly on the bed. With a hand that trembled, he dowsed all but one of the candles, and Marie could hear the breath rasping in his throat as he stripped off his clothes.

His body gleamed whitely in the light of the remaining candle, its whiteness accenting the darkness of the thick hair around his genitals and the lighter covering of his chest. Then he was beside her, his hands reaching anew for her breasts, his mouth for hers. As he smothered her face and neck with hot kisses, she could feel the hard column of his penis rising and prodding her stomach, until finally he gasped, 'Open your legs to me, my darling, open your legs. It will hurt for only a little – that I promise.' He was above her, pressing into her, dividing her. The cry that bubbled to her lips as he gained entrance was cut off by his demanding mouth. His hands seized hers by the wrists as he bore down upon her with his full weight. She lay pinioned as he heaved against her with shuddering convulsions, until the jerkings finally ceased and he lay quietly on top of her. 'Now you are truly mine, my dearest,' he whispered, 'and from now on it will be easier for you.' He stayed within her, his hands starting their light caress upon her body, and the second time he rose to a climax, she felt inside her the faint throbbing of an answering one, as he rolled over on his side, still clasping her to him.

'Ah!' he breathed in satisfaction. 'You awaken, my beautiful one.' Twice more he entered her, and he did not rest until he had brought forth the palpitating rhythm within her. Then he rested, stroking her long hair and murmuring

endearments sleepily into its tresses. Suddenly his hands
hardened on her and, quickly turning her over, he spread her
buttocks apart, heaved up, and entered her from behind.
This time she did scream as a new pain seared her, and one
of his hands clamped firmly over her mouth as the other
sought her breast. '*Allons!*' he chided. 'You will wake the
house! Again this will pass. I like to vary, you understand,
so this is necessary.' There was no completion for her, only
pain and discomfort as he had his way, but after he had
climaxed violently he seemed satisfied. Gently withdrawing,
he said with a contented sigh, 'Ah, *ma chérie*, we will rest
for a while.' And he was almost instantly asleep.

Marie was so spent that she slept a little herself, but then
awakened suddenly, her mind active and clear of sleep. She
lay looking up into the darkness trying to sort out her feelings. After the first pain had passed, she had not minded his
lovemaking; in fact, she had enjoyed the new feelings he had
aroused in her. Yet now there was a curious sense of anticlimax. Was this all there was to it?

He had possessed her body, certainly, and yet she felt he
had not reached into the deep hidden core of herself. Whatever cataclysmic thing she had expected had not come to
pass; in fact, as the lovemaking had progressed, she had felt
that he was moving further away from her, as if she was no
longer Marie the beloved, but a mere female body answering
and serving the needs of a male. A doubt stirred within her:
Was it that *she* didn't love him enough? But she had been so
sure . . .

Cautiously she raised herself up on her elbow and looked
at him by the guttering light of the dying candle. He looked
extremely young, lying on his side, his head pillowed on an
outstretched arm, the chestnut hair tousled, the long eye-
lashes shading his cheeks, a slight smile on the firm-lipped,
sensuous mouth – extremely young, extremely vulnerable.
With a sensation akin to panic, she realized that she was
looking at him with tenderness, but with no trace of deeper
emotion. Her heart began to thud uncomfortably; this
would never do! This was no marriage of convenience; this
had been what she wanted; her love, her love affair – what

would happen if he sensed this lack in herself, this reserve? Her grandmother had truly loved Charles Laveau and had held him with that love; her mother had Louis Gapion and had held him also – but without that love?

She must see, she must *know* ... Gently she started to probe ahead in the sleeping man's mind, but could get but a little way. No, that was not it. She must see herself – she would take herself to Rampart Street a year from now ...

She was there. She moved from room to silent room, but he was not there, nor was anything of his. Horrified, she probed for him. Where was he? Had he abandoned her? Married? What had happened? With startling clarity a blinding-white wall appeared before her, words chiselled into its surface. '*Ci-git*,' it read, *Etienne Pierre LeBlanc, né le dix-huit juillet, 1827, mort sur le champ d'honneur ...*' With a scream she came back to the present to find herself looking into Etienne's startled sleepy face.

'What is it, *chérie*?' he muttered thickly. 'What is wrong?'

With dilated eyes she looked at him and he took her in his arms. 'A bad dream, *chérie*?'

'Oh, Etienne!' She clutched him against her. 'Hold me close! Don't let me go – ever!' But her heart, as his hands once more began their play upon her body, was as cold as ice, for now she knew that unless she could alter in some way the path of Fate, her lover would be dead and buried before a year had passed.

Chapter Thirteen

Their night of love spurred Etienne to greater action, and within a week they were installed on Rampart Street. She had hoped in the totally feminine atmosphere of her grandmother's bedroom, she would feel – that Etienne would make her feel – the total commitment that she felt love required. But it was not to be. The more he made love to her, the further removed she felt; there was no sense of merging, no sense of oneness. He was an enthusiastic lover whose needs, she found, must at all times be met whether she felt like it herself or not. If he were typical of his kind, she began to understand why Creole ladies tended to suffer from so many evening headaches.

Wondering about herself and him, she tried to find out from others what they felt. It did not help her greatly. Marie-Philome said merely, 'Jean-Paul is an older man. We are comfortable together and we understand one another.'

Jacqueline blushed prettily and would only confess: 'Dominic is so wonderful and thoughtful. There is nothing I would not do to please him.'

She thought about asking her mother, but decided against it. She did not want her to know that all was not perfect in the Garden of Eden she had chosen for herself.

She had left the house on St Ann Street with mixed emotions. Amelie and Patty had cried bitterly, and Marie-Jeanne had vowed she would visit her every day, but then had rather spoiled this proof of affection by starting to re-arrange the bedroom before Marie's valises were even out of it. Her brothers, in the background, had seemed uneasy and shame-faced, as if her departure somehow underlined anew the shadowy role in society they were doomed to play.

Only her mother seemed her normal calm and enigmatic self. 'So you have got what you want,' she observed glancing sideways at Marie with a faint smile. She handed her a pair of large gold hoop earrings identical to her own. 'Here, these are for you. Wear them in good health and happiness.' She watched as Marie replaced the smaller hoops with them and remarked, 'I don't know if your young man knows it, but it is customary for you to be given a piece of jewellery as you start your new life.'

'He knows, Mama,' Marie said, 'and has already asked me what I want.'

'What did you tell him?'

A twinkle appeared in Marie's eyes. 'A diamond for my tignon, or one for my finger. He laughed about the tignon, but he is getting me a diamond ring, which I intend to wear from now on.'

'Then I suggest you do not flaunt it. The rich will envy and resent it and the poor will envy and want to steal it,' her mother said dryly. She went on in a more serious vein: 'I'm not going to load you with advice about your new situation; you'll get plenty of that from others. But there are just two things I would like to say. First, you should not attend the rites for a while – it will be too difficult for you to get away, and there is no particular reason that you *have* to come just now. But second, it is equally important that you keep up with everything I have taught you – on *no* account must you let your Powers fall into disuse.'

'Well, I certainly will if I have the time,' Marie said doubtfully.

'Oh, I think you will soon find you have plenty of that on your hands,' her mother said with a trace of cynicism. 'Creole men don't spend that much time around the house.'

In this case, Marie found her mother was entirely right. After the first month of hectic and unwedded bliss, Etienne returned to his normal social rounds.

Rising late, he would be off with Dominic Montal or Justin or one of the younger Valdouxes, either to his favourite absinthe bar at Bourbon and Bienville to sip his preferred drink, or to practise his fencing at the Salle d'Armes at Conti and Exchange. From there he went on to the gaming tables and the many entertainments New Orleans had to offer to a young man of means and leisure. Marie would rarely see him before evening, and sometimes not until night. She had so rapidly become a creature of candle-light and the bedroom that sometimes she wondered if he would even recognize her fully dressed in street clothes.

However, when she found out from others that his behaviour was in no way unusual, and had adjusted to the idea that for him she was no longer of any great consequence, but merely part of his round of existence, she realized that she, too, had a measure of freedom she had never known before, and it was up to her to do something with it.

She relished the ease and the comforts of her new life. Etienne was generous, so her wardrobe of rich and exotic clothes and the contents of her jewel box grew by leaps and bounds. She snuggled in the large, downy bed, listening to the bustle of the busy street outside, and waited for one of the slaves to bring her *petit déjeuner* on her tray. She thought smugly that it certainly was a whole lot better than walking around the streets, rain or shine with a heavy basket on her arm and catering to the whims of fussy, bad-tempered women.

Not that all the house slaves were entirely amenable to her. The old woman had been Etienne's nurse and never ceased to fuss and fume over him, spoiling and cosseting him as she had evidently done from his birth, which he equally accepted as his due. The young male Negro was light-skinned and fine-featured, echoing faintly the chiselled LeBlanc profile, which indicated some local activity on the part of the late Monsieur LeBlanc; he went by the unlikely name of Billy Boy. He was quiet and respectful enough when Etienne was around, but tended to be mysteriously absent when he was not at home. Both of them, being plantation slaves, had not liked this move into the city. When Etienne was absent, they were at no pains to conceal their grumblings and dislikes from her; they liked neither the city nor its people nor its ways nor their quarters, and so on, ad infinitum. When she felt after a while that this grumbling had probably gone on long enough, and that they were beginning to get back at her in sundry small ways, she contrived to have them find out, via Marie-Philome's slave girl, exactly who she was. After that she had no further trouble. Being a Mambo, even a non-active one, she decided, certainly had its advantages.

Nor was her life a lonely one. Her sisters were frequent visitors and she got to know Marie-Philome much better than she had at home. She admired her older sister for her serenity, her amiability, and her good sense. If indeed she was so like their grandmother, the beautiful Marguerite, Marie could quite see why Charles Laveau had been so faithfully devoted to her.

Jacqueline Delambe was also a frequent visitor, and Marie found her completely disarming, if a little exasperating at times, with her unconquerably naïve and romantic outlook on life. In Jacqueline's world nothing and no one were evil. She was already pregnant and looking forward to this new proof of their love with the same rosy sentimentality as she viewed her relationship with her lover.

When apprised of Jacqueline's news, Marie had experienced a twinge of apprehension on her own account, and had accordingly hurried off to her mother for Indian powders that she knew were a guard against conception. When putting these away in her reticule, a thought suddenly struck her and she asked her mother, 'If you knew about these, why didn't you ever use them? Aren't they any good?'

Her mother laughed. 'Oh, yes. The Indians use them all the time. They are as good as any of these things can be. As to why I didn't use them – well, I just happen to love babies.' She looked at Marie with a twinkle in her eyes. 'Until you've had one, you'll never know what I mean.'

Through Jacqueline, and because she and Etienne often made a foursome with them, Marie also came to know Dominic Montal a lot better. Away from St Regis and his shadow, he seemed like an entirely different person, warmhearted, fun-loving, and inclined like his lady-love to be naïvely credulous. The insecurity of being the dominated twin showed on occasions when he felt himself threatened.

Then he had the tendency to bluster and strut and to fly into tantrums. But, all in all, Marie found him increasingly likeable.

She said as much to her mother and was much taken aback by the latter's reaction. 'Twins!' Marie Laveau had hissed. 'Devil's spawn – always devil's spawn. No good ever came from them. Two lots of twins, I had, but the Gods took them all, praise be! Twins are the curse of God on any family. It would have been better for the world if the Montal twins had been taken, too, and the farther away you keep from them, the better off you'll be!'

Of St Regis they saw very little, for which she was duly grateful, although Etienne would occasionally drop a news item about him. Emile Valdoux had married at Easter. He had gone off to Europe with his bride, and St Regis had gone with them, ostensibly to learn business methods along with Emile. Some ugly rumours filtered back about his activities in Paris. And when he had returned to America some months later, he had gone directly to the family's plantation and had not returned to New Orleans. Marie learned from Justin – also a frequent visitor and the self-appointed Mercury of the group – that plans for St Regis's betrothal to Marie-Thérèse were almost settled, and that pressure was again being put on Dominic about Claire so that a date for a double wedding could be set.

This bit of news again worried her, but since neither Jacqueline nor Dominic seemed to be in the slightest bit ruffled or concerned, she told herself angrily that she was being stupid. It was their business, anyway, not hers, and she should mind her own

Much to her surprise, she now had some business to mind, none of it really of her own seeking. She was beginning to get 'clients' tapping at her door seeking the same services from her as from her mother: the mother seeking a missing child; the lover with a broken heart; the wife with a straying husband; the mistress with fading charms. 'Tell me!' 'Help me!' 'Save me!' The cries were the same ones she had heard at St Ann Street, only the faces were different.

The dark ones shuffled downcast inside the back door.

'Please give me a gris-gris, Miz Marie, please! Mah man done run off, an' Ah needs 'im back!'

The white ones, some timorous, some imperious, came into the front parlour. 'I have need of your services ... My daughter does not care for the man we have chosen for her. It is important that she should. Could you ...?' Or: 'My husband has begun to suspect ...' There was a surprising number of those. She promised them nothing, but did what she could, and was startled herself sometimes at the results.

Had her white clientele been different, she would have suspected that her mother was siphoning off her own surplus clients in her direction, but many of the whites were Anglos, for whom her mother had little time, understanding, or liking. Marie surmised that this she had probably brought on herself. Towards the end of her hairdressing days, she had become so frustrated by her Creole clients that she had ranged farther afield beyond the confines of the Vieux Carré and had taken on some Anglo business.

Her mother had once said that the Anglos would one day be the powers in the future city, and from what she herself had seen, she was inclined to believe it. The Anglo men were certainly more dynamic and more interested in business affairs than the pleasure-loving, tradition-bound Creoles. As for the Anglo women, though they were certainly very different from the Creole ladies, they were not as different as she had hoped. She had heard much talk of the 'freedom' enjoyed by them, but to her disappointment she had not seen many signs of it. True, their relationships with their husbands tended to be less formal than in the French households, and their rigid control over their family was less in evidence. However, they, too, seemed like captives, insecure and trapped in an amorphous world with few guidelines and fewer privileges.

She had divided them mentally into two main groups, the larger being the 'clinging vines' who practised an unending series of female coquetries, playing on their helplessness and their feminine charms to gain their ends with their menfolk. The other, much smaller, group, she had labelled the 'other-worlders': women who cultivated the arts or the church, who wrote much poetry of the sentimental variety, who played or sang with diligence and who had a propensity towards 'good works'.

The clinging vines took considerable pains to suppress any signs of native intelligence in themselves and their daughters. The other-worlders took pains to display theirs, but only in areas where their menfolk would not feel threatened. If anything, they catered more to the male ego than did their French sisters, though in some Marie sensed a deep frustration that felt like a rumbling volcano. When whispers had reached them – as they always did – that she was something more than a dresser of hair, both groups had held out their palms to her, opened their hearts, and whispered their secrets into her discreet ear. On the whole, she had more sympathy with the Anglos, being alien and outside her own world, than she had for her Creole clients.

Marie had to learn discretion now to mask her activities both from Etienne, who would not understand, and from her mother, who would understand all too well. So the fiat had been broadcast far and wide that she was only available when and if the '*M'sieu*' was from home, and if she were not otherwise engaged with friends. It worked well enough and her double life added a certain zest to her existence.

As summer lifted its hot and heavy hand from the city, the new social season came to life, and she and Etienne were quite busy savouring its endless variety with their little coterie. Just before Christmas Jacqueline gave birth to a girl which, to Marie's quiet horror, the young couple promptly baptized as Claire Montal Delambe. She even went to Dominic before the christening for a quiet word on the subject, only to be told off-handedly, 'I've always liked the name Claire, and Jackie thinks it's pretty, too.'

'But ... under the circumstances ... don't you think another name would be better – I mean, what about Claire Valdoux?'

'What about her?' he said coldly. 'What does she matter?' This almost staggering lack of taste and feeling was underlined by the announcement at Christmas of the Montal twins' joint betrothals.

'At last Mama Valdoux is in seventh heaven,' reported Justin, 'Mama Montal in about fifth. After all, it is no great feat to marry off one's sons, and she has two daughters now of marriageable age, with Geneviève soon to be treading hard upon their heels, and yet no sign of an acceptable offer on the horizon. Mind you,' he confided in Marie, 'I think she has her eye on Etienne for Anne, and her eye on *me* for Yvonne – but me, I have other plans.'

'Valerie?' Marie inquired with interest.

He grinned at her impishly. 'Perhaps! One of these days when we are both ready – but neither of us is in any hurry. Currently Valerie is *folle d'amour* for a handsome tow-headed Anglo, and I have some little friends here and there who keep me amused.'

'Should I start shaking in my shoes, do you think?' She smiled.

'Not on account of Anne Montal, anyway. She is like her mother, not a very *comfortable* woman. However, if I were you, I'd keep Etienne away from the Anglos. He is developing a bizarre taste for blondes,' he countered. 'I really don't understand this preoccupation with fair hair myself – such pallid people! But never fear, I shall be your faithful *cavaliere servente* and keep you well apprised of any dangers that may lurk unseen, *chère* Marie.'

'I'll remember that, dear, wise, and aged counsellor,' Marie said with mock solemnity, 'and in the meantime will keep him well away from the Anglos – blonde or brunette!'

Chapter Fourteen

To keep him away from the Anglos was easier said than done, Marie discovered. Etienne had an appetite for new things and new excitement that she found hard to keep up with.

Up until the death of their parents, the LeBlancs had led the typical, rather rigid and reclusive life of a rich planter's family. They had been spoiled in some ways, rigidly controlled in others, and since the death of their parents and the lifting of these controls they had been making up for lost time, flitting hectically from new sensation to new sensation like a flock of frantic butterflies. Etienne had boasted to Marie that he had fought his first duel and wasted his first thousand dollars on gambling within a month of his arrival in New Orleans.

In his first season there he had run the gamut of everything Creole society had to offer, culminating in his capture of her at the end of it. Now, in his second season, he was beginning to show signs of restlessness and boredom and of ranging farther afield after new sensations and amusements. He had even talked to her about going abroad. 'Maybe we should take a trip to Europe, Marie. It would be fun to visit Paris and London and all the rest, would it not?'

It would, indeed, she had agreed with just a twinge of apprehension n her own part. For what would life hold for her beyond the protection of the two waters?

'*Eh, bien.* I think I will look into it, then,' he had said. 'Perhaps we could all go.' But a certain natural laziness also prevailed and, so far as Marie could make out, he had done nothing definite about the plan.

The search for new amusements had inevitably led him into the different world of Anglo society, and this worried Marie a great deal because it was obvious that her lover had no liking for them. Etienne had imbibed at his father's knee this dislike of 'interlopers', a reactionary mode of thought reinforced by the archly conservative Montal-St Yves clan, and unlike that held by the Valdouxs, who were far more realistic about it. To him the Anglos had no business there on land which, only by an accident of history, was other than French, and he felt that they should be treated as intruders and 'kept in their place'.

'Keeping them in their place' was easy enough with the few who ventured into the Creole area of society, but on their own ground it was a different matter, and there he became imperious, arrogant, and sneeringly supercilious – all of which Marie found a great strain. It had led to some very tense social situations, and it said much for the patience and forbearance of the Anglos, she reflected, that nothing serious had resulted from it.

Still, the fear that had been at the back of her mind since their very first night together would not be banished, and with Carnival once again stimulating the city to new heights of merry-making and excitement, it came more and more to the forefront. If only she could get him safely through this period, then Fate would be defied and all would be well, for he had announced that as soon as Lent began they would take a trip upriver to the LeBlanc plantation. She leaped at the suggestion, for what trouble could he possibly get into on his own land? Besides, she had never seen anything of plantation life and was eager to see the rumoured splendours of Castle Blanche with her own eyes.

To get through these dangerous shoals of Carnival, she decided she could use some help and advice, so she repaired to seek a consultation with her mother.

She got to the house on St Ann to find the entire household in disarray and her mother in an exceedingly bad temper. 'Can you imagine!' she fumed, flourishing a letter in Marie's direction. 'That fool of a girl has gone and got herself married without as much as a by-your-leave, and she has the gall to think she has done something extremely clever just because she has married a white man! White man, indeed! Poor white trash, most likely! Long will she rue it!'

'What fool of a girl?' Marie managed to interject.

'Your sister Celeste,' her mother snarled. 'Oh, I knew she

was up to no good when she moved out of Marguerite's – poor Margot, who put up with her sulking and complaining all the time. It seems she met up with a crony of her half-brother Jacques – some layabout river rat called Jean LeGendre – and just married him out of hand. A wedding Mass, she says proudly, as if there was any other way to marry! Chances are he's only after her *dot*, and when that's gone it'll be the last she'll see of *him*. I know his kind. Bah! What an *idiot*!'

'But, *Maman*,' protested Marie weakly, 'surely that is what you wanted for Celeste – an early marriage?' She had not much sympathy or feeling for her sister, but she felt her mother's violent reaction arose more from the fact that by not being consulted, her authority had been openly flouted.

'Certainly I wanted her to marry, but to one of her own kind – a good, steady man like Marguerite's Marc Crocker. But to this river filth? Marguerite is as upset about it as I. She says he is a man of no good reputation or standing. And now Celeste asks – no, she demands! – that I give her the *dot* I had promised her because she intends to set up a little shop.'

'Well, *Maman*,' Marie said slowly, 'since she is already married and there is nothing you can do about that, perhaps that would be the best thing to do. If he is the type of man you say – and I hope he isn't for her sake – it would be as well if she had something of her own to fall back on.'

'Oh, I'll see she gets her shop, all right,' Marie Laveau said, calming down somewhat, 'But this Jean LeGendre is not going to see a cent of that money. I'll arrange it all through Marguerite, and Celeste will just have to make the best of it. If it was not bad enough that Daumeny took up with white trash, and now this . . . !' She lapsed into brooding silence.

Marie felt she had not arrived at a very propitious moment to broach her own problem and was just about to make her excuses and leave when her mother said suddenly, 'And what's worrying you so? Some trouble with Etienne?'

'In a manner of speaking,' she answered. 'Not *personal* trouble, but . . . well . . . I am a little worried . . .' Hastily she sketched out some of her anxieties while saying nothing of her deeper fears.

Her mother did not seem impressed. 'If you feel he is heading for some trouble with the Anglos, then surely you have enough influence to keep him away from them.' She shrugged. 'A little tact, a little manipulation – I do not see why you worry. What trouble, after all, could he get into?'

'He is so hotheaded at times, I am afraid for him.'

'He strikes me as a young man well able to look after himself – a *beau garçon*,' her mother replied. 'Is that all it is, or is there something you aren't telling me?'

Marie hesitated. If she told her mother the whole truth, she would have to reveal that she had a power her mother did not know she possessed, a power which she had vowed never to use again. Once her mother knew of this, she would be constantly after her to utilize it, develop it, and she would know no peace. 'No,' she said at length. 'It's just that I have this very bad feeling. I shall be glad when Carnival is over and we can go away for a bit. I look forward to that. Etienne is taking me to Castle Blanche.'

Her mother laughed shortly, a hard note in her voice. 'I have my little Maison Blanche and you your big Castle Blanche. Truly you are going up in the world, not like your fool sister!'

'No, *Maman*,' Marie murmured. 'No, I would never be like Celeste.'

But as she made her way home again, she felt that now it was all up to her, and the thought made her depressed.

But when they had reached the last week of Carnival, her hopes began to rise. Nothing had happened and she had scored one major victory – she had persuaded Etienne not to wait for Lent but to leave for the countryside on Mardi Gras. 'Think how different that will be!' she had pleaded. 'All the world flocking to New Orleans, and we two the only ones going in the opposite direction! Will that not be truly chic!'

He had laughed and agreed, and she had even begun to pack the valises and trunks with a happy heart. Then the day before Mardi Gras she awoke with her nerves all a-jangle – only one more day to go and she would be free of this omen that rested so heavily upon her. She wished the hours away until they were safely aboard the paddle boat. Etienne went out early and she tried to keep herself busy with odds and ends of packing, but the day seemed to drag by endlessly.

When he came back with Justin and Bayard Valdoux, she saw with dismay by their flushed faces and uproarious spirits that they had all been drinking heavily. 'Get your glad rags on, Marie,' he called to her. 'We're all going to a ball over in the Garden District. Think of it! Three gallant escorts! What a lucky girl you are!'

Her fears revived. 'Oh, do we have to, Etienne?' she pleaded. 'After all, we leave tomorrow, and I thought to-night we should get some rest for the trip.'

'Nonsense! You can rest on the boat if you're fatigued. This is our last night of Carnival – we must live it up!'

With ill grace she went to dress, dawdling over the process as long as she dared until routed out by the increasingly impatient Etienne. By the time they arrived at the ball, it was already in full swing, the music loud and the large crowd even louder. It was in one of the new big hotels that had been put up at the edge of the business district, and the opulent ballroom was surrounded by a 'sitting-out' area of almost equal size, crowded with small tables and chairs. They contrived to find an unoccupied one, uncomfortably crowded up against a potted palm. And when she had settled down and looked around, her spirits sank still more; the majority of the participants were Anglos, few of whom she recognized. She danced a few dances with Etienne and Justin in turn, but Bayard Valdoux, who, though much younger than his kinsmen, had been trying to keep up with them in their drinking and was already too drunk to participate. He sat staring blearily into his champagne glass, hunched over the table.

To add to her dismay, Justin said after an hour of this, 'Well, I must be off now. I've got to drop in on the Delancey ball and keep an eye on Valerie and her fair-haired beau.'

'Oh, don't go, Justin!' Marie exclaimed. 'What on earth

136

do you want to do that for? Mama Valdoux will be there, so you know Valerie will be quite all right.'

'Ah-ha! But you know as well as I do what can go on behind the chaperone's back' He grinned, fingering the leaves of the palm. 'With my eagle eye around, Valerie will be forced to be circumspect, whether she likes it or not!'

'I'll walk you to the door,' Etienne said immediately. 'There are one or two things you can do for me here in the city while we're up at the plantation that I forgot to mention.' Their tall, slim figures were instantly swallowed up by the crowd and Marie glanced uneasily at the now semi-comatose Bayard.

Hurry back, Etienne, she prayed silently, *hurry back*.

'And how about the next dance, pretty lady?' The voice booming in her ear made her jump convulsively, and she turned to see a large, fair man smiling down at her.

'Oh, thank you, but no, *M'sieu*,' she stammered. 'I have already promised the next dance.'

He shot a quizzical glance at the slumped figure of Bayard. 'Your companion does not seem in great shape for dancing – or anything else, for that matter. Come on, just one little dance, eh? I've had my eye on you all along.'

'Then you must be aware, *M'sieu*, that I am here with a party,' she said in an icy voice. 'Please go. My partner will be here in a moment.' With dismay she saw Etienne rapidly approaching them, his handsome face flushed and angry. 'Please go, go now!'

'Now, is that a nice way to treat a stranger in town, and at Carnival time, too?' The Anglo bent over her confidingly, and the slight slurring of his voice told her that he, too, was more than a little drunk.

'Please go and leave me alone,' she begged in agony, but already it was too late. Etienne had reached the table and was glowering furiously at the man.

'What is this?' he demanded. 'What are you doing here?'

The stranger straightened up and looked him in the eye. 'Just asking the little lady for a dance, that's all. Is there anything wrong with that?' he said evenly.

'Ah, truly, this is too much!' Etienne cried out. 'Have you

137

Anglos no manners at all? You are very ill brought up, *M'sieu!*'

A smaller, dark man, hearing the raised voices, had hurried up and was now standing by the fair man, a concerned look on his face. 'What is this, Joe?' he demanded in his turn.

'It is nothing, *M'sieu*, just a little misunderstanding, that is all,' Marie broke in fearfully. 'Etienne, please, don't make a scene!'

'It is *not* nothing!' Etienne stormed. 'I have just told your boorish friend here that he is *mal élevé!*'

'Now, look here, sonny, no need to lose your temper. It's nothing to get worked up about. I didn't say anything out of the way to your lady here – just asked her for a dance, that's all,' the fair man said. 'I'm sorry if I upset her. I apologize.'

'How dare you!' Etienne cried. 'How dare you insult me by calling me your son, you ill-bred cur!'

The man bridled. 'How'd you like a poke in the nose, Frenchy?' he said, shaking off his friend, who was tugging vainly at his sleeve. 'No one gets away with calling me that.'

'Precisely! You have finally got my point,' Etienne said, calming down. 'Since the code of honour – about which you evidently know nothing – precludes physical violence, I shall be only too happy to give you satisfaction on the field of honour, *M'sieu.*'

'What the hell's he mean?' the fair man asked his persistent friend.

'It seems that he's just challenged you to a duel, Joe,' the man said grimly. And there was a little murmur of assent from the curious crowd that had now gathered around.

'A duel! You've got to be kidding! Why don't we just step outside a minute?'

'Because it is not the way things are done here,' the dark man said in a tight voice. 'Would you be prepared to accept a full apology from my friend, *M'sieu*? As you can see, he is a stranger to our ways and acted only out of thoughtlessness.'

'Etienne, for Heaven's sake!' Marie broke in. '*Please,*

please, do as he says! He has already apologized to me. The incident is over. Please let it go.'

Etienne shot her an angry glance. 'This is nothing to do with you,' he said icily. 'It is *I* who have been insulted; it is *my* honour that must be satisfied.' He turned to the two Anglos. 'No, I am afraid an apology would not suffice. I demand satisfaction – the choice of weapons is yours.'

Looking a little dazed, the fair man took his friend aside and spoke to him in a soft, urgent voice. Then he turned and said, 'Well, I guess if we've got to fight, it better be with pistols. But can't we talk this over?'

Etienne looked a little taken aback. 'I had thought perhaps you would choose one of the gentlemen's weapons, but that is too much to expect, I see,' he sneered. 'But since the choice is yours, of course I agree. At dawn, then, at the Duelling Oaks at ten paces? My seconds will wait upon yours to arrange the details, and I will arrange for the surgeon to be on hand, if that is agreeable to you.' He proffered his card, which the dark man silently accepted and then produced his own. Then bowing, he tugged the bewildered-looking Joe away into the crowd.

'Oh, Etienne, how *could* you!' Marie said, then burst into tears.

'*Ma foi*,' he returned calmly. 'To teach an Anglo a lesson in manners for me will be a very fitting end to Carnival!'

He had taken her back to the house on Rampart and had departed with the pale and shaken Bayard to find Justin and another friend to act as his seconds. Marie was far too upset to do anything but sit tensely waiting for his return. She tried to calm her screaming nerves and to concentrate on what she must do.

All appeals to Etienne to reconsider had failed. There was no recourse now but to avert the threatened disaster with her own Powers. She felt no animosity towards the large Anglo; he was but the instrument of Fate. But if it was a choice between him and Etienne, he would have to be the one to suffer; all it would require would be a simple deflection of his firing arm at the right moment. She would have to go to

139

the duel; then she knew she could do it. She must begin the summoning . . .

When Etienne returned towards dawn with the concerned-looking Justin, she was prepared, a heavy cloak thrown over her ball gown. 'I must go with you,' she announced firmly.

'It is out of the question – a duel is no place for a woman,' Etienne returned.

'I tell you I must be near you at this moment,' she said with such determination that his eyes widened in surprise. 'If you never grant me another wish, you must grant me this one.'

Now completely sober, he was tense and ill at ease, obviously concerned about fighting with weapons he was not that familiar with. 'All right,' he snapped. 'I'm in no mood to argue. You may come and wait in the carriage until it is over. Then we'll come back and go directly to the boat. Does that satisfy you?'

'Oh, yes – yes, indeed. Thank you, Etienne!'

They rode in silence out along the Esplanade to the bridge across the Bayou St John, where the carriage stopped and the three men got out. Before going, Etienne leaned over and kissed her. 'Don't worry, *chérie*, it will soon be over,' he murmured. 'Everything will be just fine. No one shoots to kill in these affairs, you know.'

She watched his tall figure disappearing towards the grove, where the Spanish moss draping the old oaks reached out ghostly arms in the light dawn wind. Then she closed her eyes and began to concentrate. She would take no chances; a slight deflection was all it would require, nothing she could not accomplish . . .

Determinedly, she held the thought. '*Now!*' she murmured as two muffled shots echoed from the grove. She relaxed with a sigh and opened her eyes. A long silence followed in which the only sound was the pounding of her own heart. Then footsteps approached the carriage and she tensed expectantly, hopefully.

The pale stricken face of the fair Anglo appeared at the carriage window. 'I'm sorry,' he choked out, 'I didn't even

140

try to hit him ... it was just like a blow on my arm ... I jerked and ...' He turned away and she could hear him begin to retch.

Still uncomprehending, she saw the dark man's head appear. 'I'm sorry, I truly am,' he muttered. 'Accept my profound sympathy, *Madame*. My friend is much upset. He had no intention ...'

Marie looked at him with slowly dilating eyes. 'Etienne?' she called. 'Etienne?' And she was flying out of the carriage, over the dew-soaked grass towards the grove, terror tearing at her heart.

She saw Justin and two other figures bending over the prone shape on the ground. 'Etienne!' she screamed and hurled herself upon him. He lay outstretched, eyes open, quietly gazing up into the grey-blue of dawn; only a small patch of blood on the frilled white shirt showing that anything was amiss. She turned a frantic face to Justin as she cradled Etienne's head in her arms. 'How bad is he hurt?' she panted. 'Why aren't you helping him?'

The stricken face of Justin wavered before her eyes. 'There is nothing to be done,' he said in a voice that held all the pain in the world. 'He's dead, Marie – the shot went right through his heart. An accident, a terrible accident.'

She let out an anguished scream. 'Oh, God! I've killed him! I've killed him!' she sobbed.

Justin took her by the shoulders and shook her. 'No!' he said roughly. 'Stop that! It has nothing to do with you – nothing, you understand? It is the terrible will of God!'

She crouched over the body of the man she had so wanted and whom she had been unable to love and looked up at Justin with panic-stricken eyes. *We do not control the powers*. Her mother's voice echoed in the chambers of her mind. *The powers control us.*

'Why?' she muttered brokenly. 'Why?'

Chapter Fifteen

She had killed her lover; not only had she foreseen his fate; she had caused it. This was a fact she had to live with; this was the thought that kept her numb and frozen through the sadness of the days that followed, to which the wailings and lamentations of his old nurse echoing from the slave quarters provided poignant counterpoint.

Justin had taken his brother's body back to the family burying ground beneath the weeping cypresses of Castle Blanche, the home that now she would never see. She sat silent in her grandmother's ghost-filled drawing room, to which was now added a ghost of her own, and wished that she could retreat among their shades, shutting out the world entirely. But the outside world would not let her.

Visitors came in a constant stream, the sympathetic, the consoling, the concerned, and the merely curious. They passed by in an unending flow, only touching the outer fringes of her consciousness. Some, though they did not make much impression on her at the time, were to be of consequence.

Bayard, much sobered from his natural exuberance, had been among the first. 'Emile is newly returned and has heard the news. He asked me to tell you that if at any time you should need his help in any way, you are to call on him.'

'Thank you, Bayard,' she had said dully. 'And thank him for me.'

'Please do as he says,' Bayard said with sudden force. 'If I hadn't been so drunk that night, if I had looked after you properly, none of this would have happened.' His voice choked. 'It was my fault.'

'No, Bayard,' she said, 'not yours.'

A more puzzling visitor had been Christophe, who came bearing a message from her mother. 'She says to tell you that if you want to close the house and come home, it would be fine with her.'

'Thank you, Christophe. I'll have to think about it.'

He had stood in front of her, his dark maroon eyes searching hers hungrily. Then he burst out: 'Don't do it, Miz Marie! Don't come back!'

She was amazed, until it occurred to her that he was probably still embarrassed at the thought of how she had surprised him in her mother's arms. 'You needn't worry,' she assured him. 'What you and my mother do is no business of mine; it doesn't matter to me.'

His eyes dropped miserably, but he shook his head. 'It ain't that. There's somethin' goin' on over there. It's been goin' on fo' some time, and it's somethin' 'bout you, an' it ain't good. Ah've heard them talkin', her an' Crocodile – things Ah don' rightly understand, but things 'bout you. Ah got a feelin' they're up to no good. Ah got a feelin' they're plottin' 'gainst you.'

'Plotting? Whatever for?

A mystified expression crossed his face. Christophe was a very strong young man, but none too bright. Even Patty, who was not exactly the most stable or intelligent mind in the world, could out-think him on most occasions. 'Ah don' know,' he confessed, then appeared to go off on a tangent. 'You know Ah'm a free man. Ah don' have to stay there at all if Ah don' want. But Crocodile, he say one day if Ah stick around, maybe Ah can learn to be a Voodoo man like him. Yes, ma'am, a *real hungan*.'

'What's that got to do with it?' Marie was nettled.

His face resumed its puzzled frown. 'I don' know, but it's always when they talk 'bout the rites an' Voodoo an' all. That's when their voices drop an' they starts a-whisperin' 'bout you. Somethin' to do with Voodoo, Ah reckon.'

None of it had made any sense to Marie, although it underlined uncomfortably the long-standing feeling she had had that all was not as it appeared to be on the surface. She had never understood her mother's great haste in having her made a Mambo, nor her weird insistence that the two of

143

them were, in effect, but one for most purposes. She had even encouraged Marie to walk the way she did and to imitate her style of dress. But the purpose behind it all was quite beyond Marie's comprehension, so she dismissed it with a shrug. She had plenty of other things to worry about, the most pressing item being what she was going to do now.

Justin returned briefly to New Orleans and came to see her. His new role as head of the family sat oddly on his youthful, slender shoulders, and his bland young face was set in sombre lines. 'I'll be leaving New Orleans for a while,' he informed her. 'Going back to Castle Blanche. My sister Clarisse, who is still in the school room, has been very hard hit by all this. She and Etienne were very close. I feel I should stay with her up there until she is ready to make her debut. There is much also I have to learn about the running of the plantation. I never expected . . .' He broke off and his voice choked.

'No, of course not,' Marie murmured. She wondered if he found this interview as uncomfortable as she did.

He stirred, obviously ill at ease, and then went on. 'Before I go, I wish you to take this.' He produced a white slip of paper from an inner pocket and handed it to her. It was a draft on the Valdoux bank for a thousand dollars.

'No!" Marie exclaimed involuntarily. 'No! I don't want it!'

'But I insist. Etienne would have wanted it, I know. He had already talked about a future settlement . . .' Again he broke off and flushed under her steady gaze. 'Well, I mean, when he did eventually marry, there would have had to have been . . .'

Something hardened inside of Marie. So they had already talked of it, had they? Where? she wondered. Casually sipping absinthe at the bar on Bienville, or while matching foils in the Salle d'Armes, or seated around some gaming table? 'How much do you think would be reasonable? I mean, she deserves *something* . . .' And how many years would it have been, one, two, five? She knew now that while she would always mourn for Etienne as a young man who had met an untimely death, she had no longer to mourn for him as a lover; his feeling for her had been no more than her feeling for him.

She slowly held out her hand for the proffered paper. 'In that case, Justin,' she said, 'I thank you.' A trace of bitterness crept into her voice. 'It is indeed most generous of you.'

After he had gone, she sat staring at the draft – a thousand dollars. How long would that keep her going? A year, two, perhaps, if she were careful? No. That was not the way to think; money like that was not to spend; money like that should make money. She had no idea how that was done, but she knew who did. She would take it to Emile . . .

Marriage was obviously suiting him, she reflected as she sat across the large mahogany banker's desk from him at the Valdoux counting house. He had put on weight, which made his stocky figure even more solid and dependable looking. Clothed in sober banker's black, with a black stock at his throat, making his pale face appear even paler, he could already pass for a middle-aged man. Despite a certain embarrassment, he was also quite evidently as delighted to see her as she found she was glad to see him.

'Bayard gave me your kind message,' she began. 'And I have come to avail myself of your expert knowledge.' She handed him the draft and explained as well as she could what she wanted. 'Can you do anything with it?' she finished.

He nodded slowly. 'Yes. Things are booming in New Orleans just now. The port has never been busier, nor the river traffic heavier. There is much talk that the new railways in the east will make a difference to us, but frankly I think that is just scare talk; things have never been better here. We haven't had a bad flood in years, there have been no epidemics to speak of, and you can see for yourself how much new construction is going on all over the city, and it's the same up on the plantations. No, Marie, I think I can promise you that if you want to leave the money with me, I can double it for you in a year or even less, but . . .' – he hesitated – '. . . are you sure you don't want to keep some of it back? I mean, how are you going to manage? What are you going to do now?'

'Oh, I'll manage,' she assured him. 'I'm not sure how at the moment, but I will, never fear.' She smiled faintly. 'After all, if the worse comes to the worst, I can always go back to hairdressing!'

In actuality, it was the last thing she wanted to do. She had other ideas, and so apparently had the rest of the world.

The mourning wreath on the door had scarcely begun to wither when the first approaches were made. Some came in the form of invitations to intimate little dinners 'where we could discuss your future.' Some bolder souls had actually come to the house bearing small gifts and the same suggestion. The notes she ignored; the callers she sent away with words that were pleasant enough but sufficiently firm to discourage all but the most hardened roués.

One such visit was different from the rest and gave her much to think about. She was alone in the house now, Billy Boy and the old nurse having returned to Castle Blanche with their new master, so when the knocking came on the front door she answered it herself. She found a plump, middle-aged woman on the step, richly dressed in a rather bright shade of blue velvet and wearing one of the largest and most improbable hats she had ever seen in her life. It was so beplumed that the high-coloured, beak-nosed face with the shrewd blue eyes under it gave the impression of a bird of prey peering out of a tropical forest.

'I'm Flo Winfield, dearie. Maybe you've heard of me?' the woman said in one of the oddest Anglo accents Marie had ever heard. 'Anyway, I'd like to talk over some business with you, if I may come in.' She extended a plump, limp hand with diamond rings winking from every finger.

The name meant nothing to Marie, but she ushered her in, thinking that this was probably a new Anglo client. Flo Winfield settled herself down with mighty rustlings of countless petticoats and looked around her with curiosity. 'Nice place you've got here. Very pretty things, very pretty! You've got good taste, I see. That's always a help.'

'They belonged to my grandmother,' Marie said with a touch of frost in her voice. 'What can I do for you?'

'No – it's what I can do for *you*. That's why I'm here,' Flo Winfield said with a little chuckle. 'I've heard all about your bit of trouble, m'dear, and being a business woman, I says to myself right off, I says, now here's where you can do yourself a bit o' good, old girl, and that poor young thing, too.' The hard blue eyes started at Marie. 'Now I want you to hear me out before you say anything, and if I seem to ramble a bit, don't pay no mind 'cause you've got to know what's what.'

She took a deep breath. 'I know all about Rampart Street and you gals who live here, and ever since I came to New Orleans from England I've always thought how daft the lot of you were, to put up with what you do: spending your best days at the beck and call of one man, with often nothing to show for it at the end but a broken heart and a few sticks of furniture! What a waste, what a terrible waste!' She stopped and peered again at Marie. 'Have you any idea how *rich* this city is? How much money there is to be made here? I came without a penny piece to my name, and now look at me! Oh, I know how you Frenchies stick together and think you've got it all, but it's not true – the real money is coming down the river every day: business men from the north, ranchers from the west, southern planters, all here with only one idea – spend, spend, spend! Now, I run a real high-class establishment over on Magnolia – only cater to the best, mind you – and even the least popular of my girls there never earns a penny less than fifty dollars a night. And the popular ones – oh, my! – the sky's the limit for them!

'And you, my dear, the first time I set eyes on you in the street, with that proud walk of yours and the way men looked after you as if they'd like to eat you up, why, you could be the talk of the town! You get my meaning?'

'Oh, yes, I get your meaning,' Marie said coolly. 'You want me to be one of your whores.'

Flo winced. 'That's a harsh word for it,' she said primly. 'There's a lot more to it than that, you know. As I said, mine's a high-class place – good food, good music, good dancing – and no force. The number of times a night my girls want to open their legs is up to them. I don't believe in force,' she repeated, then dropped her voice and went on in a wheedling tone. 'I've heard all about the goings-on you organize out at the lake – the dancing and such. If you don't fancy the other at the start, you could organize some of those for me – my clients are always on the lookout for something a bit different, you know . . .' She paused expectantly.

Marie was secretly amused that she was being confused with her mother to her own credit, but still she said nothing, and so the plump madam, sensing her unresponsiveness, hurried on. 'Even though you're such a young girl, it shows what a good head you must have on your shoulders to do that sort of thing. Who knows? When you've learned the ins and outs of the business, you could perhaps come in with me on the management side. There'd be enough picking for both of us. With your brains and mine, we could end up the richest women in New Orleans. What do you say to that?'

This time Marie felt some sort of reply was necessary. She got to her feet slowly and smiled at the plump woman. 'You have certainly given me a lot to think about, *Madame*. At the moment I am not prepared to give you a definite answer, since there are other matters I have to take care of first. But I will certainly consider your proposition and let you know.'

Flo Winfield let out a relieved sigh and heaved herself to her feet. 'You do that, dearie, and you'll never regret it – you mark my words!' She fumbled in an elaborately beaded bag and fished out a card. 'Here's my business card. Whenever you feel like it, come on round and give this to the darkie at the door. I'll be glad to see you at any time – day or night – and the sooner, the better.' She gave Marie an admiring glance. 'My word, you're a cool one, you are – you'll drive 'em wild, you will!'

Marie urged her gently towards the door, and when it was shut upon the stout back, she leaned against it, tapping the card reflectively against her teeth. Some of the things Flo Winfield had said made a lot of sense. She had already seen much of what went on in Rampart Street and its little houses: the ones where deserted mistresses eked out meagre existences on what their lovers had left behind, or those who had married mulatto husbands and half the time worked their fingers to the bone at some small business to barely make a living. And there were worse cases: the ones who, when their lovers left, took their own lives in despair, or who took to drink and ended up in the gloomy, sordid houses down on Gallatin Street. Yes, it was so true, what Flo Winfield had said – little of the enormous and increasing wealth of New Orleans ended up here on Rampart.

She thought of all the young girls she knew – banana-coloured, coffee-coloured, cream-coloured – all yearning for brighter lights, softer lives, richer clothes. Yes, there was an awful lot in what Flo Winfield said . . .

She liked money and she had seen already its power. Though she was still but eighteen with life stretched ahead of her as a shadowy and rather frightening enigma, she was determined that both money and power she would have. But she would not do it in Flo Winfield's way, she decided, she would do it in her own.

Chapter Sixteen

She was floating on her back in the lake, the voodoo drums throbbing with her pulses. The lake was getting rougher and rougher, the drums louder and louder, and she was having difficulty keeping afloat above the choppy waves. 'I must get out of this.' She started to panic, and she awoke with a thudding heart to find the Voodoo drums had become someone pounding at the front door. It did nothing to calm her racing heartbeat, for it was still pitch-dark and she was alone in the house. For a moment she lay frozen, then crawled out of bed and made her way cautiously down to the front hall. Pressing her ear against the vibrating door, she could hear a peculiar thin wailing and harsh sobbing breath. 'Who is it?' she called.

'It's me, Jacqueline! For the love of God, let me in!'

Marie fumbled with the bolts, threw the door open, and the cloaked figure of Jacqueline thrust a small wailing bundle at her, tottered across the threshold, and fainted dead away across her feet. Marie hastily kicked the door shut, bolted it again, set the crying infant down on the drawing-room carpet, and, lighting a candle with shaking hands, hurried back to the unconscious figure of her friend.

The dim light showed a livid bruise along the creamy skin of the jawline. There were other dark bruises on her throat and shoulders. And the nightgown under the cloak was torn and blood-spattered. In her anxiety Marie seized Jacqueline by the shoulders and shook her. 'Jacqueline, wake up! What has happened? Who did this to you?' But Jacqueline merely moaned and did not open her eyes. Marie hastily examined her, but, apart from a cut across the palm of her hand, could find no other wounds. So she ran into the kitchen, got a dipperful of drinking water from the crock, and sloshed it into the unconscious girl's face. Jacqueline moaned again and stirred but still refused to open her eyes. 'Come *on,*

Jacqueline!' Marie commanded. 'How can I help you unless I know what has happened What is wrong?'

The eyelids fluttered open to reveal the startling deep violet-blue eyes dilated and fixed with fear. Then Jacqueline began to scream, thinly at first, but growing in volume until the hallway rocked with the hysteria.

'Stop it!' Marie yelled. 'Stop it!' And she slapped Jacqueline hard across the face.

The screams died to a whimper, and tears filled and spilled over the fearful eyes. Jacqueline began to weep hopelessly, rolling her head from side to side.

Marie sat back on her heels in exasperation. Between the hysteria of the mother and the answering wails of the baby, her own head was rocking and she could not think straight. What on earth could she do? She dared not leave her friend in the state she was in to seek help. She would just have to wait until she calmed down. Something terrible had happened – but what? Not Dominic? No, of course it couldn't be Dominic. He wasn't even in the country ...

The double wedding of the Montal twins had not taken place as planned. With Marie-Thérèse LeBlanc in mourning due to Etienne's death, they had decided that it should be postponed for six months. Then to everyone's surprise, the up-to-now completely quiescent Claire Valdoux had suddenly insisted that she wanted *her* wedding on the date originally planned, did not, in fact, *want* a double wedding at all and, to complete everyone's stupefaction, had insisted on going on a European trip for her honeymoon.

She had found a ready ally in her mother, who was only too anxious to have her long-thought-of plan brought to completion. And so the reluctant Dominic – not one to stand up to the united efforts of two determined women – had walked meekly down the aisle and sailed off to Europe with his new bride. They would not be back for three more months. So, not Dominic – but who?

'Come on,' Marie said again to the sobbing Jacqueline. 'You can't stay there on the floor. You'll catch cold.' She hoisted her up and led the tottering figure into the drawing room, deposited her on the couch, and drew the cloak around her. Since Jacqueline continued to wail and sob, Marie picked up the screaming baby and tried to comfort it. It was soaked, so she carried it upstairs and, searching out one of her own sanitary towels, proceeded to change it.

Every time she looked at the unfortunately named Claire Delambe, she felt a twinge of unease – the baby was very dark, more like a mulatto than the octoroon she really was, and, in addition, she had inherited the most unfortunate combination of features, including the distinctive Montal nose. She showed no trace at all of her mother's great beauty.

The baby still wailed, though on a more subdued note, and Marie carried it back to Jacqueline and thrust it at her. 'Here,' she said roughly. 'The baby needs feeding. So if you don't want her to cry herself sick, you'd better nurse her.' Automatically, Jacqueline took Claire and put her to her breast. The act of nursing seemed to have a soothing effect on both mother and child, because after a few minutes the baby fell into an exhausted sleep, and Marie again took her and stood looking down at her quietly sobbing friend. 'Tell me,' she said in a gentler tone, 'tell me what has happened.'

Jacqueline looked at her with dilated eyes and choked out, 'It was horrible, just horrible. St Regis – he came to the house about midnight – he'd been drinking – I don't even know how he got in – suddenly he was just there – in the bedroom looking at me. He said – oh, he said terrible things, and he laughed! When he tried to get in bed with me, I fought him off – I screamed, I begged – but it didn't make any difference. He hit me so hard – I was so dazed – I just couldn't stop him – and it just went on and on and on . . .' She began to shiver violently. 'He kept saying I was family property, and if Dominic couldn't make use of me, he would! Oh God, I wish I were dead . . .!'

'We must call the police at once!' Marie exclaimed in horror. 'He can't get away with this!'

'No!' Jacqueline screamed. 'No! Not that! I would die of shame!'

'But he's raped and assaulted you!' Marie cried. 'Those are hanging crimes! He might even have killed you!'

152

'Oh, I wish he had,' moaned Jacqueline, rocking back and forth. 'How I wish he had!'

'But didn't your slaves hear you?' Marie demanded. 'Didn't they hear you screaming?'

'They're Montal slaves,' Jacqueline said hopelessly. 'What do you expect them to do? They are terrified of St Regis. They must have let him in in the first place.'

'But you'll have to do *something*!' Marie cried again. 'You can't just let him get away with it! He might come back again! At least you'll have to tell Dominic the minute he gets back, or you'll never have another quiet moment.'

'Never! Dominic must never know,' Jacqueline moaned. 'You don't understand. That's what I screamed at St Regis when he first ... but he said that if I breathed a syllable of this, he would tell Dominic that this was not the first time I had invited him – and not only him, but others, many others. He said you only had to look at Claire to know she was some nigger's child and nothing to do with Dominic ...'

'But Dominic would never believe that!' Marie cried.

'Wouldn't he?' Jacqueline said brokenly. 'Wouldn't he? If it was St Regis who said it? No, Dominic must never know.'

Marie was silent. The enormity of it left her speechless – that and the fact that Jacqueline was probably right. If it came to a choice between believing the woman he loved and the brother who dominated him, Dominic would believe the brother. 'Then we must get back at St Regis some other way,' she said with determination. 'But he'll pay – *that* I promise you!'

As soon as it was light she stopped a milk seller, out early on his rounds, and sent him with a message to her mother, that she needed her help, to bring some sedatives, and to hurry over to the house on Rampart. Jacqueline was still so distraught that Marie dared not leave her, fearing she might harm herself in some way.

Her mother arrived, grim-faced and tight-lipped. She asked no questions until she had given a soothing draught to the exhausted girl and had seen her drift off to sleep. Then she turned to Marie. 'Well?' she demanded.

Marie told her everything as briefly as possible. 'We can't let him get away with it. I'd like you to help me with this, *Maman*.'

'Devil's spawn,' her mother muttered absently. 'You'd be well advised not to get involved in this at all. You'll bring nothing on yourself but grief if you do. Jacqueline is already treading on quicksand. You know it, I know it, and if she had any sense, she'd know it, too. But she is as she is. If she were different maybe I could do something – but nothing that involves St Regis!'

'But I *am* involved,' Marie persisted. 'Jacqueline is my friend, so I must do something. And if our powers mean anything at all, we should use them now.'

'You seem to think we're the only ones with powers,' her mother responded sombrely. 'St Regis has powers, too – powers of the world and the Devil, and if you tangle with him you're likely to suffer for it. If you want my advice, there's only one way you'll bring St Regis down – through his pride, which is that of the Devil himself.'

'But won't you help?'

'Oh, I'll help,' her mother said, 'but only on a practical level. Jacqueline can't go back to that house – it isn't safe. She'll have to return to her mother and father until Dominic gets back. I'll see to it – and if he asks questions, she can tell him she became too nervous to stay by herself. And I'll send Jean over to stay here with you for a while.'

'Whatever for?'

'Because if St Regis finds out where she went and who helped her, you may be next,' her mother replied grimly. 'And if he's on the rampage, a bolted door won't stand in his way, I can assure you. If you had any sense, you'd come home for a while until this blows over. Nothing must happen to *you*.'

But Marie wanted no part of that. Though she sensed in her mother a genuine concern, again she got the feeling that the concern was for something other than herself.

Things did quiet down. Marie Laveau carried out her plans, Jacqueline was back home, Jean was installed in the spare bedroom on Rampart, and Marie went to work on her own.

Her efforts succeeded up to a point, but not as well as she had hoped. St Regis was involved in an ugly brawl down by the waterfront and emerged from it with a broken leg and covered with mire and humiliation. She had wanted something more permanent in the way of damage, but she reflected philosophically that at least the injured leg would keep him inactive for a while.

She tried again. This time a fire broke out in the Montal household – a fire which effectively demolished St Regis's bedroom and most of his wardrobe, but unfortunately left him only a little singed, but otherwise intact. Word went around that he had been in his cups and had knocked over a candle, but this afforded surprise to no one, and St Regis himself said nothing. She would have tried yet again, but another urgent matter claimed her attention and she was forced to postpone her operation of revenge.

With Jean now in the house, there was more work to do, so Marie had hired an old mulatto friend of Bessie's to come and do most of the household chores. Her mother had protested against this, pointing out that over a period Marie would save money if she invested in a slave, rather than waste it on wages, but there was something about the idea of slave-ownership that was repugnant to Marie, so she followed her own path.

It was, therefore, old Eugenie who answered the door one morning and ushered in a couple of well-dressed Creoles. Their appearance surprised Marie, since the woman was well into middle-age and the man somewhat older, and they were neither the age nor the type who usually came seeking her help. She assumed they were man and wife but was quickly disabused of this idea. The woman introduced herself as Madame Grison and the man as Jean DuBois.

Madame Grison was of the imperious type that Marie had come to know well, but she was also evidently ill at ease and kept shooting sharp little glances at her companion. He was a fleshy man, with a high-coloured, equally fleshy, face, in which the small black eyes looked like currants in a bun. He had lost most of his hair, but the few long strands that remained were plastered carefully over the shiny bald pate. Marie decided she did not like the looks of him, nor the way he was looking at her.

After some hesitation, Madame Grison finally explained the object of their visit. 'Monsieur DuBois,' she said, bowing in his direction, 'has done our family the honour of asking for our daughter Veronique's hand in marriage. If you know anything of such things, you will already know that Monsieur DuBois is a man of great eminence in this city, and so it is a very suitable match in every way, and one which we are most anxious should take place as soon as possible.' She paused.

'Well?' prompted Marie.

'The trouble is,' Madame Grison went on slowly, 'that my daughter Veronique is still a very silly child in some respects. She has her head filled with stupid romantic notions, culled, I fear, from those ridiculous romantic novels that girls read nowadays, and of which I thoroughly disapprove – a lot of silly stuff and nonsense!' She tightened her lips and sighed. 'In fact, she is being very difficult and obstinate over this matter and has tried our patience to the limit. There is no reasoning with her . . .' She hesitated, then plunged on. 'Having heard you are somewhat skilled in matters of the heart, we were wondering if you would undertake to bring her to a more reasonable frame of mind by whatever means you can. Once the marriage is celebrated, I am sure that she will see that, with such a fine man as Monsieur DuBois for a husband, she has indeed been incredibly foolish.'

For the first time Jean DuBois broke his silence. 'It would be a most valuable service you would render me, *Ma'mselle*,' he said in a silky voice. 'What Madame Grison says is correct. Once married, I am sure I will overcome Veronique's childish objections, for I love and desire her *à la folie*. So I would be suitably grateful if you can bring this to pass.'

'How grateful?' Marie said bluntly.

The little black eyes regarded her shrewdly. 'Shall we say a thousand dollars?'

The amount practically took Marie's breath away, but she still didn't like the looks of him. So she said, 'Make it two thousand and I'll do it.'

Madame Grison started to say in an outraged tone, 'Really! This is quite outrageous! I had no idea . . .' But she was waved to silence by Jean DuBois.

'In affairs of the heart, money is of minor importance,' he said smoothly. 'I am ready to accept your terms – one thousand dollars when the marriage contract is signed, and the rest on the day the marriage takes place. Can you do it?'

'Oh, yes,' Marie said with far more confidence than she felt. He was eager, much too eager, so she temporized. 'Of course, it may take a while. I must get to know your daughter, Madame. Do you have a likeness of her?'

Jean DuBois fumbled in his coat. 'I had a daguerreotype of her made,' he said with a touch of pride and handed it over to Marie. As she looked at it, her heart smote her. Madame Grison was a rather ugly woman with a bulbous nose and a distinct moustache on her upper lip, but the childish face that gazed at her, wide-eyed and with shining black curls framing the piquant elfin features, was one of great charm and attractiveness.

'How old is she?' Marie inquired.

'She will be seventeen next month,' her mother said stiffly. 'What has that to do with it?'

'Nothing,' Marie murmured. 'But age is always a factor, is it not?' she looked levelly at Jean DuBois – he was in his late fifties, if not older, old enough to be the girl's grandfather. She began to understand Veronique Grison's objections. However rich and influential he might be, I certainly wouldn't want to take him on, Marie thought. Aloud she said, 'I assume you want this done with as much dispatch as possible: I shall have to meet Veronique. Will you arrange that? Can you bring her here?'

Madame Grison looked uncomfortable. 'We have been keeping her in a summer house we have outside the city,' she mumbled. 'We thought that away from the city and her friends, who might encourage her in her ridiculous notions, she might come to a more reasonable frame of mind. My

157

husband and Monsieur DuBois have been visiting her there. I suppose we could arrange for you to go out with them.'

'The sooner the better, then,' Marie said with decision. 'In the meantime I will give you some powders to put in her food.' She went to a cabinet she had had installed and in which she was slowly building a collection of gris-gris and medicaments similar to her mother's.

'What is in them?' Madame Grison asked with suspicion.

'Nothing to concern you. A mild sedative which will calm her nerves, and another substance that will increase her desire for matrimony.' She slid a sidelong glance at Jean DuBois, who licked his lips. 'And there is something I would like Monsieur DuBois to wear from now on.' She solemnly handed him a gris-gris and tried to keep the irony out of her voice. 'It is something that increases virility and attractiveness to the opposite sex. It is reported as being most efficacious.'

Before taking their leave, the pair arranged with Marie for an expedition to the summer house to take place in a week's time. 'To give the powders time to take their full effect,' Marie assured them. In reality, she wanted the time to make further inquiries about the principals involved and to decide how she was going to proceed.

What she did find out neither increased her confidence nor cheered her up. Rich and esteemed Jean DuBois most certainly was, but he had also already had and buried three wives – one of whom he had reportedly bullied to death, another who had died in childbirth, thankfully, it was reported, and the third, who, according to an ex-slave of hers, had died of 'the miseries'. Marie was no longer in the least surprised at Veronique's lack of enthusiasm. She found in addition that the Grisons were in dire financial straits and that they were both almost frantic with anxiety to sell their only daughter to Jean DuBois.

Still, two thousand dollars was a lot of money, so Marie hardened her heart and went ahead. On the way out to the Grisons' summer place, she made it very plain to the two men that she must see Veronique alone and that she must have a free hand with her.

But at the first sight of the pale, drawn face of the girl, dark circles under the sad, reddened eyes, Marie's heart again misgave her, and she realized that she would have to come up with something spectacular to pull this situation out of the fire.

Once they were alone, she spoke urgently to the frightened girl. 'Look, I know you've never set eyes on me before and have no reason to trust me, but trust me you must. I have told your parents and Monsieur DuBois that I will convince you that this proposed marriage is the best thing for you. But before doing anything, I must know exactly how you feel in the matter. Please, you must be perfectly honest with me, because now that I have seen you face to face, I want above all to help you.'

The girl continued to gaze at her with wide frightened eyes. 'It's no use,' she choked out. 'No matter how long they keep me imprisoned here, no matter how they badger me, or my father beats me, I will *never* marry Jean DuBois.'

'Do you not wish to marry *him* in particular? Or are you against getting married at all? Or is there perhaps already someone else?' Marie said shrewdly. The bright rush of colour to the girl's face gave Marie her answer.

'Ah, so there is someone else! Why hasn't he come forward, then, and spared you all this?'

'He can't,' Veronique whispered. 'He's not even in the country. He went off to the West Indies in the hope of making some money. He is a younger son, you see, and his family is not a rich one. Though we love each other dearly, we cannot think of marriage yet. I have no *dot* to bring to him, and he has no money of his own. It will be years before we are in a position to marry.'

'In that case,' Marie said, 'I do not think you are being very sensible about this. Monsieur DuBois is a very rich man. Also, he is a great deal older than you are and may not live many more years. You would be a very rich widow, and you could bring to your lover all you possibly need – or even if you were *not* a widow, since your heart is not involved in this marriage, what would prevent you from having your lover, as *well*?'

Veronique shook her head violently. 'You don't understand,' she whispered. 'Don't you think I have already thought of all such things? If Jean DuBois were a different man ... well ... I would *like* to help my parents; I would love to aid my lover; I do not *want* to be an old maid withering away because I have no dowry – but I just can't *stand* him! Every time he takes my hand, my flesh creeps – and to be married to him . . .!' She shuddered.

Marie looked at her in silence, for as the girl had been talking an idea had come to her, which, the more she thought about, the better she liked. So she said, 'Listen. I stand to get a great deal of money if I carry out your parents' wishes, and it's money I badly want and need. What if I can fix it so that we both get what we want? What if I promise you that, even if you marry him, you will never be his wife, never have to live with him?'

'How could you possibly do that?' Veronique was wide-eyed with astonishment.

'I can do it, but you'd have to trust me absolutely and you'd have to *help* me. I can't do it without your help. *Do* you trust me?' She gazed hypnotically into the girl's eyes.

'Yes – yes – I think so,' Veronique stammered. 'You make me feel so strange.'

Marie smiled in triumph and continued to gaze deeply into the girl's eyes. 'Then I promise you solemnly that within two months you will be a bride but not a wife ... that you will never be the wife of Jean DuBois. Listen to me, listen to me carefully, for this is exactly what we have to do . . .'

160

Chapter Seventeen

'They're talking about Marie and the Grison affair all over town. I suppose you know that.' Crocodile was pacing up and down the front parlour before Marie Laveau, who was seated in her great wooden chair regarding him moodily.

'Yes, I know that.'

'It's not the only thing she's up to, either.' He stopped before her and held out two cards. 'She's been spreading those around, too.'

Marie Laveau took the cards and regarded them in silence. One read: MARIE LAVEAU – HEALER AND ADVISOR ON MATTERS OF THE HEART – MEETINGS BY APPOINTMENT. The Rampart Street address was attached. The other read: MARIE LAVEAU – ELEGANT SOIREES ARRANGED FOR GENTLEMEN OF TASTE. It had the same superscription. She smiled faintly. 'So that's why she asked me if she could borrow Maison Blanche from time to time! Well, well! How she is coming along, to be sure!'

'Are you going to let it go on?' Crocodile demanded.

'Why not? It says a lot for her spirit of enterprise, does it not? And it does me no harm.'

'Then you have given up on your original plan?' There was something like relief in his voice.

She became serious again. 'No, not at all. I am ready now, and so, by the looks of it, is she. But the time and the circumstances have to be right, exactly right – and they will be soon now, quite soon.'

He stopped pacing and gazed down at her, worry showing in every wrinkle and seam of his ebony face.

'You realize how dangerous it is. You are trying something that, to my knowing, no one has ever really done. There is great danger in it for both of you, and particularly you. What if you fail?'

'I don't intend to fail. I *can't* fail. I need her, I need what she has too much. There is so much that has to be done, so much that can be done – but I need time, all the time ahead: first through her, then after beyond her, another and another and another if need be.' The dark eyes glowed at him in the room's dimness, their remarkable irises slitted into half-moons like a cat's. 'What will the world be in a hundred, no, a hundred and fifty, two hundred years? I must know, I must see, I must *be*!'

'And what of her?'

'It is not that I will give her nothing in return – it is not that *I* am nothing.' Her tone was impatient. 'All that I am, all that I have, will be hers; she could have twenty, perhaps even thirty, good years.'

He shot an uneasy glance at her. 'Everything except what is really hers,' he mumbled. 'I wish I had never told you about it. I wish you'd give up the whole idea.'

'But you *did* tell me about it – giving me hope where there was none. Your role is done – you need fear nothing; you should regret nothing. Now it is only between her and me.'

He shook his head unhappily. 'I don't know. I just don't know. Sometimes I get the feeling that she is already beyond reach.'

'Not beyond mine,' Marie Laveau whispered. 'Not beyond mine when the time is ripe.'

The same day the pre-nuptial contract between Veronique Grison and Jean DuBois was signed, to the vast relief of the Grisons and the delight of Jean DuBois. A few days previous to this, a strangely calm and detached Veronique had informed her parents that she no longer had any objections to the marriage and would like to return home from her exile, so that the appropriate preparations could be made. So overjoyed was Jean DuBois, who was well aware of the Grisons' straitened circumstances, that he had declared his willingness to underwrite the most lavish wedding and reception that money could buy in New Orleans, and he ordained that the wedding should take place as soon as humanly possible. The date was set for two weeks after the signing of the settlement, the wedding to be a High Nuptial Mass at the Cathedral of St Louis, to be followed by a reception at Jean DuBois' huge town house on Jackson Avenue.

There Marie had gone an hour or so before the signing to collect the first instalment of her fee. She had not been too surprised to find a less than enthusiastic welcome from Jean DuBois. After some equivocating, he had handed over the draft for a thousand dollars. He then began to talk about the changeability of the female mind and how that all that was required was patience and a little firmness. Marie could quite well see where his thoughts were leading, so to forestall them she said in a quiet, firm voice, 'Look, Monsieur DuBois, before you say something you may later regret, let me tell you a few things. In a very short time I have achieved a seeming impossibility – turning a girl who could not stand the sight of you into one who is willing to marry you ... something, I may point out, that all the badgering, brow-beating, and brutality of her own family had not been able to accomplish in months. I think you may be under the impression that you no longer need me. Believe me, you do, and you will until the very day of the wedding. Veronique is a very sensitive girl whose nerves are not of the strongest and who can easily change her mind. It is my job to see that she doesn't, and one that I will carry out provided you carry out your end of the bargain. I think, in view of the circumstances, I should like the second half of my fee on the morning of the wedding, and in return I will guarantee that you will not merely get a quiescent bride, but a very willing one. Do you understand me?' She gazed levelly at him.

A hot gleam came into the beady eyes and he nodded, and she was interested to see a blue, knotted vein throbbing at his temple, as his high-coloured face took on a deeper hue. 'Yes,' he said in a thick voice, 'I understand. You drive a hard bargain, *Ma'mselle*, but I did not mean to imply you had not earned the money.' There was grudging admiration in his voice.

'Good. As long as we understand one another,' Marie said coolly. 'There are one or two other small matters in which I

163

feel I can be of service to you. As you say, young girls some-times have strange notions, and one of Veronique's objec-tions to your suit in the first place was that she declares she cannot stand the sight of a bald head.' She dropped her voice confidingly. 'Now, I don't know if you are aware of it, but I am knowledgeable in hairdressing and I was wondering – just for the occasion of the wedding, you understand – if I made you a toupee of hair to match your own, would you might not humour her in this respect?'

'Wouldn't that look ridiculous?' Jean DuBois said dubi-ously.

'No, not at all. It would cut years off your age,' Marie assured him, 'and I think it might make everything go a lot smoother.'

'Well, all right.'

'And the other thing,' she went on. 'I am sure you have found the gris-gris of help.' A smug smile appeared on the wet mouth and he nodded. 'But to make quite sure every-thing goes well for you on your wedding night, I will give you a powder which you can take with your wine at the reception.'

'A powder?' he echoed suspiciously. 'What kind of powder?'

'You have heard perhaps of Spanish Fly? Taken in ap-propriate doses, it is a marvellous stimulant for one's own abilities. Since I have assured you that you will have a wil-ling bride, I know you would not wish to risk disap-pointment.'

'All right,' he agreed with some eagerness. 'And her, too?'

'I will see to it,' Marie said silkily. 'I will see to everything!'

She lost no time in hurrying with the draft to the Valdoux bank on Royal Street, counting on Emile to use his own brand of magic to bring forth further fruit from it. One of the things she so liked about him was that he never pried – he would merely take what she had to give him, courteously ask her wishes, and go about his business. On her way home to Rampart Street, she was somewhat surprised to run into Jacqueline, who greeted her warmly. Although the violet-blue eyes still held a haunting sadness, there was a soft radiance about her that brought a twinge of envy to Marie's heart.

'Dominic is back,' she announced with a dazzling smile. 'And all is well again. Oh, Marie, he is so wonderful that I feel I can now put the nightmare behind me. How can I ever thank you for what you did for me that terrible night?'

'There is no need for thanks between friends,' Marie muttered. 'But I still think it would be wise to tell him what happened.'

Alarm leapt into Jacqueline's eyes and she drew back. *'Never!'* she whispered. 'And you must promise never to breathe a word of it to anyone.'

'Of course I wouldn't,' Marie said hotly. 'But I'm not the only one who knows – the slaves must know, and, worse, St Regis. It would be terrible if Dominic got wind of it from any of them and you had said nothing.'

'Oh, I'm sure that would never happen,' Jacqueline said serenely. 'Why should it?'

It was all very well for Jacqueline to take refuge in her rosy cloud, Marie thought grimly as she hurried home, but to blind herself to the possibilities of what the evil genius of St Regis might do was absurd.

What would happen when the house on Bourbon Street had been renovated after the fire and when the Montals returned from the plantation – what then? Marie only hoped for Jacqueline's sake that the respite her powers had achieved for her would last a considerable time.

To make Veronique's lot and her own easier, Marie had decreed that Jean DuBois should keep his visits to the Grison household to a minimum during the two weeks before the wedding. Accordingly, when she again repaired to the house on Jackson the morning of the wedding, she was not surprised to find him testy and impatient. She produced the toupee, which she had had made to her own specifications, and on which the heavy black hair was sewn to a base net of fine silk She had expected to suppress her mirth when she adjusted it on him, but it did make him look a lot younger, a fact he obviously appreciated as he preened in front of a mirror. She handed him the powder, also, and repeated her instructions about drinking it during the reception.

Since he made no move to pay her, she asked for her money, and with great reluctance he made out the second draft, grumbling under his breath all the while. 'I will be on hand in case you need me all through today,' Marie said when the draft was safely in her pocket.

He looked her up and down coldly. 'There is no way I can prevent you from attending the church ceremony, of course,' he sneered, 'but your part is finished, and I certainly have no intention of entertaining such as you in my house. So, good day, *Ma'mselle*. From now on I am quite capable of handling my own affairs.'

Any pity or doubts evaporated in Marie at that point, and as she made her way out through the mad bustle of preparations for the evening reception, her mind was already busy with her next moves. Despite Madame Grison's protests, Marie had insisted that she attend Veronique on the morning of the wedding, and she was expecting a hostile reception. To Marie's surprise, Madam Grison pounced on her with obvious relief when she arrived. 'Oh, I'm so glad you're here! I am afraid there is more trouble!'

One look at Veronique's distraught face, with its staring, panic-stricken eyes, and Marie's heart sank. Shooing Madame Grison and the slave who was helping Veronique to dress out of the room, she closed the door and turned on the frightened girl. 'Now what's the matter?' she demanded.

The eyes dilated even farther.' 'I can't go through with it,' Veronique whispered. 'It's no use talking – I just can't do it. Mama started to talk about my duties as a wife, and I knew then it was impossible. Rather than be his wife, I would kill myself!'

'But we've been through all this before. You won't *have* to be his wife, I promised you that!' Marie cried.

Veronique just hung her head and shook it.

'Is it because you're afraid I might betray you?' Marie said in a gentler tone.

'You said you were doing it for the money,' Veronique

said in a choked voice. 'And now you've got that. Why shouldn't you just walk away and leave me to it? I'm nothing to you.'

Marie went over to her and gently lifted her face between her hands. 'It is true about the money – but there are two very important reasons why I will not betray you: one is because you are a woman, just as I; and the other is because you are a woman in love. This might not make much sense to you now, but I hope it will one day. I happen not to like the idea of anyone's freedom being sold, particularly any woman's freedom. And though you have not been stripped and stood up on the slave block, there is not much difference in what is being done to you. That is why I could never betray you – because I would never know another peaceful moment. In this time of the world our lot is not an easy one, so we must help one another and trust one another. Please trust me.'

Veronique lifted miserable eyes to her. 'I still don't think I can get through today,' she whispered.

'Then don't think of today. Think of tomorrow, when it will be finished with. What news of Denys?'

'I did as you said, I wrote and told him to settle his affairs as soon as he could and to come back because I was in desperate need of him. But I did not tell him anything else, anything about the wedding.'

'Good. And you have heard in return?'

'Yes. He wrote he would be home as quickly as he could get passage, but he was very worried. Oh, what if things do not go as you plan? He will arrive to find me dead!' She began to weep.

'Nonsense! As long as you do as I have said, all will be well. Come. As soon as you are dressed, I will do as I have done before, but this time I will shut your mind entirely to what is happening. For the rest of today until it is finished, you will hear nothing you do not wish to hear, see nothing you do not wish to see. It is Denys who will put a ring on your finger in the cathedral, Denys who will walk down the aisle with you, Denys with whom you will laugh and talk at the reception, and with whom, when the grand waltz starts, you will take the floor. You will talk to him as a lover does, and you will promise him the delights of paradise. And it is only when what has to happen happens that you will leave this dream and be yourself again, but I will be near at hand, so do not worry.'

Madame Grison, who had been waiting in an agony of impatience in the hallway outside, practically swooned when the door opened to reveal her gently smiling daughter in full bridal array. She was clad in an exquisite satin gown with an overlay of white lace, a priceless pearl necklace – her bridegroom's gift – around her creamy throat, the diamond from her betrothal ring winking from her left hand.

Madame Grison was no more surprised than the Creole aristocrats who had packed into the cathedral to relish this bizarre affair at the sight of the poised and smiling girl walking gracefully down the aisle on the arm of her suddenly rejuvenated groom. And as they trooped off to the reception, the amazed whispers and conjectures rose to a crescendo. What miracle had happened? What magic had Marie Laveau wrought?

Marie had quietly made her way to the kitchen quarters of the great double-balconied DuBois house, now ablaze with lights from every window and gay with the scent of banked flowers, music, and laughter. The slave who had owed her a favour and given her entrance had seen to it that the others knew who she was, and as they bustled in and out with the trays laden with delicacies and the magnums of champagne, they saw that she was well supplied with both before they hurried away again with frightened backward glances.

The guests were getting gayer and gayer as Jean DuBois's bounty continued to flow without stint, excited by the spectacle of the flushed and vivacious girl who whispered confidentially into the ear of her red-faced bridegroom, who was perspiring freely under his heavy wig, but laughing as well with fever-bright eyes at her sallies. When the grand waltz struck up after the cutting of the many-tiered bridal cake, there were cries and applause from all around the crowded room. *'Danse, danse pour les mariés!'* And a wild enthusiasm broke out as the slim figure of the bride rose and held out her hands to the portly figure of the groom. With all the vivacity of a young man, he swept her out on to the dance floor, and they whirled to the mounting crescendo of the waltz, around and around the polished floor, which mirrored their spinning, kaleidoscopic shadows.

Faster and faster they whirled until, suddenly, Jean DuBois faltered in his steps, stopped dead, and started to tug vainly at the high stock at his throat, his face turning an ugly purple. The bride broke away from him, her hands flying to her mouth. He stood there swaying for a few seconds, then crumpled at her feet like a bag of old clothes as she began to scream. The screams grew in volume as she looked with horror at the little old man, his toupee slipping sideways off the bald head, who lay contorted and dead at her feet.

Pandemonium broke out as the guests crowded around. And, out of nowhere, Marie Laveau was there supporting the half-swooning Veronique. She turned to find herself looking into the panic-stricken eyes of Madame Grison, who hissed at her, 'What have you done ... you ... you witch! You have tricked us! You have broken your promise!'

'*Allons, Madame!*' Marie said very softly with a slight, enigmatic smile. 'Do not get so upset – you are mistaken in that. I promised only that the wedding would take place, and it did! You have a very rich widow for a daughter, *Madame*. If I were you, I would think about that.'

Chapter Eighteen

1849

On the afternoon of 3 May, Monsieur Pierre Sauvé, sugar-planter, was enjoying a most pleasant dream. He was telling Emperor Napoleon III what a bumper year this had been for his sugar crop as they strolled elegantly down the Champs-Elysées viewing the 14 July fireworks beyond the Arc de Triomphe. 'I knew this spring,' he was telling Napoleon, 'that this would be a special year. Never had I seen the cane so high, so early – and I was right! My fortune was made, and so here I am hurrying to enjoy its fruits in your beautiful capital.'

'How interesting,' His Imperial Majesty murmured. 'And where did you say your plantation is situated?'

'On the Mississippi River, Your Majesty, about fifteen miles upstream from the city of New Orleans. You must really pay us a visit . . .'

The beautiful dream shattered at this point, and Monsieur Sauvé found himself gazing into the worried face of a house slave who was gingerly shaking him. He let out a roar of annoyance, sending the slave reeling back in alarm. 'What is it?' he roared, furious that his delightful *tête-à-tête* had been broken for some minor domestic matter.

'It's one o' de field hands,' the slave stuttered, anxious to shift the blame away from himself. 'Sez he's somethin' mighty 'portant to tell ya. Ah argued with 'im, but he sez it's mighty 'portant.'

Since there was now no salvaging of his post-prandial nap, Pierre Sauvé heaved himself up from his couch, yawning and grumbling. The frightened field hand was ushered in and was so intimidated by his master's scowling mien that he just hung his head and muttered unintelligibly at the carpet.

'Straighten up and speak up, damn you!' Pierre Sauvé said testily. 'I can't hear a word you're saying! But it had better be important to disturb me like this!'

The slave looked up furtively and started again. The words were still garbled, but one word caught Pierre Sauvé's ear and electrified him. 'Crevasse! A break!' he yelled. 'Where?'

'In de levee by de crushin' mill, sah. Ah was a-goin' back to de mill after Ah et, an' Ah seed dis stream o' water lak, an' Ah sez to mahself: where dat water from? An' den Ah looks an' Ah seed it a-comin' from de levee.'

Every trace of colour left Pierre Sauvé's face as his rosy dream punctured. 'How long ago was this?' he cried.

The two slaves glanced uneasily at one another. 'Don't rightly know,' the field hand mumbled, 'but Reuben here sez he on no 'count goin' to wake ya, but Ah sez it was 'portant, so . . .'

'My God, let's get out there!' Pierre Sauvé cried, his pulse clamorous with foreboding.

Half an hour later he was looking at the ruin of all his dreams, as the overburdened river spilled itself through a thirty-foot gap it had torn in its containing dyke and roared on towards the sea. He was wiped out, ruined, but perhaps it was still not too late to save others . . .

'Call all hands,' he ordered grimly, 'and send word to all the other planters, and have a runner go to the city. If the other dyke goes, they'll be underwater in New Orleans by morning.'

The other planters hurried to his aid, but the city of New Orleans was in no such hurry. Breaks had happened before; this was nothing new; let the planters handle it – it was their business, after all! What could happen to this most thriving and gay of cities? The season was just moving into high gear after the penances of Lent and before summer's hot hand clamped down on them. Let the planters look to their own levees; New Orleans was too busy enjoying itself!

In the days that followed, some enterprising businessmen even organized trips for interested citizens to see the thirty thousand acres of plantation land which had become a lake. They enjoyed the sight, ignoring the important fact: parallel to Pierre Sauvé's broken levee ran the Metairie ridge, which, when the thundering waters reached it, neatly funnelled them towards the great bowl in which New Orleans lay. It was only when the water had reached the outskirts of the city that some inhabitants woke up to the fact that something should probably be done. And, belatedly, help was sent to the beleaguered planters.

But the river had now got used to its wild rampage, and as soon as one break was fixed a new one would appear somewhere else; the river would not be slowed in its inexorable journey onward. Optimists said that the New Basin Canal, with its own high levees, would act as a barrier against flooding in the city. Those who lived on the wrong side of the canal pointed out that it wouldn't save *them*, and they proposed to cut the canal levels to spread the flood in at least a democratic manner.

Tempers got so hot that the police were called in and the canal was manned by armed patrols to see no such breaks were made. Meanwhile, the Vieux Carré, which was on the wrong side of the canal, sank deeply and quietly under the whispering waters, becoming in the process a latter-day and unwilling Venice. People huddled on second floors, or crouched on top of their household goods, as the muddy water swirled into their homes. Boats, skiffs, and rafts of all sorts appeared on the placid surface of the flooded streets. Sounds became muted, voices hushed, as the city began to take things seriously at last.

To Marie it was like a dream, a bad dream with no bearings, as the waters closed in. For with their coming had fallen upon her a deadly lethargy of mind and body, which puzzled and alarmed her. She was suddenly so weak that getting out of bed was a major effort, and dressing became a monumental task. She watched dull-eyed as Jean, with the help of Charles-Louis and François, rescued the things from the ground floor. These now crowded higgledy-piggledy the upstairs rooms, but she made no effort to bring order to her soggy domain.

What ailed her? She could not afford to be sick – not now, when things were going so well. Her parties at Maison

172

Blanche had been a wild success – good food and drink, some willing girls of assorted colours, a little Voodoo music to heighten the excitement, and the 'gentlemen of taste' had come flocking in. She had taken a leaf out of Flo Winfield's success story and had profited greatly from it. And the Grison affair had raised her reputation as a wonder-worker to such an extent that she had more clients than ever before, more than she could comfortably handle. Her account with the Valdoux bank was fat and growing, and she was well set on the course she had plotted for herself. Now was not the time to falter – if only the wretched, stinking waters would go away!

She couldn't understand herself. Why hadn't she gone with Jean and the others to escape the flood at Maison Blanche? He had urged her enough. 'Mama wants me to take Amelie and Marie-Jeanne and the boys up there. Marie-Philome is coming, too, since Jean-Paul is up with the rest of the planters working at the levees. Come, too, Marie! What good can you do here? People are too busy with their own miseries to turn on others. The house will be safe enough. Come with us!'

But something was holding her, and the thought of making so much effort was too much for her. 'No, I'll stay,' she had said. 'I'll be better here.'

'You're as bad as *Maman*,' he had grumbled. 'She won't leave, either – she almost seems to be enjoying it. I did not want to go without her, but she says she wants me with the younger ones. The streets are getting too dangerous, what with snakes and rats everywhere and all the rotting dead things, and she's afraid we'll all get fever if we stay. I told her the same applied to her, but she just laughed and said that nothing from the waters could harm her; her strength is the strength of the river.'

Why hadn't she gone? She was alone here, with the waters sucking and sapping at her just as they were sucking and sapping at the foundations of the house. The noise of someone moving about below and calling her name brought the knowledge of her aloneness more sharply into focus. 'Who is it?' she called. 'What do you want? I'm up here.'

Christophe appeared at the door of the bedroom, his eyes wide and staring. 'Ah came to warn ya, Miz Marie – ya got to get out o' here quick. Ya got to get right away. Ah found out what she's doin' – Ah found out! That devil woman's tryin' to make a zombie out o' ya, that's what! Ah heard her talkin' with Crocodile 'fore she sent 'im away. Ah didn' understand nothin' then, but the way she's been goin' on the last three days, that's it, sho' enough. She's been holed up in that room an' been at the Voodoo the whole time. She's after ya, Miz Marie – body an' soul, she's after ya!'

Marie struggled up on to an elbow. 'Have you gone crazy, Christophe? What on earth are you babbling about?'

'Ya ain't seen 'er. Ah have. She ain't et, she ain't slept. She got the roosters an' the snake in there with her. She been a-chantin' an' a-callin', an' that *ogan's* been soundin' off night an' day, an' the drums been answering all by themselves. Ah's scared to death, Miz Marie. Ah ain' stayin' 'round no more. Ah'm off. Come with me, please come with me, or she goin' to make a zombie out o' ya, fo' sho', mebbe a zombie out o' me, too, fo' a-warnin' ya.'

'If you're so scared of her, why did you come at all?' Marie said. She could not begin to fathom the purpose of his wild imaginings.

' 'Cause the ol' Indian said Ah had to. "Go to her," he says. "Tell her the time is now." '

Marie's heart skipped a beat. 'Indian? Who? Where?'

Christophe looked at her, dazed. 'Ah don' rightly know.' he mumbled. 'He was jus' there by the ol' magnolia in the backyard. "Go to her," he says. Seemed mighty 'portant to him.'

'But where is he?'

He shook his head in confusion. 'Gone. One minute he's there, the next he ain't. Ah's scared, Miz Marie. Ah jus' don' know what's happenin'.'

Marie's pulse was thudding uncomfortably. 'All right,' she said. 'You go along now, Christophe. You've done well. But go now and take care of yourself. I'll take care of it. Don't you worry.'

He looked at her with miserable eyes. 'Ya ain't comin'?'

She shook her head and he made slowly for the door. At it, he turned and looked at her for a long moment. 'Ah jus' wants to tell ya, 'case the Voodoo gets me,' he mumbled softly, 'that Ah've always loved ya, Miz Marie – remember that, Ah've always loved ya.'

With his going, Marie sank back on the bed, exhausted from the effort of talking. She felt she was draining, dwindling into nothing. None of it made any sense. Why should her mother want to turn her into a zombie, a creature without intelligence, enjoyment, or willpower – a mindless slave?

She knew all about zombies. She remembered one time talking with Mama Antoine about them. In fact, it was a conversation that her mother had overheard and quickly put an end to. What was it Mama Antoine had said? Something more, something about people worse off than zombies. She remembered now – they had been talking about African Mambos. 'Some o' them are sure fearsome,' Mama Antoine had said. 'Why, Ah've been told that when they feel themselves gettin' old an' they want a handsome man or somethin' special, they jus' go an' take over some young girl, body an' soul – move right into her, they do!'

'What happens to the girl?' she had asked.

'Well, she done get their old body – 'course, at times it jus' kills her right off or drives her mad. But there ain't nothin' she can do 'bout it; she's jus' trapped inside. No, those ol' Mambos are surely somethin'. 'Course, it's mighty difficult to do . . .'

Marie lay rigid as she recalled the conversation. Was that it? Was that why all this time . . .? Casting her mind back, it even began to make a crazy sort of sense. But why to her? Why should her mother hate her like that? There was only one thing to do – she had to find out, she had to confront her.

The effort of thinking had somehow brought her new strength, and she slowly got out of bed. She must think, she must act, she must protect herself without delay – but how? She tried to concentrate on the Helper. She had never seen him since her first vision, but there had been times when she had felt his presence very strongly, and if ever she needed him, she needed him now. *Your mother cannot harm you*, he had said. Was it he who had sent Christophe with the warning? No. That made no sense. *An old Indian*, he said, and her Helper had not been old. Her father – the man with the power of Earth? *Yours is the power of Earth and Water*, her mother had said. *Mine is of the Waters*. She thought of the world of water that encompassed her and shuddered.

Earth – if she was to fight this, she must have earth. With shaking hands she scrabbled in some potted ferns that drooped on the window ledge. Some of the fine, dry earth she put in her shoes; the rest she emptied into a gris-gris bag and hung around her neck. Was it just in her mind, or was she already feeling stronger? She smeared more dirt over her face and arms. She must go now and she must summon the Helper. She began to concentrate.

An old Negro poling down Rampart Street in a home-made skiff was startled to see Marie Laveau, her face dirt-streaked, her long, dark hair falling in disarray about her shoulders, clutching an *ogan* and an *asson*, and summoning him urgently from a doorway. 'Take me to the house on St Ann Street as quickly as you can,' she ordered, pressing a silver dollar into his hand.

'Why, sho' thing, Miz Laveau, glad to take ya home. What you goin' to do with dem things? Voodoo away dis ol' flood? Ah didn't know ya was still here. Thought ya was gone out o' de city with de rest of de family.' And he was surprised at the look of horror she gave him.

Arriving at the house, Marie tried the righthand door, only to find it locked, but the lefthand parlour door opened to her touch. And as she hurried in, the old Negro called after her: 'Ya take care now, Miz Laveau – there's lots o' nasty bitin' things around.'

There was no panic in Marie's heart. Was she already too late? Had the change happened? She sloshed through the foot of water that lay all over the floor to the communicating door. Under cover of the noise that was coming from the inner room, she tried it. It opened silently at her touch.

At the strange sights and smells that met her, she recoiled. On the surface of the black silent water floated rooster heads and rooster feathers, oily coils of blood and great globs of blackened wax, fallen from the guttered candles that stood on everything. The room was in semi-darkness and thick with shadows, but she could make out the outlines of the great sleeping python on one of the chests, and in the great chair sat the crouched figure of her mother. She was naked and squatting back on her heels, her head thrown back, as she chanted with eyes closed, the *ogan* in her right hand tolling and bringing forth an answer from the drums, which had been raised above the flood along one wall. Incense curled sluggishly from a large burner that sat on a table in front of her, adding its heavy scent to the melange of smells and vibrations that made the room a living thing, and over which the heavy miasma of the river waters rose like a harbinger of death. Her mother's figure seemed to be outlined by a pulsating red aura that waxed and waned with every breath she drew.

Acting on pure instinct, Marie silently stripped off her own clothes and smeared herself with more of the earth before crossing the threshold. Then, with a single dramatic gesture, she sent the sounding drums splashing into the foul waters and leaped upon their resting place. 'I have been warned, so I am here,' she panted. 'Now we are face to face, your powers against mine. This is not of my seeking or understanding. Stop now, before it is too late. You will not conquer me!'

For a second, Marie Laveau's eyes slitted open and fastened upon her, the hand with the *ogan* faltering momentarily in its action. Then the eyes closed again and the chanting rose anew, the red aura pulsating and reaching out towards her. Marie closed her eyes and concentrated all her willpower on the force she felt within her, driving it out to combat the seeking tentacles of her mother's power; in her hand her *ogan* began to toll a counterpoint to her mother's, shattering the shadows with discordances.

Time ceased to have any meaning, as in the world beyond them day paled into night and dawned into another day. The voices of the *ogans* gradually died and fell silent, and all that troubled the surface of the still waters was the harsh, sobbing breath of the two women. There was nothing now but mind against mind, will against will.

At one point Marie had felt her soul slipping away from her and she had cried out in a tongue she did not recognize and had clutched at the bag of earth around her neck, and for a second the red aura had shrunk and wavered, only to reach out once again.

In the time beyond time, she felt it happening again, this terrible tugging at the very roots of her being. This time she cried out to the Helper – if he did not aid her now, she knew she was finished. She felt a change in the vibrations of the room, a shaking in the atmosphere. She opened her eyes to see a flurry on the water, as of a shadow passing, a glimpse of black braids, a hint of gold, and the encompassing red cloud that threatened and loomed, shrank and shifted. There was a sudden choking cry from her mother, and she slumped sideways in the great chair, twitching feebly as the red cloud withered and died, its tattered remnants disappearing within her.

Marie stirred on her own pedestal, then stood up. The bonds were snapped; she was free again, conscious now only of aching exhaustion. Stiffly she stepped down into the waters, which were now merely muddy remnants of a river's wrath and not a source of threat or danger. She went over to her mother's unconscious form and stood looking down. She had triumphed, but there was no sense of victory within her, only a weary sadness. Her mother moaned and the eyelids fluttered open on dull darkness within.

'Why?' Marie said. 'Why?'

The flaccid mouth worked and the words came out thick and slow. 'I needed you, I needed what you are. I must not go – there is so much I must do. Death shall not, must not, have me!'

'What have I ever done to you that you should hate me so?' Marie cried in sudden anger.

The dull eyes fixed on her. 'I do not hate you,' her mother said softly. 'I love you. You are flesh of my flesh, bone of my bone. There was only a greater need – and the need remains.'

'A need you will never fulfil,' Marie said savagely. 'Oh, I know now that you will probably try again, but I am warned. I know now also the face and force of my enemy, and I am ready. If you cannot beat me now, you cannot beat me later. My powers rise; yours fail.'

A frightened look crept into the dull eyes. 'What are you going to do?' her mother croaked

'Do?' She laughed angrily. 'Why, nothing! I will live my life and you will live what is left of yours, but if there is anything of yours that I want, I shall take it and you will give it to me, because you will know well that I *can* take it if I wish.'

'And the Voodoos – you will be Queen of the Voodoos?' Her mother's tone was fearful.

'No – why should I be? I leave you to your games and your dances and your petty powers. For the moment they do not interest me. I have other plans, but when I *choose* to be Queen, then I will be.'

'You will have to kill me first,' her mother whispered.

'Oh, no, Mama!' Marie cried triumphantly. 'All I have to do is *wait* and let Death himself take care of that. From now on, *I* am Marie Laveau!'

Chapter Nineteen

The river, having fulfilled its purpose, retired quietly to its bed. By the third week of June the sun was shining brightly again on the havoc the river had caused, and the people of New Orleans had begun the tedious task of removing its sludgy traces from the face of their fair city. Though the flood had been a ruinous one, it had not been very lethal. The toll: two men swept from a levee and one poor Negro found floating on Gallatin Street swollen and blackened from snakebite.

It took Marie several days to find out that the Negro was Christophe, and there was little doubt in her mind that somehow her mother had made him pay for his act of devotion with his life. She resolved that her mother must pay, also, that now should be established the pattern their lives must take from hence forward. She would take Maison Blanche, which she needed and for which she had plans, and she would take something else, something that would cause her mother much pain – she would take Patty.

The first objective was easy to accomplish. It was merely a matter of dollars and cents. She went to her mother with a fair offer, and after some haggling and a grudging assent, it was done.

The second was a more delicate task to accomplish. She had long realized how fond her mother was of the little slave; she had also long been aware of the fact that her mother had used the same method on Patty that she herself had used on Veronique Grison. She would use her mother's own weapons against her.

First, she waylaid Patty and took her to see the cameo perfection of the house on Rampart Street. There she talked at length to her about Christophe, to whom the slave girl had been pathetically attached, planting in her mind the fact that he had displeased her mother and had suffered death in consequence. She wanted to frighten Patty but not terrify her – this was not part of her plan. Easily she led Patty into a mild hypnotic state in which she described how pleasant life would be with her, how she would get her new clothes and a big room of her own, full of things that would be a slave's dream of paradise. 'A real mirror?' Patty had said wistfully. 'Mah own mirror, an' an oil lamp? An' a real silk tignon? Oh, Lawdy!'

The groundwork laid, Marie went to her mother. 'I am going to take your advice – I am going to buy a slave,' she informed her.

Her mother was cool and wary. 'Oh, have you seen one that would suit you, at last?'

'Yes, indeed. I'd like to buy Patty.'

'*No!*' her mother said violently. 'Never! I'd never consider it!'

'Not even if Patty were happier with me than with you? With Christophe gone, she is unhappy here. You must have seen that.'

'Ridiculous! She's just having one of her spells; she isn't unhappy. What gave you such an idea?'

'She told me. If you don't believe me, why don't you ask her about it?'

'Certainly ... Patty!' her mother called. The slave girl came sidling in, a sullen expression on her face, which lightened and brightened into a sudden grin as she saw Marie.

'What's this I hear about you telling Miss Marie you're unhappy?' Marie Laveau said sharply. 'What are you unhappy about?'

The sullen look settled back on Patty's face and she hung her head. 'Ah don' lak it here no more,' she muttered finally. 'Nothin' but work, work, work, an' nobody 'tall to help. Ya done send Christophe off, ya bad woman, ya, an' he's all daid 'cause o' ya. Ah don' lak it here no more – Ah wanna go with Miz Marie. She got a nice place, an' she won' work a body to death!'

A look of pain came into Marie Laveau's eyes. 'We'll get another boy,' she assured Patty, 'soon, very soon. A nice one, one maybe you can marry up with, not like Christophe,

181

who wouldn't have anything to do with you, being free. You go along now, and everything's going to be all right.'

Patty, her head still hanging low, sidled out again, muttering to herself. Marie Laveau turned on her daughter. 'So, you've been at her,' she hissed.

'Only with her best interests at heart,' Marie informed her coolly. 'She's frightened. She feels what happened to Christophe could happen to her.'

A veiled look came over her mother's eyes. 'The answer is still no,' she said shortly.

'I know what you have done to Patty since you first brought her here,' Marie informed her. I know how you have blocked her mind against the past. Well, if need be, I can undo what you have done – I can unblock her mind.'

'You wouldn't!' Marie Laveau said in horror. 'You know that would destroy her!'

'I would if I were forced to,' Marie countered. 'And if you do not sell her to me, I will be forced to. It's as simple as that.'

Their eyes clashed for a long minute; then Marie Laveau's dropped. 'Then take her and be damned,' she faltered miserably. 'I'll not have her destroyed because of what lies between us. But if you don't treat her right, I swear you'll suffer for it.'

'Oh, I'll treat her right; in fact, I'll treat her like a human being and not a creation,' Marie said. 'After all, why not? She will always remind me of you.'

She took Patty back to the house on Rampart like a prize trophy of war – as it turned out, it was to be one of the best bargains she was to make in her entire life.

In 1850, Zachary Taylor, of Baton Rouge, Louisiana, moved into the White House as president of the United States. Although he was not a native son, the inhabitants of the state, lacking one of similar eminence, proudly claimed the old Indian fighter and general as theirs. It was good, they said, to have someone connected with this most thriving of states in the White House. In the summer of 1850, Marie moved into her own White House for the summer; the event passed without notice.

When she had taken it over from her mother, Maison Blanche had consisted of just one huge room, the site of her soirées, with an equally large portico running along the front, Southern plantation style, and a few shanty outbuildings tacked on at the rear. She had transformed the house, adding on several small cubicle bedrooms – for those 'gentlemen of taste' who were too fatigued to take their ladies of the evening elsewhere – a large bedroom for herself, and spacious kitchen quarters. The main room – with its simple gracious lines, whitewashed walls, and long French windows giving on to the portico – she had left alone, save to add some suitable embellishments, such as a polished parquet floor for dancing, sundry large gilt-edged mirrors, and velvet-upholstered banquettes along the walls for the weary. She had also added a large carved teak chair, somewhat similar to her mother's, from which she could 'preside' over the proceedings. She thought of it as being a rather neat touch, emphasizing as it did that it was she who controlled, who dominated the soirées, not the paying customers. It also underlined the fact that she was special and generally unavailable.

It was not that she had been entirely continent since Etienne's death. Sometimes she had taken a man because he had been pleasing to look upon, or attractive in some way, or, more rarely, because she needed some hold over him. But none of them had ever touched her heart, even to the extent Etienne had done, and sometimes she wondered if there was a man born who could ever reach the inner recesses of her being, a man with whom she could ever truly meld. She had in the process, however, become skilful in the management of men, so that those who had started out as lovers generally came back as friends. From what she had seen of male-female relationships thus far, she felt that this was no mean accomplishment.

So satisfied was she with her new arrangements that she lingered at Maison Blanche long after the new social season had begun in the city, and she would have lingered longer had not a pressing circumstance drawn her back.

Veronique Grison DuBois, now Veronique Devereux, had sent an urgent messenger in the shape of her husband, Denys Devereux. Marie had met him briefly after his return, and had not been overly taken with him. His eyes were a mite too close together, his chin a little in retreat, and he seemed a young man of no particular wit or charm, and she wondered if Veronique had perhaps made a bad bargain. However, they had married after the proper period of mourning for the unlamented Jean DuBois had been observed, and had appeared to be extremely happy. Now, as he descended from his elegant carriage, his undistinguished face looked worried and anxious, and without wasting time on any polite preliminaries, he burst out, 'Veronique begs you to come to her. She needs you most urgently. And I beg you to humour her wish. She is expecting our first child shortly, and of late has been quite unwell. Please, will you come?'

'Naturally I'll come to see her,' Marie said. 'But what does she expect of me? I am not a doctor or a midwife.'

'We have a doctor, the best in the city, supposedly, and a midwife has been arranged for, but Veronique has something on her mind, something only you can take care of, she says. I don't know what it is – she won't tell me.'

Intrigued, Marie went with him. She found Veronique, her face pinched and her belly swollen, but otherwise in a calm enough frame of mind. Denys, who obviously was used to doing what he was told, was dismissed, and the young women settled down to a *tête-à-tête*. After an exchange of news – for they had not seen one another in over a year – Veronique finally spoke of her problem.

'Marie, I need your help again, the same kind of help.' She got up and began to pace laboriously back and forth in her elegant boudoir. 'I'm frightened. The doctor says the baby will come at any time now, and the way it kicks it feels like it may be here any minute. He also says that because I am so small, the birth may not be an easy one. Mama has told me such terrible stories of my own birth ...' – Marie gave a

184

cluck of vexation – '... that now I am terrified. I've always been afraid of pain, and the thought of it is almost too much for me. Please, will you, could you, be here when the time comes? Not to deliver the baby, but to block my mind against the pain, as you did before? Could you do that?'

'Yes, I suppose so,' Marie said slowly. 'I've never done anything like it before, but I don't see why I couldn't do that. But I'm not sure how a doctor would react to my presence. Also, I'm not sure I'd *want* him to see what I do,' she went on, with sudden decision. 'The very *first* labour pains you feel, you send for me at once, before you send for either the doctor or the midwife. I'll come and put you under before they get here, and I'll stay till it's over in case there is further need. Is that agreeable?'

'Oh, Marie, you're an angel!' Veronique cried. 'You're the most wonderful person I know! I'm sure the good Lord will take you straight to Heaven when you die.'

'Well, perhaps not *straight* up,' Marie murmured with an ironic twinkle in her eye.

To be near at hand, she moved back to Rampart Street, and, walking in its familiar environs, she ran into Jacqueline, who was surprised and delighted to see her. She was looking more beautiful than ever, a soft bloom to her fair skin, a lustrous sheen to her hair, her eyes sparkling.

'I thought you had deserted us entirely,' she reproached Marie gently. 'Dominic and I have missed seeing you so much. Why must you hide yourself in that old bayou?'

'I like it out there, and I came back only for the *accouchement* of a friend; otherwise, I'd have probably stayed until Christmas.'

'We, too, are expecting again,' Jacqueline informed her shyly. 'This time we are hoping for a boy. It should arrive about the time of your birthday, so we plan to call it Yves-Marie.'

So that explained her added radiance, Marie thought, but her heart sank slightly. Now, if anything happened, there would be two burdens, not one, upon those exquisite shoulders. Then she gave herself a mental shake – nothing had happened so far in spite of all her forebodings; nothing probably would ever happen. She was just being stupid. She parted from the radiant Jacqueline with a promise to come and see her soon.

Veronique Devereux went into labour two nights later, and Marie, summoned by the distraught Denys, hurried to her side. 'You will feel nothing,' she informed Veronique, who was grasping tightly at her hands and staring at her with eyes fixed in panic. 'You will feel no pain and you will do what the doctor and midwife say. You will hear only them, see only them, until it is over. With the first cry of the new-born, you will awaken from this, and you will hear and feel and see as normal, but you will not remember.' The convulsive grasp of the hands loosened, the panic faded and died, and Veronique lay quietly back with a sigh on the birth couch, which was stretched along the foot of the great Seignouret bed. Marie went quietly out.

'Send for the doctor and the midwife,' she told the anxious Denys. 'The time is here.'

The waiting time was long. Marie sat quietly in the boudoir adjacent to the bedroom and watched the frantic Denys pacing up and down. He began to make her nervous, as well. She barely remembered her youngest brother's birth, but it bore no comparison to this, since her mother had had her children as a cat had kittens. What if she had done the wrong thing? What if Veronique or the baby died?

Her increasing fears were finally put to rest by a tiny wail followed by a sudden moan from the bedroom. Denys stopped frozen in his tracks, and a short time later the frock-coated doctor emerged solemn-faced from the bedroom. 'Monsieur Devereux, you are the father of a fine son,' he informed Denys. 'And I have to say that your wife is the most courageous and·remarkable patient I have ever had. She bore that long and tortuous labour with scarcely a whimper. She is all right. You may see her, but only for a moment. Understandably, she is exhausted.'

As Denys disappeared with alacrity, the doctor looked curiously at Marie. 'Are you perhaps the Marie Madame Devereux called out to during the labour?'

'Yes. I am Marie Laveau.'

'Ah, so that explains it. I have heard of you,' he said softly. 'Well, Marie Leaveau, I do not know how you did it – I'm not sure I want to know – but that is a great gift you have. I had serious doubts about this case, for I have seen more young mothers die from the exhaustion of pain than I care to think of, but somehow you took her pain away. God keep you for that. I only wish you could be on hand for all my cases. My name is Dr Franke, and if you ever stand in need of employment, please remember me.'

'Thank you, Doctor, I'll remember that,' Marie assured him.

'At your service, Marie Laveau.' He bowed, then was gone.

Since she was back in the city, Marie decided she might as well stay for a while; there were a lot of things to catch up on and a lot of family news. Marguerite, her eldest sister, was also back in town on the sad errand of burying yet another Crocker baby in the family grave in the old St Louis cemetery. She brought news of Celeste, who had produced three babies of her own in rapid succession, and was supporting them and her lay-about husband on the proceeds of the small haberdashery she kept. It surprised no one that she and her husband did not get along.

There was a family gathering after the interment. Marie-Philome was there with her new baby; what a year it had been for them, thought Marie. And all the rest were there, too, except for Celeste and Daumeny, from whom there had been no word for a long time. Outwardly, her mother and she were on the same terms they had always been. Only Jean, so finely attuned to his mother's feelings, sensed a difference, and Marie could see him glancing at them both from time to time with a puzzled expression.

There were similar get-togethers at Christmas and at New Year's, with much laughter and feasting and exchanging of gifts. Families were fun, but definitely exhausting, Marie concluded as she made her way back to Rampart Street in the small hours of the first day of the new year. Fond as she was of them all, she felt increasingly aware that in her lifestyle and in her thinking she was drifting far away. It was not only on account of her mother; that struggle was quite a separate thing. She was thankful to be a single entity, to be returning to something she had made completely her own.

She slept late and heavily, and was awakened at last by a pounding on the front door. She got up and went out on to the landing in time to see Patty almost bowled over by a figure that rushed through the door and up the stairs towards her. It was Jacqueline's slave girl, and she was clutching a howling Claire in her arms. 'Come quick, Missus,' she bawled. 'Der's all hell broke loose down at our place. Ah caught Missus tryin' to kill dis po' chile with a pillow. She's taken leave o' her senses – she's a-carryin' on lak a mad thing. Come quick!'

Marie grabbed her cloak and threw it over her night things. Thrusting the howling child at the startled Patty, she cried, 'Look after her!' And then she followed the running slave. They raced down Rampart to the astonishment of passersby and burst into Jacqueline's house on South Rampart. All was quiet.

'Where are you, Jacqueline?' Marie called.

'She's in dere, Missus – look!' The slave quavered, tugging at her sleeve. Jacqueline was sitting silently on a couch in her drawing room, attired in a ball gown, and staring fixedly, straight ahead.

'What is it, for God's sake!' Marie rushed in to her.

Violet-blue eyes devoid of expression gazed blankly at her from a swollen, distended face. 'He's gone,' Jacqueline said dully. 'Dominic has gone. He has left me.'

Marie almost groaned in despair as her worst fears were realized. 'How did it happen?' she said quietly. 'Did you have a quarrel? Or is it something more than that? Whatever it is, you've got to take hold of yourself. I'm sure nothing has happened that can't be fixed up. Tell me, tell me everything.'

'It was St Regis,' Jacqueline began in a flat monotone, and Marie's heart sank still further. 'They were drinking together. Dominic was boasting about the son he was going

188

to have. St Regis said maybe a Montal was going to have a child at last, since Marie-Thérèse and Claire had no children or any sign of having them. Dominic asked him what he meant. St Regis said that surely he knew Claire wasn't his – that she was some nigger's child. Dominic hit him. St Regis got angry. He said he'd had me and a dozen others had, too. Dominic called him a liar. St Regis laughed and went on to describe some moles I have – one under my left breast, one on my private parts. St Regis has a good memory.' She spoke mechanically. 'Dominic believed St Regis. He came to me with his accusations. I tried to explain. It was no use. He has gone!'

'I'll get him back – I'll *make* him believe what happened!' Marie cried. '*I* know the truth, and I'll make him see St Regis for what he is.'

'He has gone,' repeated Jacqueline. 'And my world has gone. I cannot live without him – and I will not!' Her breath was coming in slow, labouring gasps.

'Now, there's no sense to this!' Marie cried. 'Jacqueline, I'm going to take you to your mother's, and then I'll go and find Dominic – I promise.'

'It's too late for that.' Jacqueline's words began to slur. 'I am going. I wanted to take Claire with me so I could look after her, but now it's too late for that. Look after Claire for me, my dear Marie.' She started to slip sideways on the couch and her eyes closed.

'My God! Has she taken something?' It was Marie's first fear, and she yelled at the slave, who was cowering near the door.

'Ah don' know, Missus! Ah don' know! She was jus' cra-shin' 'round de house when Ah left with Miz Claire.'

'Quick, go and get Dr Franke! He lives over on Dauphine Street, number sixty. Run all the way! Tell him Marie Laveau needs him!'

'Yes'm.'

Marie tried to shake Jacqueline back into consciousness, but she shook and slapped and chafed the icy hands all to no avail. Jacqueline's breathing was slowing, now shallow and almost imperceptible. She was at her wits' end when the door burst open and Dr Franke hurried in.

'She's taken something, maybe some kind of sleeping draught. I can't bring her out of it!' she cried desperately. 'For God's sake, do something!'

He bent over the unconscious form and took her pulse. 'Look around and see if you can find what she took,' he barked. 'I've got to have something to go on – it could be a dozen things.'

Marie rushed out and began searching the house frantically from top to bottom. She was rushing downstairs when she saw Dr Franke slowly emerge from the drawing room. He shook his head at her. 'I'm sorry,' he said shortly. 'There is nothing I could do. She's gone. Have you any idea what killed her?'

Marie stood transfixed on the stairway. 'I don't know what killed her, but I do know *who*,' she said with the bitterness welling up in her. 'The Montals killed her, Dominic with his love, St Regis with his hate – *they* killed her.'

Chapter Twenty

Jacqueline had been spared the final ignominy of a suicide's grave thanks to the connivance of Dr Franke, who had stated that she had died while under his care, apparently of heart failure. Madame Delambe had suffered a slight stroke on hearing of her daughter's death, which had left her confused and a little wandering, so that Marie perforce had to assist the bewildered, grief-stricken Monsieur Delambe with the sad task of burying his only child. Having done all she could for her dead friend, she turned her thoughts to the future of Jacqueline's daughter.

She told Monsieur Delambe the true facts of the case and what she proposed to do about it. 'You had best leave it alone,' he said heavily. 'Nothing will bring Jacqueline back to us, and, God willing, I will take care of Claire for as long as I live or as long as she needs me.'

'You don't know what you're saying!' Marie cried. 'Claire is Dominic's child – we know that – and no Creole father ever turns away from his children, even in a *mariage à la main gauche*. Not to do anything would not only deprive Claire of her rights but would condemn Jacqueline, who never did a wrong thing. Surely you would be the last person to want that!'

'One cannot always have what one wants in this life.' Monsieur Delambe was sombre. 'Dominic believed a lie about Jacqueline, and I see little hope of you persuading him otherwise. What is more, you will be coming up against the power of the Montals, and that can only hurt you. There has been enough pain. Let it go. I know Jacqueline was innocent – that is enough!'

But it was not enough for Marie. She was determined that Dominic should know the truth and that he should recognize his daughter. She went to the Montal town house only to be told by the old butler that Dominic was 'away from home'. He had gone upriver to one of the Montal plantations, and no date had been set for his return.

'Then I will see Monsieur Montal,' Marie persisted. 'This is a matter of great importance.'

The butler left her cooling her heels in the hallway and returned after a few minutes to say that Monsieur Montal would see her in the library. She followed him into that grandiose and seldom-used room to find Vincent Montal standing by the long window, his hands clasped behind his back, and St Regis lounging at ease in a winged-back chair. She gazed into each stony-faced countenance. At the sight of St Regis, her hatred welled up with the bitterness of gall, but she fought it down. This was no time for emotion; this was a time for clear thinking.

'What do you want?' Vincent Montal barked at her.

Marie took her time in replying, vividly aware of St Regis's feral gaze. 'I come on behalf of your granddaughter, *M'sieu*. I had hoped to speak with her father on the matter, but I understand he has left New Orleans. I therefore come to you, as head of the family.'

'What the devil are you talking about? I have no granddaughter,' Vincent Montal barked again.

'Oh, come now, *M'sieu*, you are as aware as the rest of the city of the existence of Claire Montal Delambe, the child of your son Dominic and Jacqueline Delambe, who is untimely dead because Dominic's mind was unjustly poisoned against her.' She shot a venomous glance at St Regis. 'It is too late to do anything about that, alas, but I intend that he knows the truth about all this – and I know the truth of the matter – and that he do justice by the child, who up to now he has most dearly loved. So for the honour of your house, *M'sieu*, I beg you to assist me in this.'

'What is this claptrap? Have you any idea?' Vincent Montal appealed to St Regis. His feigned astonishment sounded a false note.

'Well, it's fairly obvious what a woman from Rampart Street wants,' St Regis sneered. 'Money – what else? A little polite blackmail on account of some bastard that another Rampart Street whore with whom Dominic was involved

192

tried to foist on him. Luckily, he finally came to his senses.'

'St Regis, haven't you done enough?' Marie cried. 'Do you really want me to tell your father – and, for that matter, the world – the truth of this matter? You knew Dominic and Jacqueline loved one another. Was that why you hated them, hated *her*, so? Because they knew a happiness that you have never known? Because with her, Dominic was his own man and not your shadow? When Dominic comes to his senses, he will know the truth in his heart and will have to live with his own hell, but at least for a time he was a *man*, which is more than you'll ever be!'

St Regis's eyes narrowed. 'Have a care,' he hissed. 'By God, much more of this and I'll destroy you.'

'Destroy me as you destroyed Jacqueline? Oh, no! I am a different proposition; Jacqueline was the soul of goodness, who never did or thought a wrong or evil thing. I am not of such a sweet disposition – and for what you have done, I intend to make you pay. It was to me Jacqueline came the night you forced yourself upon her like some wild animal. I can tell Dominic the truth and *make* him believe me. And where will that leave you, St Regis, you and your lies?'

'Your word against mine?' He laughed scornfully. 'And against the word of others I can produce? You would be laughed out of court!'

'Who is talking about courts?' Marie demanded. 'I should think a court of *justice* would be the last thing you would want! Who would you produce? Some brow-beaten slaves who would say anything to spare themselves what you would undoubtedly inflict on them? And I am not alone in my knowledge – my mother was there that night, too.'

'So the two of you are in it together – the infamous Mesdames Laveau. But it would still be against my word, the word of a Montal,' he grated. 'So take care. You have said enough.'

'I have not even begun,' Marie said quietly. She turned to Vincent Montal, who had been standing gloweringly silent during the exchange. '*M'sieu*, I intend to have justice. Do you really want New Orleans to know what St Regis has done, what he is really like? Nothing can undo the terrible thing he has done to his own brother and the woman who loved him, but he must be stopped. You must already know this is so. If he has done this, what else might he do? He will bring your house tumbling down around your ears if he is not curbed; he will destroy you all, for there is nothing in him but destruction. Do justice by your granddaughter and I will leave his fate in your hands; the responsibility is yours – but wash your hands of it and I will be forced to become involved.'

For a second Vincent Montal hesitated. Then St Regis sprang out of his chair and roared, 'Enough! Father, there is nothing to be said. Either you believe her or me. I intend to throw this strumpet on to the street, where she belongs, something I should have done the moment she walked through that door.' He strode over and, seizing Marie roughly by the arm, started to propel her towards the door.

Vincent Montal made a little fending-off gesture with his hands. Then he muttered defensively, 'You have no case, Marie Laveau. It is none of my affair. I shall do nothing.'

'Wait!' Marie tugged herself free and turned to him. 'Monsieur Montal, if you turn your back on your own granddaughter, it will be the saddest day's work you will ever have done. There will be no Montals beyond this generation to carry on the name of which you are so proud. Your house will be barren, *M'sieu*, that I predict, that I foresee – you will condemn your own house!'

St Regis seized her again and thrust her though the doorway. Dragging her across the hall, he flung open the front door, then twisted her savagely to face him. 'Now listen to me,' his voice grated. 'If I hear anything of this breathed around New Orleans, or if you try to contact Dominic in any way, I swear I'll destroy you. I would not have to look very far for the means. Don't forget what you are! Those rings you flash on your fingers are enough to get you whipped and flung into the parish prison. And that would only be the beginning. I'll have you run out of this city.'

For the first time Marie let some of the hatred she felt for him show in her eyes. 'And you listen to me, St Regis,' she returned. 'I intend to make you pay for Jacqueline's murder – for murder it was. It may take me the rest of my life, but I will do it.'

St Regis laughed savagely. 'Should I look for poison, like the unfortunate Monsieur DuBois? Oh, yes, I know about that! Or a knife in a dark alley wielded by one of your nigger friends? Oh, you don't frighten me with your silly Voodoo tricks, Marie Laveau. I have more tricks up my sleeve than you'll ever know.'

'I don't want you to die, St Regis – that would be too easy,' Marie said between gritted teeth. 'I want you to suffer, and suffer you most surely will.'

With an exclamation of disgust, he heaved her into the street and slammed the door. As she got up and dusted herself off, Marie was under no delusions about the seriousness of the situation; she had failed in her objective, and she had made an implacable enemy of St Regis. She realized she would have to look to her own defences and tread very carefully. She only hoped she could get some warning where the first attack might fall, and she wondered what allies she could possibly find to counteract the weight of his name and his money. One thing she did know – she had no intention of giving up the fight.

The warning came from an unexpected direction. She arrived back at Rampart Street several days after the confrontation to find Patty lurking near the front door with the message: 'Some woman been hangin' 'round here all mornin' wantin' to see ya.'

'What woman?' she asked, Patty never being too well versed in the social graces.

'Nobuddah Ah seen befo'. Got a pretty skirt on,' Patty volunteered in a loud whisper, and with a jerk of her head. 'She's in dere.'

Marie went into the drawing room to find herself face to face with Valerie Valdoux. It was a surprise; she had seen little of her since Valerie had become a busy socialite, and she had never been near the house on Rampart Street since Marie had first moved there.

As befitted a society belle, she was dressed in the height of fashion, wearing one of the brand-new basques of deep emerald velvet, with a matching bonnet, both of which set off her chestnut hair, and with a very full skirt of bronze-coloured silk.

Secure in her knowledge of Justin's affections, her father's favourite, and indulged by her mother, who highly approved her marital choice, she had had a lot more freedom than most girls of her age and station, and had built up quite a reputation for herself as an extravagant 'madcap'. Now she was very much a woman of the world, but one who to Marie's practised eye was very ill at ease.

After they had greeted one another with something of their old warmth, Valerie said all in a rush, 'I know I should not have come here, but in view of our old friendship I felt I had to warn you.'

'Oh?' said Marie guardedly. 'About what?'

'I don't know, and I don't think I want to know, but it's St Regis. Bayard overheard him talking to a bunch of cronies in an absinthe house – something about Friday night, a police raid, a house on Bayou St John. Your name was mentioned. He said he was going to get you, run you out.' She looked at Marie. Her eyes were full of questions.

Marie's heart sank. Well, at least now she knew! 'Thank you, Valerie. It was very kind of you to let me know.'

'Yes. Well, now I've paid you back for Fifi!' Valerie exclaimed with relief. 'Now we're all square.'

'Not quite,' Marie said with sudden decision. 'There's one more thing you owe me. Sit down!'

Surprised at her abrupt tone, Valerie did as she was told.

'Years ago, when St Regis poisoned Fifi, you never told me why. This I must know; it is very important because St Regis and I are at odds over the death of a very dear friend of mine, a death he caused. Tell me, did he try to assault or rape you, and was he thwarted?'

Valerie's colour rose. 'No, of course not,' she said hastily. 'It was really nothing, and Emile stopped . . .'

'So Emile knew of it?' Marie said quickly, and something clicked into place in her mind.

'It's nothing I want to talk about,' Valerie said, with something of the imperious manner of the St Yveses.

'All right.' Marie was suddenly amiable as a plan started to form in her mind. 'I won't pester you further.' Valerie looked at her with troubled eyes. 'Is everything all right with you and Justin?' Marie went on in a gentler tone. 'How are the wedding plans coming along?'

'Oh, slowly,' Valerie sighed. 'We were going to get married at the end of Carnival, but there has been some trouble on the plantations, and so now it will probably be at Easter, or even after that. Those *wretched* Abolitionists!' she went on in a vexed tone. 'Have you heard of them? Damned Northerners who know nothing of the South. They've actually had the nerve to propose the abolition of slavery, and they've sent agitators down here to *encourage* the slaves to run away to the North. Can you imagine! There has been a lot of unrest on the plantations and several runaways at Justin's. He's furious about it, of course. You knew one of them – Billy Boy?'

'Yes, I remember Billy Boy. That does surprise me.'

Valerie looked uncomfortable. 'Well, that case was *most* unfortunate. He got accused of something and was punished – or going to be – and then they found out he probably hadn't done it, after all, but by that time he had already run off.'

'What was he supposed to have done?' Marie had a familiar stirring sensation, one she usually had when something important was about to happen.

'Well' – Valerie lowered her voice – 'you promise you won't tell anyone about this?' Marie nodded. 'Remember Geneviève? She's been staying up at Castle Blanche as company for Clarisse, Justin's younger sister. She has become such a handful that I think the Montals were glad to get her out of the city. They hoped Clarisse, who's a sweet, amiable child, might calm her down, I suppose. Anyway, Geneviève claimed that Billy Boy tried to kiss her and ... er ... make other advances to her. That, of course, is a hanging matter, but I doubt if Justin would actually have ... But, anyway, Billy Boy ran off, and then the very next day, mind you, Justin himself came upon Geneviève throwing her arms around a fourteen-year-old slave boy and trying to kiss *him*! Can you imagine! And when Justin faced her with it, she climbed all over *him*. You know the way she goes on; she burst into tears when he fended her off, and she said everyone hated her and was against her. Justin didn't know what to do, so he sent her back home. I just don't know what they are going to do with that girl!'

'Hmm,' said Marie, deep in thought as yet another plan began to take shape. 'Very interesting, very interesting, indeed!'

After Valerie had taken her leave, Marie sat for a long time lost in her thoughts. Finally she nodded, and a slow smile curved the delicately moulded lips. 'Yes,' she said with satisfaction, 'that might do very well, very well, indeed.'

Chapter Twenty-one

Marie whirled into action. Her next 'elegant soirée' at Maison Blanche was but two days away, and in that short time she had to subvert St Regis's plans for her ruin. She alerted the girls to stay away and got hold of the few men she thought she could trust enough to help her. When the police broke into Maison Blanche, prepared to break up an orgy and carry off the perpetrators to durance vile, they were startled to find a soberly dressed circle of gentlemen of the most impeccable Creole lineage, grouped around the great chair of Marie Laveau, who was chastely attired in deep blue velvet, listening with rapt attention to one of their group who was reading selections from his own newly published book of poetry. The Creole gentlemen were not amused. One of them, Aristide Sautelle, went so far as to remark acidly that if this was the way the New Orleans police force wasted its time, he personally would see the commissioner and make sure that certain heads, namely theirs, rolled. The police were routed out, covered with confusion.

Although she had headed off disaster for the moment, Marie knew that she was still in serious trouble. The 'elegant soirées' were her main source of income; without them she would be forced to spend her savings all too quickly. She had to find some means of getting the police to leave her alone. She decided it was high time she made her long-delayed call on Flo Winfield, for she had one good reason for supposing Flo might help her.

Since she was sure that Flo was well aware of her own activities, she was not expecting a very warm welcome when she presented Flo's now-tattered card at the plush bordello on Jackson. She was absolutely right.

'What do you want?' Flo snapped ungraciously when Marie was ushered into her heavily furnished and perfumed office.

'Some advice, and possibly some help,' Marie returned. 'I'm battling for survival at the moment, and I believe you know my opponent, St Regis Montal.'

Flo Winfield's bird-like face took on a pinched expression, her beady eyes hard. 'Yes, I know St Regis,' she said. 'He doesn't come here.'

'But I have heard he did come here quite a lot at one time, until a certain incident occurred,' Marie said softly. 'An incident that involved the "accidental" death of one of your girls.'

A haunted look came into the narrowed eyes. 'Yes, I've no love for St Regis,' Flo Winfield said, 'but I want no trouble with him, either. State your business.'

'He's trying to close me down, to get rid of me, and I'll tell you why...' And Marie told her.

Flo listened quietly, then said with a snort, 'What did I tell you? The girls on Rampart Street – fools, that's what they are, fools!'

'I agree,' Marie said with the hint of a smile, 'which is why I took your advice. You know, I'm not in competition with you, Flo; there's plenty for both of us in New Orleans. But I've got to keep going, and he'll stop me if I don't get help. And you know what St Regis is.'

'So what do you want of me?' Flo said again.

'I want to spend some money for protection in the right places, but I've got to know *who* to spend it on. I think you can tell me that. Who must I buy?'

Flo thought for a long moment. 'All right,' she said at last. And she told her.

To make doubly sure, Marie contacted a few Anglos who owed her favours and who she knew either bore no love for the Creoles in general or the Montals in particular; some of them were on the city council; others had contacts in the police department. There were no further raids on Maison Blanche, and the 'elegant soirées' began again and continued more elegantly than ever.

It was time to take the next step. Marie went to see Emile. 'I want you to do something for me,' she said. 'You are not going to like it, but it's something that has to be done. I have

200

here a long letter I have written to Dominic Montal concerning the true fact about the death of Jacqueline Delambe. I want you to give it to him and to see that he reads it – but first I want you to read it yourself.' She handed him the bulky letter.

He read it through, then looked up at her, his mild hazel eyes deeply troubled. 'Is this true?' he said.

'Have I ever lied to you, Emile? Every word in there is the truth. I know this is difficult for you, Claire being your sister, but I also know you are a good and honest man, and a man who, I think, knows firsthand what St Regis is capable of.' She looked steadily at him and his eyes dropped. 'Valerie has told me something, but not all, and I think I can guess the rest. Dominic *has* to know the truth – for the sake of his daughter, if nothing else. I have tried to reach him myself, but there is no way I can do it. I am depending on you.'

He made a grimace of distaste, then slowly put the letter back into its envelope. 'As you say, a very unpleasant task, but I will see that it is done.' He looked at her with concern. 'I wish with all my heart you had never become involved with this. St Regis is a highly dangerous man!'

'I know, Emile, but I am being very careful.' She smiled at him. 'And you'll let me know the outcome?'

He continued to stare at her. 'Yes,' he muttered, 'of course. But I should not build your hopes too high, Marie; I should not count too much on Dominic.'

Nevertheless, when she received his summons two weeks later, she went with high hopes. 'Well?' she demanded eagerly, as he sat sober-faced across from her at the big banker's desk.

'I did what you asked,' he said, and cleared his throat nervously. 'I gave Dominic the letter, and I saw that he read it.'

'And?' Marie prompted hopefully.

'And then he tore it up and said St Regis had warned him you would probably try something like that,' Emile said heavily. 'For what it is worth,' he went on, 'I told him that I thought he should give the letter serious consideration, that I had never known you to lie.'

'And?' Her tone was grim.

'He laughed and said that I had always been a fool where you were concerned. It was as I feared, Marie – St Regis's hold is as strong as it ever was. Dominic will do nothing.'

'I see. So be it, then,' Marie said slowly, her eyes suddenly cold and blank. As she got up, Emile gazed at her with concern.

'If there is anything I can do – about the child, I mean . . .' he said awkwardly.

'No. She is being well taken care of by her grandparents, and I will take care of the rest.' Her tone was bleak.

'But what more can you do?' A frown creased his forehead. 'Can I help in any way?'

'No, you have done your part, Emile, for which I thank you. Dominic has chosen his own hell – as have the rest of the Montals. The only one I am sorry for is your sister.' She looked at him for his reaction to find his gaze still fixed on her. 'Why are you staring so, Emile?' She was testy all of a sudden. 'This need concern you no further.'

'It is just that you have such strange eyes,' he murmured. 'Do you know that when you are deeply concerned about something, the irises constrict into half-moons? It's remarkable.' He was startled to see the look of horror on her face.

'I hadn't realized that,' she muttered. 'It must be a family trait; my mother's do the same thing.'

'Are you sure there is nothing else I can do?' he persisted as she turned to go.

'No . . . I mean, yes, there is one thing.' She turned towards him again, with decision. 'I would be very much obliged if you would contact Justin and see if he is willing to sell me one of his slaves . . . a particular slave – Billy Boy.'

'But, but . . .' He was bewildered. 'Isn't that one of the runaways? Why on earth would you want to do such an insane thing – to buy a slave that isn't even here?'

'Not insane – just call it a sentimental whim.' She was all smiles. 'Billy Boy was Etienne's and mine, once. I happen to know there were some special circumstances involved in his

202

running away. Justin as a plantation owner is duty-bound to hunt him down, but he will have little taste for it, unless he has changed out of all recognition. If he sells Billy Boy to me, he'll no longer be under that obligation, and I hate to think of Billy Boy being hunted down like a wild animal. Besides, I might be able to find him, where I'm sure Justin wouldn't. It's a gamble, and I'm a gambler. Will you do that?'

'Why, yes, I suppose so.' He was dazed. 'Sometimes I confess you absolutely bewilder me, Marie, really you do. Most of the time you are a sensible, hard-headed business-woman, most admirably so in my opinion – and then, some-thing like this!'

Marie laughed at him. 'Don't concern yourself, Emile. Just humour me. I have my reasons.'

An equally bewildered Justin agreed to let her have Billy Boy's bond for a token price, and she embarked on the next stage of her gamble. She was guessing that Billy Boy was still around and that he had not already fled to the North. It was a gamble which, putting two and two together, she had high hopes of winning. She remembered his lengthy and unex-plained absences from Rampart Street, and she had been aware, for some time, of rumours that were much talked of by bunches of young men at the Voodoo dances, rumours of an organization that was being set up from hidden bases in the bayous, an organization to help slaves get to the free territories, an organization called the Underground Rail-road. She remembered Billy Boy, despite all his grumblings and lackadaisical ways, as being extremely intelligent – the sort of man an organization like that would have to have. Now she had in the palm of her hand something he needed and could use to good advantage if her suppositions were correct – his freedom. If she could find him, this she would gladly give him in return for one small service . . .

She spread the word through the underground grapevine that ran deep through the roots of the city and beyond it to the Louisiana bayou country, then settled down to wait. Results were not long in coming. A young Negro accosted her in the street, wanting to know if she was interested in meeting a certain party. A meeting was set for the next night at a lonely stretch of the bayou out by Maison Blanche. She was to come alone.

With some qualms she drove herself in a gig to the deserted spot and waited as patiently as she could. For a long while there was nothing but the symphony of the frogs and the mournful call of some lone nightbird to keep her company. Then suddenly there was a rustling in the reeds and Billy Boy stepped into the dim circle of the gig's lamp. He was taller and gaunter than she had remembered him, and the dark eyes that glittered in the light were hostile.

'I hear tell you're my new owner,' he said. 'What do you want of me?'

'To tell you that no one is looking for you any longer, for one thing, and that, back at the house, I have your manumission papers all made out,' Marie said. 'Your freedom is yours . . . in return for one small service to me.'

'What might that be?' he asked guardedly.

She told him and he threw back his head and laughed, disclosing a flash of white teeth. 'Is that all?' His tone was incredulous.

'That's all. But we must wait for the right moment. I don't want you around until then. Keep on doing whatever it is you have been doing, and don't tell me about it. But when I call for you, you come at once. Is that understood? And after, you'll have to get out of town, at least for a while, and I'll have to know how to get in touch with you, because we'll have to move fast. Will you do it?'

Again he laughed. 'Sure thing. It will be a pleasure, Missus, a *real* pleasure.' And he told her how to find him when the time came.

She moved on to the second stage of the plan, for which she needed expert assistance. She decided against calling on her mother, who would probably not approve and might even take advantage of the venture to gain more power over her. Instead, she went to Mama Antoine and explained what she had in mind.

' "Fe Chauffé" dances for Erzulie – out on the lake? Yes,

that been done befo'. An' you want *me* to arrange them?'

'Yes. There are some good reasons I don't want to appear as having a hand in this, just now. But I'll stake you for the expenses, hiring the barge and so on, and after they're back we'll split: seventy-five, twenty-five – the seventy-five for you.'

The old woman looked at her shrewdly. 'Yes, Ah heard tell you was havin' some trouble. What you up to, Marie? Ah seen that look on yo' mother's face plenty o' times, an' now Ah'm seeing it on yours. You're up to somethin' fo' sho'!'

'Don't you want to honour Erzulie?' Marie countered, knowing well Mama Antoine's devotion to the Voodoo love goddess.

'Oh, sure thing. I don't mind doin' the dances – I jus' don't want no trouble, that's all!'

'No – the dances will be the real thing. You can start as soon as you like. But there will be one special dance at which *I'll* arrange who comes – that you don't have to know anything about. All right?' And there'll be a few people at the others who'll be my guests. I'll tell you about them when the time comes.'

'Guess so, but I'd sure like to know what you're up to,' Mama Antoine grumbled.

There was only one more thing before the final move. Marie contacted a certain Regine Nicaud, a Creole of reduced circumstances and bizarre tastes. She had two things that were important to Marie: she moved in the same circle as the Montals; and during her convent days, Geneviève Montal had had a crush on her and had been inclined to follow her lead ever since, although Regine was several years her senior. Regine was invited as Marie's guest to the 'Fe Chauffé' dances and accepted with alacrity. When she had expressed her appreciation for Marie's generosity, the latter had said with studied vagueness, 'Oh, maybe you can do a favour for me one day,' and had left it at that. Now the trap was set, needing only the moment to spring it. When it closed, Marie wanted St Regis to be out of town – and for that she knew she had to wait.

In the meantime she stilled her impatience by compiling all the information she could on the Montals. It was interesting enough. Anne Montal had finally been betrothed to a man as rank-conscious as herself, but of limited fortune. Yolande was holding out for a better match, though both were now well past the usual marrying age.

It was said that Dominic Montal was drinking heavily, that his gambling debts were formidable, and that he had applied to his father-in-law, Paul Valdoux, for help. It was also said that Marie-Thérèse Montal no longer shared a bedroom with St Regis, or, for that matter, a bed. And it was also rumoured that Madame Montal had been in consultation with several doctors about Geneviève. Marie had a shrewd idea what about – indeed, her whole scheme depended on it.

It was high summer before the moment arrived. News came that St Regis had taken Marie-Thérèse up to Castle Blanche to escape the merciless wet heat of New Orleans, which she found so fatiguing. Marie went into immediate action. A special 'Fe Chauffé' dance was arranged, and, with two exceptions, the female dancers were participants in Marie's evening soirées. The male dancers were to be of Mama Antoine's choosing – again, with one important exception.

Marie took the last step. She called on Regine Nicaud and demanded the long-delayed favour, a favour she had made sure Regine was in no position to refuse. 'Well, I'll do it if I can,' Regine agreed uneasily. 'But they keep Geneviève pretty penned up these days. I just don't know if ...'

'Do it,' said Marie with quiet authority. 'After all, you know Geneviève will follow where you lead and that she will enjoy it just as you do.'

The night was a warm and heavy one as Marie made for her rendezvous with Billy Boy at the same spot as they had met before. She had had a skiff moved there which they would take to the barge on the lake and from which she intended to watch the proceedings.

When Billy Boy appeared, he was not alone; with him was

one of the largest Negroes Marie had seen in her life, stand-ing well over six feet, and broad in proportion to his height.

Billy Boy grinned at her as she stepped into the lamplight. 'I brought you a present,' he announced. 'Meet Jethro. Since you're going to lose a slave-boy tonight, I got a new one. I figgered you might need him if all hell breaks loose – and it sure might after I take off! Mind you, Jethro's a free boy, but he works cheap. In fact, all you gotta do is put him up at your place, 'cos he got things to do here that you'd best not know about, but he'll be around when you need him.'

'I see. And what does Jethro say to all this?' Marie said with some surprise.

'It's all right by me, ma'am, if it's all right by you,' Jethro said in an unusually cultivated and deep voice. 'We need someone in the city now, and I'm it, but I'll look after you, too.'

'Well, that sounds fair enough,' Marie said cautiously. 'You can wait with me in the boat. We'll talk more later. For now, the important thing is for Billy Boy to play his part.' She handed him the papers and a small pouch of money. 'These should take you wherever you'll be heading. Let's go.'

The sluggish barge lay on the oily surface of the lake, its edge outlined with little pots of fire. As they approached, they could see the dancers were already moving to the throbbing rhythm of the drums. They surrounded the stocky figure of Mama Antoine, who stood in a circle of bottles and shook to the rhythm as she chanted the moves. Some of the dancers had already placed lighted candles on their heads and were doing the intricate, jerking movements of the 'Fe Chauffé', while others watched and clapped in unison.

Marie searched the crowd anxiously and it was some time before she could make out the golden glints of a mass of tawny hair on a slight, chemise-clad figure, who was already twitching in the dance and screaming with delight. Marie relaxed with a sigh. 'She's there,' she announced. 'Off you go, Billy Boy, and do not fail me.'

He stripped off his shirt, his well-muscled body gleaming bronze in the light of the fires. 'Wish me luck!' he said softly, and, climbing on board, he jumped into the dance.

Marie motioned Jethro to row them a little closer, so that she could get a clearer view of things. With Billy Boy's coming, the drums had stepped up their beat, and already some of her own girls had thrown off their chemises and were dancing naked with the men of their choice. She saw Billy Boy bounding in front of the excited Geneviève, fitting his movements to hers, but retreating as she advanced, advancing when she retreated. As they circled past her, Marie caught a glimpse of Geneviève's face: the eyes with their familiar hot, glazed look; the little mouth wetly glistening; the pink tongue shooting in and out like the tongue of a snake. Now some of the dancers dropped out and were writhing in coupled heaps on the floor of the barge. Marie saw the white sideways flash of Billy's eyes as he gauged the scene and slowly stripped off his trousers. Then he danced deliberately towards Geneviève, his large, erect penis aiming at her like a sword. With a little sobbing cry, she stripped off her chemise and stumbled towards him, her eyes wild with desire. Then they came together and collapsed in a tangled mass of black and white limbs that threshed and melded in ecstatic union.

Marie threw back her head and looked up at the stars in triumph. She closed her eyes and murmured in thanksgiving, 'Vodun, Vodun – it is done. Now it is *done!*'

Chapter Twenty-two

The news that Geneviève Montal had run away with a Negro slave flashed through New Orleans like a forest fire. Spreading from some unknown source, the news was received with shocked rejection or ribald amusement according to temperament. Missing she undoubtedly was, as were three slaves who had also mysteriously vanished from the city that night.

The Montal slaves were interrogated at length by the authorities. A further damaging statement was elicited from a frightened fifteen-year-old house slave, who stated that Geneviève had come to his room one night and had tried to get into bed with him, but that he had been too 'skeered' to do or say anything about it. Even a sound whipping got nothing further from the terrified boy other than that she had slapped his face and gone away.

Another damning bit of evidence came from a late-returning traveller from the lake, who volunteered the information that he had seen a 'reddish-haired white gal' in a skiff with a light-coloured nigger on one of the many bayous opening off the lake and that 'she was laughing fit to bust'. He had taken her for a girl from Gallatin Street out on business, and he had passed on his way, minding his own. There were no further traces of the fugitives.

The Creole community retreated into shocked silence; the rest of New Orleans, restrained by no such code, began either to laugh or to demand redress for the moral decay that was besetting the city. When it became clear that Geneviève was indeed gone and that the Montal name was besmirched beyond redemption, Vincent Montal quietly locked himself in his seldom-used study and blew out his brains with one of his own duelling pistols.

Anne's betrothed fled the city, leaving behind him a note for her saying that, much as he regretted the circumstances, he had the honour of his own family to consider. In view of that, he was sure she would understand . . .

Yolande, more realistic than the rest, repaired to her old headmistress at the Ursuline convent and declared she would like to enter the novitiate of the order, but that she would prefer to become a bride of Christ 'overseas'.

St Regis, hastily summoned from the LeBlanc plantation, arrived back in the city to find himself head of a family which was in shambles and which had suddenly become a pariah in New Orleans society. In the circumstances he did the only thing he could do. He bundled up the survivors of the family – his mother, who had locked herself in her room and had not moved or spoken since the news had broken, and the distraught Anne – and bore them off to their upstate plantation. The shuttered house on Toulouse and Bourbon bore mute testimony to the fact that, for the moment, the mighty Montals could find only one answer – silence and retreat. The rout was absolute.

It surprised no one when further news arrived that Marie-Thérèse Montal elected to stay at Castle Blanche and that she would seek a legal separation from St Regis; nor was it a surprise about the news that Claire Montal had hurried from their plantation with her husband to St Regis's and was doing what she could do for her female in-laws. It marked, Marie thought, the difference between the LeBlancs and the Valdouxs, though of the two she felt Marie-Thérèse had followed the smarter, safer path.

She had covered her tracks completely; there would be nothing to connect her with Geneviève's disappearance, if and when St Regis rallied his forces and returned – as return one day he assuredly must. The one weak link, Regine Nicaud, had been easily taken care of. 'You are not responsible for what she did,' Marie had assured the terrified girl, 'but for your own future no word must ever be breathed that it was you who took her to the dances that night.'

'But . . . but . . . you told me to . . .' the girl faltered.

'That, of course, I would deny,' Marie said smoothly. 'And to admit you had taken her would be to admit also that you had participated, in which circumstances I hazard a guess that your own betrothal would suffer the same fate as Anne Montal's – and I do not suppose you would care for that.'

'How about the other people there?'

'They were my people, who would see only what I wanted them to see, and hear only what I wanted them to hear. You understand?'

She had understood.

For the rest, only her mother guessed the role she had played, and she referred to it but once. 'I see you took my advice,' she remarked.

'On what?'

'On getting at St Regis through his pride – though even you could not have predicted such a violent and complete outcome.'

'I don't know what you're talking about,' Marie said, but her mother only laughed.

And there was another uncomfortable moment or two with Emile. 'I see you have a new Negro slave,' he remarked.

'Not a slave – he's a hired man.'

'So you have given up on Billy Boy? You found no trace of him?' he inquired with a shade of unease.

'Oh, yes, I've given up.' She had been bland. 'I'm afraid that was a gamble that didn't pay off. You were so right about that, Emile. I'll never be that silly again.' And she had passed on to less dangerous subjects. But for all that, knowing her as well as he did, she felt that he looked at her for some time after with uneasy suspicion. It did not worry her; Emile was a man who knew how to keep his mouth shut.

Life resumed its normal course. Marie felt at peace with herself. Jacqueline had been avenged: St Regis had been routed. She could resume her own path. Now the only faint cloud on her horizon was her mother, but even there she felt she had no need for great concern, only watchfulness. She was not sure her mother would even try again, so certain was she of her own growing strength. Her mother was no fool; she would surely know that, too. Thus, the year '52 slipped into the year '53 with no perceptible clouds on the horizon.

In the spring Marie was once more called upon to perform for Veronique Devereux. Another success, another boy, but she was thankful enough to hear from Dr Franke that there would be no more Devereux children; something had happened in the birth this time, something that he had taken care of but which would preclude any other babies. Veronique was tearful at the news – she had wanted a daughter – but, comforted by her two fine sons, she resigned herself to the will of God and the hand of man.

Marie would have performed a similar service for Valerie Valdoux LeBlanc's firstborn, had not that good lady surprised herself and everybody else by producing the LeBlanc heir three weeks ahead of schedule and with very little pain or fuss – after a gala evening at the opera.

Dr Franke often called on Marie's gift, though she had made it plain to him that she would only answer his call for cases that were extreme ones. It took too much out of her, she explained, and there were reasons why she could not risk its constant use. Not that she went unrewarded for her services; in fact, the Creole and Anglo ladies paid highly and willingly for their surceases from pain. To her own kind and the few blacks who had need of her, Marie donated her services – as she knew the doctor gave his – willingly enough, hoping only in return for some of the good will that had accrued to her mother in similar fashion over the years. But in this she was to be disappointed.

It was not too long after Veronique Devereux's *accouchement* that Marie started to notice something; it was slight at first, but it grew as the spring turned into summer. Her black clients began to fall off, and in the streets she was conscious of a change. There had been from the first some who were frightened of her because she was her mother's daughter: those who caught their small children to their skirts and bade them look away ' 'cause that Marie Laveau will hex you fo' sure'. Since these were in the minority, it had always rather amused than annoyed her, but now their number was growing, and people would hurry past her with frightened, downcast faces. Her 'back-door' trade for gris-gris and hexes, too, dwindled to almost nothing.

Then the contagion spread to her Creole clients, and she heard murmurs once more about the Grison affair, which had long been buried. There was no similar dereliction among her Anglo clients, so she was forced into a fairly obvious conclusion: her mother must be behind this sudden ostracism; her mother was up to a new kind of attack.

What puzzled Marie was what her mother hoped to gain by it. She had to know that Marie no longer depended on these clients for her livelihood – that, indeed, her main source of income now came from the 'soirées' at Maison Blanche and the '*Fe Chauffé*' affairs at the lake, which were now in vogue among the bored aristocracy of New Orleans. Perhaps that was it – her mother resented this intrusion into her dominion and was retaliating in kind. Knowing her mother, however, she was worried that it probably was not that simple.

The sense of being under attack grew to a climax at the St John's Eve ceremonies at the lake. As a Mambo, Marie naturally had gone, only to find that she could get nowhere near the centre of the activities; her way was blocked wherever she turned. When she tried to insist, she was met by dark looks and rough jostlings from a crowd suddenly hostile to her, and one young Mambo, whom she recognized as Eliza, a quadroon protégée of her mother's, actually went so far as to heckle her. 'You go home, bad Voodoo woman, we don't want your sort here. Vodun don't want your kind around.'

After that the crowd got even uglier, and Marie thought it wise to make a dignified retreat. But as she drove home she became increasingly upset. Although she felt none of the familiar and frightening 'draining' sensation, she wondered if all this was just a preliminary to another such attack, a softening-up process to make her feel isolated and afraid, so that she would be more vulnerable when the main onslaught was made. She thought of going to Mama Antoine for help and advice, but then she discarded the notion. Mama Antoine, despite the differences she had had with Marie's mother over the years, was still her friend and a member of her generation. Marie to her was merely a business partner, and if it came to a showdown between herself and her mother, Marie had few illusions as to whose side Mama Antoine would take.

No, she would just have to take her own counter-measures, and along lines she had been toying with for some time and for other reasons. She had been contemplating a more permanent removal to Maison Blanche, which she had grown to love, away from the smells and the noise of the city, a place where she reigned supreme and where only people of her own choosing came. She had thought of doing it when St Regis Montal returned, not wishing to confront his con-tinuing enmity at close quarters. Now she thought an earlier removal was called for.

The events of 1 July made her decide. There had been a period of unusual and incessant rain, which turned New Orleans into a stinking steambath in which only the hardiest of gentlemen and the most browbeaten of slaves ventured out into the mud-churned, sewage-seeping streets. All the ladies of New Orleans, white and coloured alike, huddled indoors and watched the downpour beating against windows, tightly closed against its onslaught and the horrible smells it brought forth. In the rat-ridden, leaky tenements along the waterfront, newly arrived immigrants, seeking their own pot of gold in this most prosperous of cities, were particularly hard-hit. Between dawn and dusk of that day, they began to sicken and die like flies. Before the night was over the dread news was out – 'Bronze John' was back: the yellow fever which had laid its heavy and indifferent hand on rich and poor alike so many times in the city's history.

By the next day it was all through the Vieux Carré and was spreading fast towards Canal Street. The rain stopped and the sun came out, but no breath of air stirred in the sudden stinking blanket of heat that suffocated the city. Travellers returning from the bayous reported unusual phenomena – all wildlife was still and no birds sang. People began to flock to the churches and to murmur about the wrath of the Lord.

The day after that the fever leaped into the Garden District, and death started to scythe a heavier path through the Anglo community there and in the suburbs beyond. People began to panic as the horror stories spread through the city: eight dead in two days in one small boardinghouse; five priests already stricken as they ministered to the sick; a whole family on Canal Street wiped out. With the number of victims the horror grew.

The authorities decreed that cannons should be fired in the city to purify the atmosphere, and their dull and constant roar was a constant reminder of the universal plague. Burning barrels of tar and pitch were lit along the streets of the growing contagion. The smoky, sulphur-laden fires turned the night city into a gloomy fantasy of hell on earth.

Marie had decided on her own course of action as soon as the news was confirmed that this was the worst outbreak of Bronze Jack the city had seen since 1837. She dimly remembered that time: the stench of the sulphur and her mother hurrying out of the house on St Ann Street at all hours of the day and night to aid the sick and comfort the dying, for it was known that the Widow Paris was the best yellow fever nurse the city had ever known. In her present uneasy state of mind, Marie found herself wondering if this, too, was not part of her mother's terrible plan to strike her down and then possess her. She would not wait for that; she would flee to her refuge in the bayou, taking all that she had with her.

The execution of this plan, however, was not so easy. Wagons were at a premium, as panic-stricken hordes tried to carry out the same plan. Although Jethro went out day after day to find one, it was only to return empty-handed. He was as worried as Marie, for it was a well-known fact that the fever often mysteriously spared those native-born to the city and exacted its heaviest toll on those who were newly-arrived: a category into which Jethro most uncomfortably fell.

The sight of a milk-seller's dray wandering aimlessly along Rampart Street, its Negro driver dead in his seat, finally spurred Jethro into inventive action. 'I'm going up-river to get a wagon in one of the unaffected towns,' he announced. 'It's hopeless here. I'll be back as soon as I can.

215

If you're so set on taking everything with you, it's the only way we're going to do it.'

Two days later Marie received an urgent summons from her mother, which she ignored. The day after that, Jethro returned with a large farm wagon, and the loading process began. She decided, after it became clear the wagon would not hold everything, to take only the best things of her grandmother's and Etienne's and to leave the rest for later. In the middle of it all, her mother arrived, the light of battle in her eyes.

'Why didn't you come when I sent for you?' she chided. 'You're badly needed. I'm doing what I can, but I need your help.'

'Whatever for? I'm no yellow fever nurse,' Marie returned. 'Anyway, it's out of the question, as you can see, I'm leaving.'

'But you can't leave,' her mother protested. 'There are literally hundreds dying for lack of attention. You can't desert your own people at a time like this!'

'*My* people!' Marie mocked. 'Who are my people? Surely you mean *your* people – oh mighty Queen of the Voodoos – the ones you have so carefully turned against me. *I* have no people – they are *yours*, so you look after them.'

'This is no time to think of what is between us,' her mother snapped. 'Forget what has happened, as I have. This is a crisis, a crisis when all your powers will be needed. Have you no feelings at all? No heart? If you won't care for your own, how about your Anglo friends, who are the worst hit?'

'My *friends*?' Marie queried. 'The ones who come to my front door, but whose homes I must visit through the rear entrance? Come, now, you will have to do better!'

'There must be some who you care for!' her mother exploded. 'How about Louise Valdoux, who lies sick to the point of death in Emile's house? He took the family there, thinking they'd be better off, but, as you know, the Garden District is the worst hit.'

'I'm sorry to hear that, but the Valdouxs can afford the best doctors and nurses money can buy, and if they have any

216

sense they'll get out of the city, just as the LeBlancs and Devereuxs have done – and just as I am going to do. Call on some of your other children, *Maman*. You have plenty of them. Why me? Why not Marie-Philome?'

'You know why it must be you. Besides, Jean-Paul has taken her and the children away. She has them to think of,' her mother snapped.

'And I have my valuable self to think of,' Marie returned smoothly. 'After all, I have to take good care, do I not, for when *I* am Queen of the Voodoos? Nothing must happen to me, must it? Take Amelie, then.' She turned to give Jethro an order.

'I *order* you to stay!' her mother exploded, white with temper.

'Your orders mean nothing to me!' Marie exploded in her turn. 'I'm going, and nothing you can say or do can stop me.'

'Then may you never come back,' her mother hissed. 'And may nothing of yours prosper or bring you happiness! You have no heart, no heart at all, and I am *done* with you!'

Marie shrugged and turned away. 'Good-bye, *Maman*,' she said. 'I will return when I am ready, and then I think it is your day that will be done. Think about that as you rub the sick with murderer's dust, or sing your little songs, or whatever it is you do. Just think about that, *Maman* – you have met your match!'

The toll mounted as the heat mounted – ten thousand, twenty thousand, thirty thousand sick – and Marie Laveau had no time to implement her curse against her daughter as the city drew into itself and died. Among the dead were Louise Valdoux and Emile's newborn son. And in August, Amelie, labouring at her mother's side, sickened with the fever and almost died. Her mother's skill and willpower saved her for the time, but her practised eye saw that she had only snatched this quietest, most unassuming of her brood but temporarily from the jaws of Death, and again she cursed the absent Marie.

In October the fever showed signs of abating, but by that time over eight thousand lay dead of it, most of the city's

217

businesses were closed, and fires and looting had become the order of the day. Fire claimed the empty house on Rampart Street, and though its loss saddened Marie, safe in her refuge, it seemed to confirm the wisdom of her decision to leave a city that had turned against her.

Crocodile brought the news of its burning to the house on St Ann Street. 'Some say it was set, but most like it was just sparks from the pitch barrel fires – people been burning their trash in 'em and everything is tinder-dry,' he explained.

Marie Laveau received the news with indifference; she had other things on her mind. 'I want to borrow that shanty of yours out on Bayou Sauvage,' she announced.

'Sure thing.' He looked at her, then frowned. 'But what do you want it for?'

She looked steadily at him. 'Because it is time to try again.'

'No!' he protested. 'No, not now. It most liked to a killed you last time. You're all worn out.'

'She must pay for Amelie,' Marie Laveau grated. 'This time I can do it; I know I can. After four days you can come and get me, and then you know what to do.'

Dumbly, he nodded.

It was with a sense of inner weariness that she placed the black and red candles around the empty shack and lighted them. The trussed roosters twitched in their bonds and followed her movements with staring amber eyes as she spread the white sheet on the ground and placed the bronze offering bowl and the incense burner before it. She stripped slowly and then squatted facing the drums, her *ogan* and *asson* in her hands, a knife before her on the sheet. Softly she began to chant, the *ogan* sounding quietly at her call. The chanting mounted in volume and the drums gave their familiar answer. She began to rock as the *loa* came, a fine line of foam appearing on her lips. She twitched and grovelled as the possession took hold, and the candles leaped and guttered as the shadows gathered around. In Maison Blanche Marie stirred uneasily in her sleep and called a name . . .

In the shack the dance of the shadows continued. Then

the hand holding the *ogan* faltered and the wild music stopped. There was silence for a while, and the candles stopped their grotesque dance and burned evenly and brightly as the shadows shrank and dwindled into nothingness. Then the large black eyes opened and a slow radiant smile appeared on the sensuous lips. 'The *loa* have spoken,' she whispered to herself. 'What a fool I have been! Not by her, but *through* her, will I gain my goal. By her own blood will she suffer, not by mine; through others she shall suffer, not through me. Long the working-out, but sure. Dark the path for her and long. As *I* have willed it, so shall it be – for *I* am Marie Laveau!'

Part II
1859-1918

Chapter Twenty-three

Marie smoothed the heavy satin of her dress and settled back into the velvet cushions of her chair. Her practised eye ran over the New Year's Eve party as it eddied and flowed in the great saloon of Maison Blanche. It was very crowded and going well – as usual. Elegantly dressed men swirled past her, their naked or near-naked partners in their arms. Occasionally, a couple would slip into one of the little bedrooms she so thoughtfully had installed, or slip out of one of the French windows, a cloak thrown over the girl's nakedness, to the circle of waiting carriages outside. There was a crowd around the buffet, and the drinks were circulating freely. There was nothing for her to do, nothing for her to worry about. She leaned back, took a sip of the champagne standing on a small table at her elbow, and closed her eyes, savouring as she always did the feeling of the fine linen and satin against her flesh and beneath her ringed fingers.

Despite her mother's gloomy predictions to the contrary, she had prospered in the six years succeeding her permanent removal to Maison Blanche. She had prospered and enjoyed greatly. She had never tired of the joys that money bought: the luxurious fabrics, the fine French wines and cognacs, the gourmet food, and the jewels. And yet – and it was this 'and yet' that gave her pause.

Recently she had become conscious of the familiar stirring inside her, the feeling that betokened something important was about to happen, and along with it had come the consciousness of time passing. It had never really entered her mind much before now. Her 'girls' at the start had been her own age or even older, but the 'girls' had changed so rapidly over the years. Some had drifted up, some down; many had taken the money they had made with her to start small businesses or to serve as dowries for their marriages with coloured husbands. A few had even married white men and had gone North.

None of her original group remained, nor, for that matter, did any of the second. The girls here tonight were mostly arrivals from the past two years, and they looked young to her, very young. Even the men seemed to be getting younger; some of the dashing cavaliers here tonight she remembered as sober-faced little boys from her hairdressing days. And it was with something like relief that she recognized some longtime customers like Aristide Sautelle, who was firmly propped against the bar, getting diligently drunk and haranguing his peers.

Life was so smooth now. The rising tide of prosperity, which even the great plague of '53 had not halted, swept her up with it. She had done more favours for and heard more secrets from the rulers of New Orleans than she cared to think about. There was not a corner of the city's life that she could not reach, not a string that she did not know how to pull. So, what was unsettling her? What change could possibly be coming? Not trouble from her mother, surely, after all these years?

She had expected, been braced for it, at the start, but nothing had happened. It puzzled her, especially since she was certain her mother blamed her for Amelie's death. She had gone to the funeral expecting some open show of hostility, but though her mother had been as distant as stone, there had been no scene, no reproaches.

They had seen one another but rarely since then: at the burial of the long-absent Daumeny, who had been killed in a factory accident in the North in '55; and at the weddings of Charles-Louis and Marie-Jeanne. Only the ever-devoted Jean and François still lived at home, and she had heard from Marie-Philome that he, too, was soon to marry – little François; it seemed hard to believe.

If she had seen little of her mother, she had seen much of Marie-Philome, the serene and devoted mother of three children. Nothing ever ruffled her elder sister, and Marie enjoyed the peaceful calm of her establishment, which she often used for overnight stays when kept late on some social occasion in the city. Even though her home was now here, there was little she had missed in the social life of the city:

the theatre, the opera, a mild flutter in the gambling establishments which now sprouted on every corner in every neighbourhood, and the endless balls. With the onrush of people pouring into the city to cash in on its wealth, there was an acute shortage of presentable women, and many of the hotels had relaxed their social barriers. It was quite common nowadays to go to a ball in which white couples and gentlemen with girls of darker hues mingled freely.

This had not been accomplished without opposition. Some of the tradition-bound Creoles had become so incensed by this growing licence, particularly during Carnival, that they had instituted a private society, the Comus, geared around the Carnival and its balls, in which membership was exclusive and highly sought after. None but the oldest and most monied Creole families were invited to join. It was rumoured, however, that the monied Anglos were also thinking along the same lines and forming a rival society with much the same rules and exclusivity, but so far nothing had come of it. Either way, it did not worry Marie; there were plenty of the other sort to meet her needs. Her life was full and rich and gay – so why was she restless?

Aristide Sautelle, followed by a gaggle of loudly arguing men, crossed the room and drew up a chair beside her. 'I come to seek your protection,' he announced with the over-careful enunciation of one who has drunk deeply but who is not yet drunk. 'I have been telling these gentlemen a few home truths which they do not seem to like.'

'Now what are you up to?' She smiled at him, for, though he was ugly and on the small side, he had a keen mind and a ready wit that always amused her. For a short while, a few years back, they had been lovers, but, finding him jealous and possessive, she had gently disengaged herself. He had sulked for a while and deserted her salons, but lately he had returned, finding in her mind a ready complement to his own.

'Oh, with all this damned travelling he's been doing, he thinks he's the oracle of God,' one of the younger men broke in heatedly. 'Don't waste your time listening to his piffle, Marie.'

225

'Piffle, indeed! Here I am prophesying our Creole doom, going forth as a crier before the cataclysm, and all I get is scorn,' Aristide said with offended dignity. 'Look at me!' he appealed to Marie. 'A typical member of our society! I have wasted my substance and my wits on a lifelong pursuit of pleasure. And there is not a man here tonight who is not like me! I have never done anything, never created anything – except, perhaps, one or two bastards – never accomplished anything. Why? Because our Creole society, this elegant cocoon in which we are all encased, decrees that to do otherwise would not be becoming to a gentleman. We live on the backs and sweat of others and ply our little games, while the busy gentlemen of the North invade our lands and pick our pockets, all of us unmindful of our coming doom.'

'Now you're talking like a stinking Abolitionist,' another man sneered.

Aristide held up a hand in mock horror. 'God forbid! Slavery is dead, dying of its own weight, but we fools of the South and those fools of the North do not seem to realize it. We cling, they clang, and before you know it, we will be at one another's throats over it. Whereas all any of us needs do is wait a few years until everyone realizes that you can get more out of a man you pay than a man you own.'

'Oh, come now! Marie chided gently. 'You don't mean to say we're ever going to fight about the slaves, do you?'

'You're damned right I mean it,' Aristide assured her. 'The North will descend on us in the shining armour of self-righteousness, swords clutched firmly in their strong right hands, carpetbags in their left. They will free the slaves – who will be a lot worse off for it, poor souls – and take everything we have in the process. It is not only we Creoles who are doomed; it is the whole woolly headed – if you'll pardon the expression – South land.'

'You talk like a madman,' someone said in disgust. 'Anyone knows those Yankee traders can't fight worth a damn. Why, if it came to a war, we'd beat 'em hands down. It was Southerners who won the Mexican war, and nearly all the officers in the army are Southerners – not that it will ever come to a war.'

'It takes more than officers to fight one. Are you going to arm your slaves, as well?' Aristide went on. 'And it takes guns and ammunition, and factories to make 'em. What would we use against them, Louis? Cotton balls from your cotton plantation, shot from sugar-cane rifles primed with molasses? Going to turn your gin mills into explosive works? Is that what you'd do?'

'Bah! I came here to have a good time, not to argue with a drunk,' Louis scoffed, then moved off with most of his audience.

Aristide looked after them and shook his head sadly. 'Change – they can't stand the thought of change, and yet it's everywhere, and nothing we can do will stop it.' He turned confidingly to Marie and lowered his voice. 'You've no idea what things I saw in the North when I was up there ...'

'There he goes again!' one of the few remaining men said with resignation, then drifted off.

'No, listen! Not only among the men, but the women, too. Some of those northern women, they're doing all sorts of things – wanting to vote, wanting and sometimes getting the same education as men, wanting to *work*! Mind you, most of them have got faces that would frighten a horse, but they're *doing* things. Some of 'em have even written books about it – saying that women have the right to have something besides husbands and homes and families.'

'Try telling that to our womenfolk,' another man sniffed. 'They'd laugh you out of town, Aristide. Besides, what could they do?'

'Most of them? Damn all, I expect. They sit around looking decorative as they've always done, trying to think up ways to make us miserable,' the confirmed bachelor replied. 'But not all – no, not all. Take Marie, here – I'd say she has a better mind than any woman in New Orleans – better than most men, for that matter. But what has she ever done? Nothing, except think up different ways to minister to our pleasure and tempt the money out of our pockets. And there is nothing she ever could do under the present setup –

she's got no education to speak of, no training, and because one of her great-grannies had the misfortune to be a nigger, she can't even lead a normal life.'

A horrified murmur rippled through the group, for Aristide had just broken part of the unwritten code of Creole society. Then one of them said hotly, 'I'm not going to stand around here and let you insult Marie under her own roof. You're too drunk to know what you're saying, so if you haven't the delicacy to leave, I am going to throw you out. I think all this travellin' you've been doing has probably turned your mind, but it most surely has ruined your manners, sir!' He made a movement towards Aristide, but Marie stayed him with an imperative gesture.

'No, let him be! Go about your pleasure, gentlemen,' she commanded. 'Leave Aristide to me.' They moved off, outraged.

Aristide took a long swig of the straight bourbon he'd been drinking and looked at her owlishly over the rim of the glass. 'I didn't upset you, did I? I didn't mean to insult you, you know.'

She shook her head at him. 'No. I take a lot of shocking, you know that, but you ought to mind your manners in front of the others. What you have been saying may well be true enough – but can you ever really see it being any different?'

'Sure I can!' He thrust his jaw out pugnaciously. 'Oh, not at once – you've seen yourself how people fight change – but sometime, somewhere . . .' His voice grew dreamy. 'A hundred years from now – what I would give to be able to see the world a hundred years from now!'

A tiny pulse began to beat in Marie's brain. 'And can you see a place for the likes of me to do things in this dream-world of the future?'

'As you are now?' He threw back his head and laughed. 'Oh, no, my dear! I'm afraid some things will take longer than that. But if you were a blue-eyed, well-born blonde? Yes. Why, I dare say then you could rule the world, or at least some part of it!' He laughed again at his own fantasy.

A suffocating feeling welled up in Marie as the pulse began to pound its message. 'Leave me now,' she said abruptly. 'Go and amuse yourself, Aristide. I have a headache.'

He staggered to his feet and stood looking down at her glumly. 'I have offended you, then – I'm sorry. I'm too drunk to behave, so I'd better take myself on home. Pay me no mind. I'm just a drunken old fool. Happy New Year, Marie, my dear.' Slowly he staggered past her, out the door and into the night. 'Happy 1859 to you, too,' she called after him absently.

What I would give to see the world a hundred years from now ... *I needed you, I need you to go on, and after you another and another and another, if need be – there is so much to be done* ... The two voices of present and past intermingled in her mind.

Her mother had reached out to the future through her, and had failed by a hair's breadth. She had failed because she had taken on an opponent as strong or stronger than herself; she had failed because she had been greedy; she had wanted not only the young body, but the powers that went with it. But what if she had started sooner, been contented with less? If she had made the attempt when Marie was just beginning? She seriously doubted whether she could have withstood her mother at that time. So it could be done – of that she was sure.

The important thing was to reach out to the future, just to get there; that was something her mother had lost sight of, a mistake she herself could profit from. As of now she knew little about the process, but she would learn – oh, yes, indeed, she would learn! The blood tie was important, it seemed – so a child, a young child, was needed: a baby, perhaps. Her excitement quickened – a baby of her own! If her mother could do it to her, why should she be more scrupulous?

The sense of Time washed over her again – she was twenty-nine years old. If it was to be a child of hers, she had best make haste. Her eyes wandered vaguely over the excited throng milling around the overheated room. To be tied to one of these by a child, she who had hated to be tied – could she stand it? No, none of these would do.

What should she do? Where should she start? What was it Aristide had said? '*A well-born, blue-eyed blonde.*' A slow smile curved her lips.

'Well, I do have to start somewhere,' she murmured. 'Item one: find a blond man whom I can tolerate long enough to give me a child.' The unfortunate vision of the dark-skinned Claire being cooed over by her fair-skinned parents rose before her eyes. 'Maybe it'll have to be more than one,' she mused. 'So I'll have to have a semi-permanent relationship with a man I like a lot – oh, dear, how trying!' For a second her resolution faltered, but the challenge of her blood overcame it. 'I certainly won't find him here in this lot,' she went on. 'So, obviously I must return to the city – and the quicker, the better . . .'

'All alone and talking to yourself, Marie?' a male voice broke in. 'That's a fine way to start the New Year, I must say!'

She looked up to see an old acquaintance smiling at her. 'I was making my New Year's resolution,' she said.

'Oh, la! Such tiresome things, resolutions! They get in the way of one's pleasures so.'

'Not this one.'

'I am intrigued. Are you going to divulge its marvellous content?'

'Not unless you have a wide circle of blond male friends,' she said with a cryptic smile.

'Ah! I am mortified,' he said languidly, running a hand over his own dark, shining locks. 'I see your thoughts are not on me at all – I am shamed!' he jested. 'I will wish you then a happy New Year and take myself away.'

'Happy New Year,' Marie murmured, then nestled back into her chair. Aristide – dear, ugly Aristide – had given her the only thing she had needed to make her life complete: he had given her a dream . . . 'Happy New Year!' she wished herself.

Chapter Twenty-four

'Ain't dat Marie Laveau? Ah didn' know she was back.'

'Sho' is. Ah been seein' her 'round all over de place. Bad news fo' someone, Ah reckon. Dat's one bad Voodoo woman, dat one.'

The two Negro women sat by their small stalls in the French Market and looked after the tall, elegant figure strolling in the bright sunlight, which struck fire from the diamond glittering in her tignon and coaxed answering yellow gleams from the great golden hoop earrings.

'Oh, she ain't so bad,' the first one said uneasily. 'She sho' helped me when mah man got his eye on dat yeller girl on Canal Street. Run her right off, she did. Anyways, t'aint safe to bad-mouth her.'

The second woman lowered her voice. 'My sister spited her some way, an' next thing ya know, she done give mah sister's man some "Follow Me" water, an' he's off after her like a tomcat. Not dat he got no place to be sure – she don't give no coloured man de time o' day, nor many o' de whiteys, de ways Ah hears it – but he never did go back to mah sister. She sho' has got somethin'!'

'Where's she at now? Her place on Rampart's gone, an' dere's bad blood 'tween her an' de old one. Ah thought she was safe up in dat ole bayou fo' good.'

'She buildin' dat ole place up again, but Ah hears she got rooms over on Bourbon. Ah seed her more 'round de streets dese days den ever befo'. Not since she was a young 'un wit dat ole Bessie, she ain't been 'round as much. Ah jus' wonder what she's at.' The tone was wistful.

Marie was still working on item number one on her new agenda. She was hunting. Half-amused at herself for taking Aristide so literally, none the less she was diligently combing the city day and night for the proper mate. So far the search had been fruitless.

In the meantime she had started the long-delayed rebuilding of the house on Rampart. It seemed that everywhere she looked, the people of New Orleans had the same idea; old buildings were being torn down all over the place and lavish modern ones being erected in their stead, many of them smaller in scale, but modelled on the great Gothic lines of the new city hall facing Lafayette Square. Emile had rebuilt his house in the Garden District to complement all the new houses on Lousiana and St Charles – a house heavy with ornamental ironwork outside and panelled in exquisite woods inside. Justin and Valerie LeBlanc, in keeping with their image of 'young moderns', had elected not to have a town house at all, but to move into one of the luxurious apartments in the Pontalba buildings by the cathedral, which were considered the ultimate in chic.

The older houses in the Vieux Carré were taking on an almost shabby, fragile look in the face of all this new flamboyance. People had even started to move out of the old district, and many houses which had been white-owned when Marie had left the city were now inhabited by coloureds.

The Montal house still stood shuttered and peeling into decay, though she had heard that Madame Montal and Anne now inhabited its upper storeys, leading a hermit's life in the dim, closed-in rooms. The rumour was things had been going badly for the Montals; there had been troubles on their estates, some crop failures, and the worst trouble of all stemmed from Dominic, who piled up gaming debts faster than St Regis could pay them off. It was a rumour Marie devoutly hoped to be true.

She had become a frequent visitor at the Delambe house on Decatur Street, where Monsieur Delambe, withered and bent under the weight of his continuing sorrows, still laboured at his little store to provide for his family. Madame Delambe had never completely recovered from the stroke she had suffered when Jacqueline died, and she had to be carefully watched. She was in the habit of wandering off towards the dangerous dock area searching for her lost daughter. Claire, now thirteen, was still at the convent, but her life outside it was one of constant care and vigilance over her ailing grandmother. Still on the plain side, she had inherited her mother's sweet and gentle disposition and was much beloved in the neighbourhood, but every time Marie saw her anxious and sad eyes as she cared for her grandmother, her own hatred of the Montals was renewed.

Returning home to her rented rooms on Bourbon Street, Marie was pondering, as she often did, what to do about Claire's future, when she bumped into a man hurrying in the opposite direction. With muttered excuses they both went on their way. It was not until she was well past him that the vivid blue eyes and a mass of shining fair hair impressed themselves on her mind. With an exclamation of annoyance, she turned around, only to find he had disappeared. There hadn't been time for him to turn the corner; therefore, he must have gone into one of the houses on the street itself – but which one? '*Merde!*' she muttered. 'The best prospect I've seen to date! Right under my nose, too! Well, I suppose I'll just have to lurk around and track him down.'

It took her three days to do it, but then she spotted the tall fair-haired figure again rushing down Bourbon Street. This time she followed him until he disappeared into number 516, just a few doors down from her own rooms. It was a boardinghouse, she discovered, run by a coloured woman, but catering mainly to Anglo businessmen from out of town. It was time to call in help.

She sent for Jethro, who was already installed in Rampart Street overseeing the rebuilding, and told him what she wanted. 'Everything about him you can find out – and while you're at it, find out about the woman who runs the place, too.' She had learned enough of Jethro's abilities in the last nine years to know that if there was anything to find out, he was the one who could.

A few days later he was back with the report. 'A Swede – from Chicago – in the lumber business – their shipping agent here. Late twenties, unmarried, no relatives here. Parents in Chicago, father disabled in some way, so he sends money back there. Job's okay, but hasn't much money.

Considered a bit strange by his fellow boarders because he reads a lot. Drinks, but doesn't gamble. Likes to dance. Visits Flo Winfield's occasionally. Name is Nils Andersen. This okay?'

'Jethro, you're a marvel!' she said, flattering him. 'And the woman who runs the place?'

'An ex-mistress of an ex-mayor, now completely ex because he's dead. House isn't hers completely, a half-interest only; the other half still belongs to his family, who lets it to her to keep her quiet, I think. Bit of a shrew. Takes mostly Anglos and charges 'em high, but sets a good table, I'm told. Name's Marie LeBeau – kinda similar to yours.'

'Hmm, very,' Marie mused. 'She take any women boarders?'

'Nary a one. Why?'

'Because I was thinking of changing my lodgings.'

'You really are up to something, aren't you? What now, I wonder?' He looked at her speculatively.

But she didn't enlighten him. 'Well, I'd better tackle Marie LeBeau,' she observed.

'The best of luck to you, then. She strikes me as a hard nut.'

'Sometimes they crack the quickest,' Marie assured him sweetly.

She tried the direct approach and found Jethro was quite right. Marie LeBeau had only one interest in life – herself. 'Out of the question,' she had snapped. 'I take only men boarders – *white* men!'

'Not even if I paid more than the going rate?'

'Why should you do that?' the woman asked suspiciously. 'Anyway, the answer is still no. I don't want a woman of your sort here.'

'My sort! What sort is that?' Marie said, quietly ominous.

Mademoiselle LeBeau was not at all abashed. 'A woman who's up to something – *what*, I've no idea. But you're not getting in here. I've heard of you.'

'I'm interested in the boardinghouse business, and I've heard you run a good one. I'd like to study the way you operate. Would you be interested in a partnership?'

234

'No, I wouldn't. Go learn the business somewhere else. You'll get nothing from me.'

'You're making it very difficult. I usually do get what I'm after,' Marie assured her, 'and I just happen to be set on this idea.'

'Don't you threaten me!' the landlady hissed. 'And don't you try any of your "hex-on-the-doorstep" routines, either. They may cut some ice with some of the stupid women in the quarter, but not with me, I can assure you.'

'Oh, I wouldn't dream of doing that,' Marie murmured, 'but I might set up a rival establishment next door and undercut your rates by half. Then what would happen, I wonder?'

For the first time the woman looked disconcerted. 'I run a good place here,' she muttered. 'You can't frighten me!' But the first seed of doubt had been sown.

Marie broke off the frontal attack and retired to attack on the flank. She went to see Emile.

'Buy a boardinghouse!' he exclaimed in amazement. 'Now what crazy idea are you working on? You've been so good the last few years, but, you know full well, these whims of yours always end up costing you money.'

'You mean I have done nothing of late but take your advice, Emile, and have had no ideas of my own,' Marie said sweetly. 'But we've got to move with the times. The boardinghouse business is booming, and this is a good, sound investment. Besides, the building is wonderful – three storeys, good solid construction of the late 1820s, when they still built with care, not like some of the places they're throwing together now, nice ironwork. No – it's a good idea. You know the Vigos personally, and I think they may be happy to sell their half-share. I'll deal with the woman who owns the other half.'

Emile sighed with exasperation. He had added some poundage to his stocky frame, and his face now looked like a solemn cherub's; save for the flaming head of impudent red hair, he could already pass as a middle-aged man. 'All right,' he agreed grudgingly. 'I'll see what I can do – but it's probably going to cost you!'

It cost her, but she got what she was after. Armed with the legal papers, she returned to the frontal attack. 'Being now part-owner, I shall be moving in,' she informed Marie LeBeau.

'It can't be done. There's no room,' her co-owner snapped, but the hand holding the papers trembled.

'I happen to know that one of your boarders is returning to Philadelphia within the week. I'll take his room.' Marie was calm but definite. 'And I may point out there is no way you can keep me out. Check with a lawyer if you like, but you'll just be wasting your money.'

'I'll not be partners with you, you can be sure of that!' The older woman was trembling with rage.

'Good. Then I'm prepared to buy you out. You can do it the easy way, or you can do it the hard way. It is entirely up to you.' Marie was suddenly dangerous. 'But I am moving in, and, if I receive no co-operation from you, I will be taking over.'

'But this is all I have!' Mademoiselle LeBeau wailed, her face suddenly crumpling.

'And I have no intention of taking it away from you – *if* you are reasonable,' Marie assured her. 'I'll not interfere with your running of the place, if you don't interfere with me.'

An uneasy pact was agreed to, and a few days later Marie was installed, bag and baggage, in one of the third-floor front rooms – one with its own tiny balcony, fronting on Bourbon Street. Her prey, she discovered, inhabited one of the less desirable third-floor rear rooms, and this suited her purposes excellently. He was one of the few 'full' boarders, returning to the house for his midday meal. This probably explained his haste on the two occasions she had seen him, she reflected, because the landlady set an excellent table. However, she herself had decided against sharing its delights, not wishing to try her unwilling partner too far, and not wishing, either, to embark on the second half of her campaign in other male company, which possibly might distract her.

She contrived the first meeting with supreme care. Having taken extra pains with her elegant toilette, finishing with sev-

236

eral touches of the heavy, and extremely delectable, perfume she used, she managed to appear at the head of the stairs just as he was rushing up them to wash up before the midday meal.

He was almost at the top before he sensed her presence. Then he looked up, his eyes widened, and he flattened his big body against the stair wall in embarrassment, trying to make room for her descent. 'Excuse me,' he muttered, and the fair cheeks flushed under her steady gaze.

'Oh, please!' Marie cooed. 'Do come up – I am in no hurry.' She moved slightly, but only enough to let him squeeze past. After a second's hesitation he did so, with another muttered apology, and when they were literally face to face she smiled at him, opened her eyes very wide, and said, 'I am afraid you will have to get used to this. I believe we inhabit the same floor. Allow me to introduce myself. I am Marie Laveau, Mademoiselle LeBeau's new partner.'

He gingerly engulfed the slim, bejewelled hand she held out to him and his blush deepened. 'Very happy to meet you,' he said in an accent that lilted up and down the scale. 'I am Nils Andersen, and *ja*, I live up here, too.' His v's came out as f's, and his o's as u's, which Marie found delightful.

The nostrils of his thin, fine nose quivered slightly as he caught the full impact of her perfume, and he stood gazing down at her, the blue eyes wide, still absentmindedly clutching her hand. He seemed at a loss for further words, so Marie disengaged her hand gently.

'I'm sure we will make very good neighbours,' she murmured with another upward, vivid glance. And, gathering up her rustling crinoline, she began to descend the stairs. '*Au revoir.*' She smiled.

'Oh, *ja – au revoir*,' he muttered as he stood gazing after her.

She could feel his eyes on her till she passed out of sight. Oh, yes! she thought. You'll do very well, Nils Andersen.

She carefully avoided him for the next two days and then proceeded to stage three. She dressed for a dance in a ball gown of pale yellow satin, huge in its crinoline and cut to reveal her tawny shoulders and emphasize her deep bosom. She curled her dark, wavy hair into the currently fashionable ringlets, until they lay in lustrous shiny rolls on her shoulders, and pinned them into place with white camellias. Even in the somewhat wavy outlines of the boardinghouse mirror, she had to admit that the result was spectacular. And to further the effect, she added a choker of jade and pearls. Arming herself with a fan and a tiny lace handkerchief, she rustled into battle across the landing and tapped timidly on his door.

After a second's pause it opened to reveal Nils in his shirtsleeves, one finger marking his page in a book in his left hand, as he held the door open with his right. The pool of light from the oil lamp on the small round table by an easy chair struck golden gleams from the shining hair.

'Oh, do forgive me for disturbing you, Monsieur Andersen, but I am in such trouble, and I wondered if you might help,' Marie said plaintively as she bowed her head and touched the tiny square of cambric to her eyes.

'Trouble? Oh, that is bad. What is it?' His deep voice showed concern.

She glided past him into the room and then stood in silence for a moment within the pool of light so that he could get the full effect of her toilette. His eyes widened again and he let out a faint sigh.

'It is like this. My brother was taking me to a ball at the St Louis Hotel – we were to meet some friends there. And now I have just received word that he is unavoidably detained out of town and will not be back in time. I am *so* disappointed, and I have no means of letting them know, and I have the tickets and all. Oh, dear! I don't know *what* to do!' Again she applied the handkerchief.

'You would like me to take a message?' he said doubtfully, but she went on as if she hadn't heard him.

'Oh, such a waste, and I was *so* looking forward to it! Do you dance, *M'sieu*? Perhaps if you have some young lady, you could use the tickets and give my friends the message . . .?' Her voice was tearful.

'Oh, *ja*, I love to dance.' His tone was eager. 'And I would be very happy to escort you, if you would do me the honour. Please do not be upset. For me it will be a pleasure, a very great pleasure?'

'Are you sure?'

'Of course I am sure. Who would not be delighted to rescue such a lovely lady in distress?'

'Well, in that case, I accept. You are truly a gallant gentleman, *M'sieu*,' Marie said smugly. 'I'll wait for you in my room until you are ready.'

Oh, yes, he would do, indeed!

As she floated around the ballroom in his arms, she liked everything about him: the way he looked; the way he looked at her; the feel of his arms around her; the way a wayward lock of the fair hair kept falling across the high forehead; even his shyness. It had taken her half the evening to persuade him to call her 'Marie', and even then he occasionally slid back into the more formal address. Gradually, under the influence of the plentiful drinks offered, which he evidently liked and downed in considerable quantities, and the gay atmosphere, his colour blossomed and his tongue loosened. All that she learned confirmed the original impression that this was the right choice.

He was twenty-seven, almost two years her junior, and heart- and fancy-free. Not rich, not poor, but a young man on the rise, the kind that New Orleans was full of nowadays. 'I was born in Sweden,' he informed her, 'but my parents brought me here as a very little boy, and now I am an American – what you call a damn Yankee, ja?'

'Some of my best friends are damn Yankees,' she informed him, somewhat mendaciously. 'It would be a dull world if we were all the same, would it not? I can quite appreciate that your ways in the North are very different from those of the South, but when you've been here longer, perhaps you will like our ways better.'

His face darkened. 'This slavery I will never like,' he informed her shortly. 'That is not a good way of life. Man should be free.'

'I'm not too wild about it myself, come to that,' Marie murmured languidly.

On their way home in the carriage, she allowed him to kiss her, and his warm, trembling lips on hers told her all she wanted to know: the fire had been lighted. Nevertheless, she did not want to rush things, and, after a moment's hesitation on his part, they had parted formally on the third-floor landing.

The next morning she had just risen when she heard light tapping at her door. She opened it to find Nils looming on the threshold, a very small bunch of red roses almost engulfed in his large hand. He thrust them towards her.

'For me?' she exclaimed in mock surprise. 'You need not have done that.'

He looked at the roses, then at her, and a slow, brilliant smile spread over his face. 'Red roses,' he informed her. 'I guess I am what you call ... er ... wooing – *ja*? Is that all right?'

Chapter Twenty-five

What had happened had been none of her planning; she had been swept up, engulfed, overcome ... She lay on her back, trying to still her thudding heart. Nils's right hand was clasped confidingly on her left breast as he lay deep in sleep at her side. The impossible had happened; she felt that merging with another human being, the oneness that she had so often sought, but in which she had ceased to believe.

His courtship had been as swift and as strong as a summer storm: no obstacles, no delays – the male animal in full pursuit of a mate. She had let it happen, for this had been her purpose, and it had reached its culmination this very night.

They had kissed good night on the landing after a night on the town, but his lips had been feverish on hers in their new hunger. He had opened the door of his room and lifted her inside, his lips still on hers. 'I need you, I want you, my dearest darling. You want it, too, *ja?*'

She had said nothing but had nestled closer to the great heated body, and his hands had started to fumble at her clothes. They had trembled so that she had had to help him, and when she was naked before him, he had looked at her with wide, dilated eyes, and, picking her up, he had deposited her on the bed, his mouth seeking her nipples as they rose to the touch of his lips.

With a sobbing cry, he had torn off his own clothes and had sprung upon her, his face flushed, his eyes unseeing, the great hands reaching, as if to tear her apart, and his hard penis seeking and cleaving into her like an iron rod, as he rode her wild and hard like some great stallion. And then ... and then the impossible had happened. As she rose with him to his frantic, throbbing crescendo, she had experienced the indescribable: an obliteration of all that was Marie Laveau, an entrance into a twinned being of blood that was not her blood, thoughts that were not hers – a being that was all fire and ecstasy and delight, and that rose far above two bodies heaving on a bed. And with little surcease it had happened again and again and again . . .

Nils stirred beside her, his hand tightening on her breast, and she turned to him, her mouth half-open, yearning towards his, yearning to feel once again what she had felt. His mouth closed on hers, his tongue diving like an arrow deep into her throat, his hands moulding her to what he wanted. He drew her left leg over his thigh and entered her again, and she could feel her own warm wetness as her vulva opened to meet him. She began to move softly against him, every nerve, every drop of blood reaching out, stretching out, towards the ultimate, and he turned on his back, drawing her on top of him and rubbing her body up and down against his, his mouth sucking and biting at her breasts. She moaned her pleasure, and once more began to fuse into this other being, this other being from which each time she so unwillingly returned. By dawn there was nothing she had refused him, nothing he had not possessed utterly, nothing they had not done. Sometimes they entwined, only to come back to the same oneness.

So this is love, she thought, as she lay looking around the shabby, meagre room, loving everything about it, from the cracks in the ceiling to the worn dresser, the narrow armoire with its blotched mirror, the faded carpet. To her it was more beautiful than the grandest house in the Garden District. Her whole body tingled with exhilaration and well-being. 'I'm happy!' she cried silently. 'For the first time in my life I know what happiness is, and I am happy!' With a pang she remembered the cause of all this and almost laughed at its absurdity. Power and the future! Whoever wanted or needed it? For her there was only now and happiness and Nils. She had found her world at last.

But the everyday world could not be shut out, much as she would have liked it to be. Nils had to get off to his work – very late. And she had to decide in the long morning hours what to do next. The boardinghouse, she concluded quickly, was no place for the love of her life, the love for all time.

242

Ready or not, they would move to Rampart Street, where at least the outside world would be less readily apparent. Nils did not need any persuading; on his part he was so bedazzled and bemused by his love that he would say *'Ja'* to anything she said and did, and reach out for her once more.

'You really run the boardinghouse very well, so I'm leaving you to it,' she informed the startled and thoroughly confused Marie LeBeau. 'But I should get those upstairs rooms redecorated – it's bad to let a place get shabby. And you can pay my share of the rent directly into Valdoux's counting house on Royal to my account there. I'm sure you won't have any difficulty letting the two vacant rooms.'

And she bore off her Viking lover to the familiar confines of Rampart Street, where their ecstasies continued amid the hammering of carpenters and the thudding of masons.

After what had gone, it came as no surprise to Marie to find herself pregnant after the first month. So far had her original purpose faded from her mind that the certainty that she would bear a child only concerned her in so far as it might interfere with the perfect delight which had now become her world. With her own reservations about it, she was taken aback by Nils's enthusiastic reception of the news that he would soon have the added responsibility of being a father.

'So we get married right now!' he said eagerly.

Patiently, she explained to him why this was impossible.

'But this is a monstrous law!' he fumed. 'These people of the South are mad! We'll go home to the North and get married. Right now we go.'

But she was not ready for that. Her bliss and her world were here; she didn't want anything to change. 'We are married in every sense that I care about,' she assured him. 'That's all that matters.' And, as usual, he had given in.

When the world found her back at Rampart Street, it came knocking at her door as it had always done, and, armoured by her happiness, she dispensed advice and gris-gris with a sunny patience that mystified and even terrified the seekers more than her former austerity had done.

One such seeker surprised her. 'Dat lady wit de pretty clothes here again,' Patty had announced.

And Marie had made the correct diagnosis and had hurried into the drawing room to find Valerie LeBlanc. As chic and elegant as ever, Valerie's face was drawn, her eyes troubled, as she greeted Marie. Waving away Marie's invitation to be seated, she moved restlessly around the room, fiddling with objects on the mantelpiece and on the small tables. Then she said abruptly, 'Marie, my whole life is in a terrible mess, and you're the only one I can think of who might help me.'

'Gladly,' said Marie. In her present state of ecstasy she wanted the whole world to share in her happiness. 'What is it?'

Suddenly, the smart society veneer that had become part of Valerie's armour crumpled, and she burst into tears, revealing the same fourteen-year-old that Marie had first known. 'It's Justin,' she sobbed. 'I think I've lost him, and it's all my fault! I was so fed up with life in general after the birth of our third child, and Justin was so busy with the plantations and such. Well, I stayed in the city and I had a flirtation with someone I knew before I was married. Oh, it was so *silly*! I no longer even like the man. I suppose I was getting back at Justin, too, because during my last pregnancy I knew he'd been seeing some horrible Anglo woman over in Carrollton. Anyway, Justin got wind of it, but he didn't rage at me or anything. He just became quiet and distant, and since then, well, he's hardly been near me, and he's been spending more and more time with that damned whore.'

'And what about the other man?'

'Oh, Marie, you know there has never really been anyone for me but Justin. However silly and flighty I was before we were married, I always came back, and he knew it, and I knew it. The other one is still hanging around, though I've tried to get rid of him, and, damn it, *he's* married and should know better!'

'Have you told Justin what you've just told me?' Marie asked quietly.

'I've tried, but we don't seem to communicate anymore. Oh, I'm so wretched, wretched, *wretched*! Why couldn't I have been satisfied with three lovely children and a good husband? What's wrong with me?'

'Nothing,' Marie assured her. 'You merely tried to reach out in a time of need for the same thing that Justin reached out for. The only snag is that the dice are loaded against you. A man can do it; a woman can't. It's that simple.'

'But what am I going to *do*?' Valerie wailed.

Marie smiled faintly, 'Well, if you were one of my darker-hued clients, I would prescribe some "Follow Me" water and sundry other things along the same line to get your man back, and, amazingly enough, they would work because they believe in them. You do not, so it is no use prescribing the same for you. So, in your case, this is what you must do . . .'

Valerie's eyes widened as she listened and she gasped, 'Why, I've never heard of anything like it! You really mean it works? But what about the other woman?'

'Just give me her name and address and I'll take care of that – that's the easy part. Yours is the hard part,' Marie informed her. 'But understand, as soon as you see signs of it working, you must forgo the delights of New Orleans for a while and insist that Justin take you and the children back to Castle Blanche for a lengthy stay. I think you'll have no problem with that, the summer is almost upon us. And let me know how things are going.'

Two weeks later Valerie returned, but this time she was radiant. She flung her arms around Marie and kissed her. 'You're the dearest, most wonderful friend I have in the world – you are a miracle worker!'

'I seem to have heard such statements from you before,' Marie reproved. 'I take it things are now all right.'

'All right! Everything is marvellous! I just came to say good-bye. We are going up to Castle Blanche this afternoon. I've never been so happy in my whole life. I have heard that woman is packing up and leaving town. Marie, however did you do it?'

'Oh, I have my methods,' Marie said smugly.

But no sooner had she smoothed out the woes of one Valdoux when she was burdened by another. She was astonished on her return to the house one day to find Bayard waiting for her. She had not seen him for years, save at a distance, and though some of his youthful exuberance had subsided, he still had the air of a dashing man-about-town – at that moment, however, a very troubled man-about-town. He paced up and down on the rose Aubusson, sneaking furtive glances at her as she patiently waited for him to state his business.

'Marie,' he finally burst out, 'I'm in a hell of a mess.' Her heart sank slightly. 'I come to you in desperation, because it is a very delicate matter and I could think of no one but you who might help me – though I know full well that you have no earthly reason for either liking me or wanting to help.'

'I've always liked you, Bayard,' Marie murmured, safe in her newfound happiness. 'The past is long buried.'

A hopeful gleam came into his eyes. 'It is like this,' he went on. 'I owe a considerable gambling debt to an Anglo, who I'm pretty sure ran a crooked game. At the moment I simply can't raise the money, and he's pressing me for it – I think he is anxious to leave town before someone else as unlucky as myself calls him out. I have tried to reason with him, but he is threatening to go to my father or Emile about it if I don't pay him in the next three days – and that's the last thing I want to have happen.' He flushed under Marie's steady gaze.

'If he ran a crooked game, why do you have to pay him at all?'

'Because I cannot prove it, and it is, after all, a debt of honour,' he informed her loftily. Oh, these Creoles! Marie thought in despair. 'You see, Clarisse's trust is tied up, and we get the money only in instalments. Similarly, I have several large bills of credit coming in from the plantation Papa gave me, but these will not be in for another month. As soon as they do come in, everything will be all right, but for now I have nothing.'

'Why can't you go to Justin and get an advance on Clarisse's dowry?' Marie demanded.

'And let him know his sister's husband is in debt to a renegade Anglo? No, I couldn't possibly.'

'Well, how about Valerie? She'd help you like a shot.'

'I couldn't burden my sister with something like that,' he explained in hurt tones.

But you don't think twice about burdening *me*, Marie thought grimly. 'Why not give him the bills of credit, then?'

'Because he insists on cash. You see, if I got it from any of our friends here, the news would be bound to get back to the bank in some way. No. Only you can help. If I could borrow it from you, I'd pay it back with interest as soon as the money comes in.'

'How much is it?'

'Five thousand dollars.'

Marie gasped. 'But I don't have that much!'

'No, but you could borrow it,' he said eagerly. 'I'm sure Emile would let you have it with no question.'

A few months before, Marie would have sympathized with him and sent him on his way without further ado, but in her newfound commitment to the world, she hesitated.

'You could do it. I know you could,' he urged her.

'Well, I could try. I can't promise it, but I'll do what I can.'

'I shall be ever indebted to you, Marie,' he said with relief. 'Could you do it right away?'

'I suppose so,' she said with a sigh. 'I suppose so.'

She repaired to the bank. 'Five thousand dollars!' Emile almost yelled at her. 'In *cash*? Are you mad? You don't have that much at the moment.'

'I know. I want to *borrow* it from you,' Marie said. 'Just for a short-term loan, that's all.'

'But what do you want it for?'

'That's my business.'

He looked at her with deep suspicion. 'That Anglo you're living with isn't getting this out of you, is he?'

Marie was outraged. 'Certainly not!' she snapped in a fury.

He looked away from her, but went on doggedly: 'Well, it's been known to happen, and I hear he is a *younger* man.'

247

'Good God!' Marie exploded. 'Is that all you bankers have to do – listen to cheap gossip? If it's of such interest to you and your friends, Nils is eighteen months younger than I am. Does that satisfy you? Anyway, he has nothing to do with this five thousand dollars. And if it will strain the resources of the Valdoux bank too much to lend it to me, just say so, and I'll go to another. I can use the deeds of Rampart Street for collateral easily enough.'

'No,' he muttered unhappily. 'There's no need for that. I'll lend you the money. You should know after all this time that I only have your best interests at heart. Naturally, I thought you might at least have some trust in my discretion.'

'And you in mine!' Marie snapped.

They parted stiffly, both of them aggrieved and cold.

Marie was still smarting when the relieved Bayard came to pick up the money. 'It's the last time I'll ever do anything like this – so don't ask me again,' she fumed at him. 'That stodgy brother of yours is simply beyond belief at times!'

'I'm sorry, Marie, I really am – it'll never happen again,' he said placatingly. Then he rather spoiled the effect by adding, 'I promised Clarisse that.'

On his way out he turned and confided: 'I hear Dominic Montal is in to the same man for ten thousand – God knows how St Regis is going to scrape that up!'

And for the first time in her life Marie felt a twinge of pity for her enemy.

Chapter Twenty-six

Bayard, that man of honour, repaid his debt in due course with grace and gratitude, and Marie repaid hers with far less grace and no gratitude at all to the troubled Emile. Both of them sulked and nursed their hurt feelings throughout the summer. Early that autumn, it was with considerable surprise that Marie answered Patty's summons for 'some gentleman in de parlour' to find Emile standing before the mantel, his hands clasped behind him and an enigmatic expression on his face as he surveyed the exquisite little room. It was the first time he had ever crossed her threshold, and she wondered uncomfortably what dire happening could have prompted his appearance.

After she had greeted him stiffly and motioned him to a chair, which he had refused with a polite bow, he cleared his throat and looked down at her, his mild eyes full of pain. 'I have come to offer you my most profound and abject apology, Marie. I realize now that I have occasioned you the most grievous and unwarranted hurt by my thoughtless remarks, when, as I now know, all you were doing was protecting the honour of my own family. In short, I know about Bayard, and I do most humbly beg your forgiveness.'

'Oh!' Marie said with relief. 'So that's it! However did you find out?'

Emile made a hopeless little gesture. 'Bayard himself. He got in his cups one night – you know how he is – got maudlin, and it all came out. The young fool! He should have known he could have come to me.'

'Perhaps he couldn't bear the thought of the accompanying and inevitable homily,' Marie murmured.

Emile flushed. 'Anyway, I am most profoundly sorry. My family stands indebted to you . . .' He hesitated. 'I also know what you did for Valerie.'

'Don't tell me *she* got in her cups and told you!' Marie said, trying to lighten the atmosphere a little.

'No, of course not.' Emile was once more the total banker. 'But I happened to be keeping a rather close eye on that situation myself. She let a few things slip and I deduced the rest.'

'Oh, poor Emile, what a trial we all are to you!' she gibed.

The pain returned to his eyes. 'I know you think me a stuffy bore, but you must believe me when I say that I and my whole family will always be entirely at your service, to help you in whatever and by whatever means we can. You can always count on me, Marie, for anything.'

She relented. 'I always have, Emile, and . . .' she began to say when the front door burst open and Nils bounded in, brandishing a bottle of wine in one hand and booming what sounded like a Viking mating call. He stopped, disconcerted, when he realized she was not alone, and peered down at the visitor. He looked so bursting with good health and vitality that Emile seemed to dwindle and pale before him, but he stood his ground, unconsciously straightening and throwing out his chest. The two men eyed one another as warily as two strange dogs meeting unexpectedly at a corner.

Suppressing a smile, Marie performed the introductions, and after a minute or two of stilted conversation, Emile took his leave. At the door, however, he turned and said to Nils, 'I feel you should know that my family has a particular interest in Marie's welfare, and that we have every intention of protecting her happiness and well-being at all times. I am glad to have made your acquaintance. Your servant, sir.' And he bowed himself out.

'What was all that about?' Nils asked, puzzled, as he gathered Marie into his arms.

'Oh, nothing,' she murmured, as his lips closed on hers. 'Just Emile being Emile.'

After a satisfactory interval, she drew away from him. 'You're home early,' she chided. 'Luncheon is nowhere near ready.'

He grinned at her impudently. 'Good! Then we have plenty of time – *ja*?' He patted her burgeoning stomach under the concealing folds of the crinoline. 'Soon you grow too big, so we make hay now while the sun still shines.'

She smiled at this expression. 'Oh, I'm sure we'll think of something when the time comes,' Marie murmured as he carried her upstairs.

Sometime later, she lay languidly looking at him as he scrambled back into his clothes, and wondered, as she often wondered, what made her love him so. Perhaps it was because his very simplicity was the ideal complement to her own complexity. He was so direct in his wants and needs: eating hugely, drinking deeply, loving mightily – enjoying life as a child might enjoy a party. There was in him not an ounce of guile, and he was so honestly trusting that she was always amazed.

Only his habit of reading somewhat irked her, for she had never read a book from cover to cover since her convent days, and when he was immersed in a book his attention was totally concentrated on that and not on her. She had asked him one day what fascinated him so in his current book, and he had obliged by an enthusiastic précis of *The Oregon Trail*, apparently by some Northern writer of note.

'It all sounds highly improbable to me,' she had observed. 'How do you know it's not just a bunch of lies? The man's from Boston.'

He had looked at her with absolute amazement. 'Oh, no, it is the truth – it is all true. Why should he lie? The only people who lie are politicians, and they have to – it is part of their trade.'

She sometimes wondered how he managed to survive in the world of business. Not that she much cared; like her mother before her, she had come to the conclusion that no matter what he did, he was her man, and that, if need be, she could always take care of them both.

Nils looked forward to the birth of the child with none of Marie's own doubts or misgivings. 'It will be a good healthy baby,' he had pronounced. 'No trouble.' He had patted her hips happily. 'You're built to be a Mama – good big hips built for the job!' And he had caressed her enlarging bosoms. 'My son never will go hungry, either.'

She wished she could be so sure about things. However, when her time came, just before Christmas, and she was brought to bed, the process was as swift and as uncomplicated as her mother's deliveries had been. She had taken the added precaution of putting herself in a state of self-hypnosis, so she was still a little dazed and exhausted when he bent over her and put the squirming bundle in her arms.

'A lovely girl,' he beamed. 'Just as good. She will look after us when we are old and feeble – *ja*? Next time we will have a boy.'

She looked down with mixed emotions at the child that had been the prime object of this whole affair and smiled weakly. It was a girl-child as fair as a lily, with a fine fuzz of blonde hair over its tiny head. How ridiculous life sometimes was! She knew she could never harm in any way this tiny scrap of humanity, that the whole idea had been a fantastic pipe dream from the start, but a dream that had somehow led her into complete happiness.

Nils wanted to call the baby Marie, which occasioned some argument, since Marie felt there were altogether too many of them around. Finally, they settled on the name Ingrid, after Nils's grandmother; it was a name that removed the infant firmly from the Laveaus and all that they stood for – which Marie thought was all to the good.

The one reaction she had not been prepared for was Patty's. From the first time she had set eyes on the baby, she had been its complete captive. Clutching it to her small breasts, she had crooned to it in some outlandish tongue, and had looked with wild, dilated eyes at Marie. 'Dis chile's fo' me,' she announced. 'Ya ain't never goin' to take dis chile from me. Ah don' belong to ya no mo'. Ah belong to her, an' Ah ain't never goin' to leave her!'

Marie got the familiar stirring sensation of something important happening, so she held her peace. In the days that followed, when the household chores sometimes went neglected, as Patty spent more and more time with the baby, Marie still held it. One possible reason had already occurred to her. 'Patty,' she warned the little slave, 'you must never ever let my mother alone with Ingrid. Is that clear? Above all, you must *not* let her take her.'

'Not dat ole devil woman,' Patty muttered ungratefully. 'No, she ain't goin' to touch a hair o' mah chile's head.'

Marie, trying to analyse her own feelings about her daughter, found to her surprise there weren't many. She was fond of the child, could not conceive of doing it any harm. But, as the tiny mouth sought and clamped on to her nipples, she felt nothing of the overwhelming tenderness and satisfaction her mother had so often mentioned as part of the benefits of motherhood. Instead, she felt this was an intrusion and a depletion of her basic self. Indeed, it was with a feeling of relief that, after she had recovered from the birth and it was evident the baby was thriving, she handed over the bulk of its care to the overzealous and jealous Patty. And she returned to her major interest, her relationship with Nils.

Their perfect idyll continued, and its very perfection aroused in Marie doubts as to whether it could possibly go on this way. For the first time since Etienne's death, she was tempted to probe into the future, and only the remembrance of that terrible outcome restrained her.

Uncomplicated as Nils undoubtedly was, he never ceased to surprise her. One day they had gone on a picnic outing to Bayou St John, Marie wanting to check on the condition of Maison Blanche, which had remained shuttered and empty since her return to the city and the beginning of her life with Nils. She had not wished to linger at the damp-smelling, deserted house, which reproached her silently with remembrances of the past and the present neglect, so they picnicked at some distance from the house by a large weeping willow which reached its sorrowing arms over the still waters of the bayou.

After they had eaten, they made love in its shade, and then she had slept for a while. When she awoke it was to see Nils leaning over the bank scooping up water into a very small cup. She watched lazily as he bore it back with him and set it gingerly down on the ground, seating himself beside it with a little grunt of satisfaction. 'What are you doing?' she inquired.

He cocked one vivid blue eye at her. 'Painting,' he announced, holding up a small sketching block in his large hand. And a miniature of the scene before them, brilliant with colour, sprang into sight.

She gasped. 'Why, that's beautiful, Nils! I never knew you could paint.'

'Oh, *ja*.' He grinned cheerfully. 'Always I paint like this – my Papa, he teach me.'

'But it's really lovely! You have a real talent, Nils! Why don't you do more?'

'Oh, it is only for amusement. There is no money in painting – not in watercolours, anyway. I know, I tried for a time, but when Papa got so sick . . .' He shrugged.

She took the small tablet from him. 'Can I have this when you're finished?'

'Of course. I did it for you. A happy memory of a happy day, *ja*?' he said as he took her in his arms once again.

Marie was returning from having this precious memento framed when she discovered another of Nils's facets she had not yet seen. She entered the house to hear the baby wailing, Patty screaming, and Nils bellowing like an enraged bull. Horrified, she rushed into the kitchen to find a tableau that stopped her dead on the threshold.

Patty was crouching against the sink, her teeth bared, the baby clutched tightly to her breast. Nils was standing over her, his face red and suffused with anger. Marie's mother stood in the centre of the kitchen like some great idol, her face calm and enigmatic.

'Give that baby to her at once!' Nils was thundering at the cowering slave.

'Wait!' Marie called imperiously, and they all turned towards her. For a second the eyes of the two Maries clashed. A slight smile appeared on the lips of the older woman, and she shook her head.

'Never have I heard such nonsense!' Nils thundered at

254

Marie. 'I tell her to give Ingrid to her grandmama to hold, and she runs away with her!'

Patty threw back her head and screamed at him: 'Ya don' know nothin'! Ah ain't goin' to do it, not if ya beat me to death, no, sir! Miz Marie say no, an' Ah ain't goin' to . . .!'

'Quite right,' Marie broke in. 'Patty was only carrying out my orders, Nils. There is absolutely no cause to yell at her.'

'You *ordered* Patty not to give the baby to your own mother? In the name of God, why?' he roared.

'Nothing you would understand, but I am sure my mother does,' Marie said with a cool glance at her.

'You're damned right, I don't!' he growled. 'Never have I heard such a thing! And if my Mama wants her grandchild, what then?'

'That would be quite different,' Marie assured him, still looking levelly at her mother. 'My mother goes much among the sick and dying. I was afraid the baby might catch something from her.'

'Oh!' His roar dropped to a rumble and he looked disconcerted. 'I didn't know that.'

'I merely wished to see my latest grandchild,' Marie Laveau addressed Marie, with the same smile on her lips. 'But I did not wish to create a domestic upheaval. I see you have continued your work on Patty.'

'Yes, indeed.' Marie for the first time smiled back. 'I'm afraid you won't get through that way.'

'I had no intention of trying,' her mother said. 'As usual, you quite mistake my motives.'

'I certainly hope so. You have plenty of other grand-children,' Marie said meaningfully.

'Oh, yes,' her mother murmured, 'but not quite like this one. She shows signs of great beauty, I see, and she has her father's colouring, too.' Her glance was inquiring.

'Yes, that will stand her in good stead when we move to the North, don't you think?'

For the first time her mother looked disconcerted. 'North!' she echoed sharply. 'You are *leaving* New Orleans?'

'Perhaps.' Marie was vague. 'A lot depends on what happens here.'

Her mother seemed to gather herself together. 'Well, there was something else I wanted to discuss with you – a matter of business.' And the two women looked at Nils, who had been following the whole exchange with a puzzled look on his face. Coming to, he hastily excused himself, and Patty took the opportunity to scuttle upstairs with her precious burden.

Marie Laveau waited until they were well out of earshot before she spoke again. Then she said with some urgency, 'I came to ask you to start attending the rites again. I don't want to go on much longer – I don't feel I *can* go on much longer. You'll have to take over soon.'

'Oh?' Marie's tone was noncommittal. 'But surely things have never been better? Why this sudden urge to retire?'

A troubled look crept over her mother's face and she shook her head slowly. 'Things aren't going that well. I don't know what it is, but there has been a great dropping-off at the rites, and there's a sort of restlessness about those who do come. It's hard to describe. Things have never been better materially for most of them, it's true, but it's as if the old ways no longer hold, no longer satisfy them. I think it is time for new blood, new ways. I have had my day. Now it is your turn.'

'This would not have anything to do with the news that I might be going north, by any chance?' Marie asked dryly.

Her mother snorted. 'The day that happens, I *will* be surprised – you would be lost without the two waters, just as I. No, it's as I said – it is time for you to take up your task and obligations.'

'My obligations!' There was savage irony in her tone. 'After I attended the rites the last time, I really did not feel I had any.'

Her mother made a brusque gesture. 'That is the past. Nothing like that will ever happen again. I think you know that as well as I do. Otherwise, why would I be here like this?'

Marie shrugged.

'It's not only for the rites or for myself,' her mother went on. 'It's just as much for you. I've got a strong feeling that you are going to need all your powers and all the force the rites can give you in the near future.' And she stirred uneasily.

'Is that a threat?'

'*No!*' her mother snapped. 'Whatever it is will not be from me. I don't know what it is, but it threatens *you*.'

'And your concern is for me!' Marie sneered.

'Whatever you may think, I have always been concerned for you,' her mother said quietly.

'Well, I'm sorry, but I am no longer interested in all this. Don't count on me for anything. Find someone else. I have had my fill of it, and now I know there is a lot more to my life. I am happy as I am, and I don't intend to do *anything* to change it.' Marie was firm.

Her mother did not argue, but looked worriedly at her. 'Enjoy your happiness, Marie, but when things change, as change they will, remember what I have said, and let me know. When the time comes, I will do what I can to help. If you believe anything, believe that.'

Chapter Twenty-seven

'You meant what you said? We go home and get married, eh?' Nils's tone was eager as he cupped Marie's face between his hands and tilted it up to his.

'Someday,' she said soothingly, as she smoothed back the fair lock that always flopped down over his forehead. 'Someday, darling, but let's not talk of it now. Your job is here, and so is mine, for the present.'

'I could get a new job.' His tone was almost wistful.

'But that would be foolish,' Marie chided gently. 'You like what you do, and there are good prospects. Besides, I know what a heavy burden you carry, what with your parents and now us, and at least here I can help you. If we went north, I would just be a burden.'

'I would like to get married.' His tone was stubborn. 'I would like the world to know you are my wife, that this is my family.'

Marie sighed inwardly. 'Well, we *will* be someday – that I promise,' she comforted. 'But we are so happy and settled as we are, so why change? You are happy, aren't you, Nils?'

'Oh, so happy,' he murmured and drew her closer. 'So happy, my darling. And you?'

'Do you need to ask? I have never been so happy in my life! And nothing is going to change it – nothing!' she whispered as their lips came together.

Since Nils had come into her life, she had put Maison Blanche, with all its profits, firmly behind her. It had led to a drastic cut in her income, but she was beginning to prosper in other areas. Her 'consulting' trade was picking up again now that she was permanently in the city, and Dr Franke was making increasing use of her services, not only for *accouchements* but for other difficult cases. She was fortunate that Nils was so accepting of her activities. He had inquired mildly at the start as to what she did exactly, and, on being told she 'helped' people with her counselling, he had never probed further.

She enjoyed working with Dr Franke. He had a keen mind and would talk to her as an equal about all manner of things as they waited long hours by some sickbed. Many of the things he talked about she did not understand too well, but she liked listening all the same.

He was currently very concerned about the political situation, which to her up to now had only been of interest in so far as the internal politics of New Orleans were concerned. She had helped so many councilmen, so many state senators, to win elections – partly by her counsel, partly by her contacts – that she felt herself as a power in the land, but she had never concerned herself in the least with the issues involved.

'Take this fellow Lincoln,' Dr Franke said worriedly. 'It seems to me that he may well be elected in November – and the South will never stand for it. A Republican, and with his known stand on slavery! I'm afraid if he wins, states in the South will start to secede from the Union, and Louisiana may well be one of them.'

'What does that matter?' Marie shrugged. 'Maybe we'd be better off on our own – let the North go its way, and we'll go ours.'

'It's not that simple. It *does* matter – it could even lead to war.'

'What – over the slaves? Nobody would ever fight over that!' she said uneasily.

'The slaves are only part of it. There are so many other important issues involved – the Union for one,' he worried on. 'I only hope there are enough men of good sense around not to let it come to that.'

'So do I!' she agreed with fervour.

In November Dr Franke's prediction became fact, and the republican Lincoln was elected. And in December, just before Christmas, the first of the Southern states – South Carolina – seceded.

'Do you think anything is going to happen here?' she

asked Nils anxiously as they made preparations for Ingrid's first birthday and their second Christmas together.

'Oh, there's a lot of talk about secession around, but that's all it is – talk,' Nils said comfortingly. 'Everything will be all right. You'll see.'

Christmas had been so happy and peaceful that Marie was quite unprepared for the next twist of Fate, which came pounding on her door just before New Year's. Her mother's man-servant, his chest heaving, stood on the doorstep. 'Come quick!' he gasped. 'The Delambes' house is on fire! Your mother say to come!'

Marie hurried towards Decatur Street, and she fought her way through the crowd that had gathered to see the tall figure of her mother outlined against the flames and smoke of the burning shop. 'How bad is it?' she shouted above the commotion.

'Bad!' Her mother thrust the quivering figure of Claire at her. 'Hold on to her! Her grandfather got her out and tried to go back for his wife – they're bringing him out now.'

Marie clutched the sobbing Claire to her, and she pressed the girl's head into her shoulder as she saw two men bearing a smoke-blackened groaning figure out of the flames. Her mother rushed to them, calling for water. Marie could see her sloshing water all over the smouldering clothing as the men held the writhing figure. Finally, she straightened from her task and beckoned to Marie, who gently disengaged herself from the shivering girl and handed her over to Mama Antoine, who had appeared at her side. 'Look after her till I get back,' she charged. And she hurried to her mother's side.

'It's no use,' the older woman whispered. 'He's burned so badly, he can't be saved. I've put him under so he'll not feel the pain, but it's only a matter of minutes, I'd say.'

'How on earth did it happen?'

Her mother shrugged. 'Possibly Madame Delambe was looking for Jacqueline in the attic with a lamp – she did that sometimes, I know. Perhaps she fell and the lamp shattered and set the place on fire. I know he had time to send Claire out, and then he tried to get to her, poor devil! You'd better get back to Claire. She isn't hurt, but she is upset. You can take care of that. I can manage here.'

There was a faint groan, and they looked down to see Monsieur Delambe lift his head and open his eyes. They fixed on Marie with a mute appeal, and his blackened lips worked, but no sound came out. Then the eyes glazed into a final, startled stare and the head dropped back.

Marie Laveau knelt down and felt the pulse at his neck. 'He's gone,' she announced, then got up brushing off her skirt. 'All right, I'll do what has to be done here. You look after Claire.' Then she dropped her voice. 'If you do not make it obvious, you may look over to your left in the crowd, and you will see someone who seems to have taken a particular interest in all this and who is now looking at Claire. So I repeat, look after her.'

Marie looked cautiously around, but she needed no further directions. She saw a familiar figure standing in a doorway, an expression of satisfaction on the long, pale face. It was St Regis.

She hurried back to Claire, who looked at her with sad, frightened eyes. 'My grandfather . . .' she faltered.

Marie took the small plain face in her hands and gazed deeply into her eyes. 'He is free of all pain.'

'But how is he?'

'My dear, he is with your grandmother and mother, where I am sure you would want him to be, rather than here, ruined and crippled.'

Tears welled up in Claire's dark eyes. 'Then I have no one left,' she whispered, 'no one at all.'

'Oh, yes, you have,' Marie said with decision. 'You have me – as long as either of us lives, you will have me.'

'But . . .' faltered Claire.

'No "buts",' Marie said. 'I promised your mother I would care for you as my own, and that I will do. My home is now your home, and your well-being is my concern. Come let us go. There is nothing more we can do here.'

She put her arm around the thin shoulders of the sobbing girl and moved her gently through the crowd. As she went, she looked around for St Regis, but he was no longer to be seen. I wonder, she thought with sudden apprehension, could it all be starting again?

Claire's entry into the life of Rampart Street necessitated some adjustments. Nils accepted the newcomer with his customary amiability, but the change from an idyllic two-some to a *ménage à trois* gave Marie many a selfish pang. Not that it was all bad; the fact of having to be a little more discreet about their passion for one another was actually an added enticement – the kisses stolen behind doors were particularly sweet, and there was a delightful air of conspiracy in messages that now had to be sent with eyes and hands rather than words. It was all greatly helped by Claire's own character. She was sweet without being sickly, and was an expert in the art of diplomatic self-effacement, so the transition was as smooth as any such major change could be.

Another shock lay in store for Marie after the Delambe burial. Emile had rather surprisingly turned up to pay his last respects and had drawn her aside. 'I've something for Claire,' he explained in an undertone. 'When you've a free moment, come to the office and I'll tell you about it.'

She had gone, more than a little puzzled, because – as far as she knew – what little money there had been left by the Delambes had been swallowed up by the joint funeral.

Emile was at his most solemn and pompous best. 'I have here a credit on the bank for Claire Montal Delambe in the amount of one thousand dollars. If you need it for her upkeep now, of course, I will apprise her of the situation and see that an appropriate allotment is made. However, I suggest, if you do not stand in need of the money, that I just pay her the interest to cover her clothing and incidentals, and that the capital remain intact to provide a dowry when the time for her marriage arrives.'

Marie was taken aback. 'Oh, you shouldn't have done that, Emile! Really, it's too generous of you ...' she began.

But he cut in quickly: 'This has nothing to do with me. I am merely serving as banker and messenger in this.'

262

'If not you, then who?' Marie was amazed.

His eyes dropped and his fair skin coloured. 'Dominic Montal.'

'Dominic! Where on earth did he get a thousand dollars? Surely not from St Regis!' Marie gasped.

Emile shook his head. 'No. He came in several days ago, dropped the money in cash on my desk, said he'd had a good night at the tables for a change, that it was to go to Claire, and that on no account was St Regis to learn of it.'

'Does that mean he has finally accepted Claire?' Marie said with some eagerness.

Again Emile shook his head. 'No. Don't expect too much, Marie. His exact words, to my recollection, were: "Give this to the poor little bastard for old time's sake. Lady Luck smiled last night, and perhaps if I do some good with it, she'll go on smiling."' Emile sighed. 'Anyway, it's a bit late for it to do the child any good, isn't it? There's not much left of the Dominic you knew.' Almost as an afterthought, he added, 'I've been trying to persuade my sister to separate from him for some time now. The situation is quite hopeless, but so far I have been unable to make her see that.'

'Poor Emile,' Marie murmured automatically, but her mind was busy elsewhere. 'Well, we'll do as you suggest with the money for the time being. Claire will be going on to school until she is sixteen. Then we'll decide whether to use the money for an apprenticeship or not. I certainly do not wish to see her follow in her mother's footsteps.' And there was pain in her voice.

The knowledge that she was not a penniless orphan had a cheering effect on Claire's spirits, and the household settled down to a happy tranquillity, which contrasted sharply to the atmosphere of feverish activity and exaltation that had the rest of the city in its grip.

In February, Louisiana had seceded from the Union, along with five more Southern states. There was much talk of a Southern Confederation of States, but Louisiana, in her wealth and pride, decided to go whole-hog and set herself up as an independent Republic; and New Orleans, that belle of cities, started to think of itself as the Paris of a new France. Carnival had never been gayer or more frenzied. Its colour was added to by the vivid new regimental uniforms that the men of the city were donning like so many peacocks. Each little section and clique was trying to outdo the other in the gorgeousness of its plumage, as many disparate bands were formed for the defence of the new Republic.

No one took it very seriously, and the ladies of New Orleans were loud in complaint that the new uniforms quite eclipsed their own Carnival ball gowns, and they muttered at the conceit and horrendous expenditures of their menfolk. Since it did not really concern her, Marie listened to their complaints with wry amusement, and only worried about the fact that the growing anti-Northern feeling in the city might be bad for Nils and his business activities.

She secretly wished everyone would calm down, for the nervous excitement was getting to Nils, who talked more and more about moving to the North, with all its advantages. It was a decision she did not want to be pushed into, and she was glad of Claire's presence in the household, which would make such a tremendous change even more difficult. Nevertheless, she had the uneasy feeling that a crisis was approaching, and she braced herself for it.

When it came, however, early one April morning, it was not in the shape she expected. The household was quiet: Claire at school, Nils at work, Jethro absent on one of his many mysterious errands, Patty absorbed with the baby. So when the knock came at the door, Marie answered it herself, anticipating a client.

A tall, elderly figure stood on the doorstep, clad in black broadcloth of an old-fashioned Spanish cut, with a dark beaver hat of Spanish design crowning the grey straight hair. The face beneath the hat was as brown and as seamed as a walnut, but the dark eyes were bright and imperious in their glance, as the man stood silently gazing at her.

Taking him for a businessman seeking Nils, Marie said, 'I'm afraid if it's Mr Andersen you seek, he has already gone to his office on Canal Street – number one hundred and ten.'

The man spoke, his words slow and deliberate, as one using a strange tongue. 'I do not seek this man. I came for you, Marie Laveau. I am Don Thomé di Sonora – your father.'

Chapter Twenty-eight

'The whole situation is impossible – it's the last thing in the world I expected,' Marie muttered angrily, as she paced back and forth in her mother's room. 'It's so impossible as to be absurd!' Then, inconsequentially: 'I had no idea he would be so *old*.'

Her mother, who had been watching her with a certain degree of wariness, shrugged. 'He can't he *that* old,' she murmured placatingly. 'Let me see, I was thirty-three when you were born, and he couldn't have been more than ten years older. So he must be in his early seventies.'

'He *looks* older than the hills,' Marie said again.

'And what exactly does he want of you?'

Marie threw up her hands in an angry gesture of despair. 'The same thing he wanted of you – to go back with him to the desert. His powers fade, he says; he needs me. *Me*, mind you, not Nils. When he heard there was a baby, he very condescendingly said I could bring her along. Good of him, I said, but no, thanks! And he just ignores it! Keeps right on babbling that the French are coming and there will be ill times in Sonora and that I'm needed by *my* people! I ask you! As if there wasn't enough trouble at the moment. I don't know what I'm going to do. I've told him "No" a thousand times, but he just won't accept it. He says he'll stay in the city until I change my mind or events change it for me. He frightens me, he seems so *certain*.'

'Yes, that sounds like him.' Her mother was calm. 'But there's no need to panic, you know. You're as strong as he is, maybe even stronger by this time.'

'I've a good mind to throw it all up and do what Nils wants – go north as soon as possible,' Marie said angrily.

The wary look returned to Marie Laveau's eyes. 'That's not a decision I could make in a hurry,' she cautioned.

'Your life is here, Marie, like it or not – and so are your powers.'

Marie snorted. 'My life is with Nils – that's all that matters to me. I don't care about my powers any more – they've been more of a burden than a blessing, anyway.'

Her mother raised her eyebrows but said only, 'I should wait for a while until you see what else he has on his mind. Where's he staying?'

'Somewhere down by the waterfront – I don't know exactly. He made a point of saying *he'd* contact me, and that I should not seek him out.' She shot a sudden suspicious glance at her mother. 'You haven't seen him, have you?'

'No – I doubt he would come here.' Her mother met her gaze levelly. 'What was between us was finished long ago. He *can* be faced – it is important to remember that.'

Marie sighed in exasperation. 'Oh, yes – I'm not afraid for myself, but I am anxious not to have any collision between him and Nils.' Her face softened. 'Nils would not understand; he knows nothing of that side of me.'

Her mother looked at her with something like pity in her eyes. 'Perhaps, then, it is time that you told him,' she said quietly. 'If he loves you as much as he appears to, it will make no difference – it didn't with Louis.'

Marie looked troubled. 'But that was different – very different.'

'No, my dear, it wasn't – you're not unique, you know. Nor is he.' But they pursued the subject no further.

The situation got no better. Every time she went out, Marie felt haunted by Don Thomé's presence. Sometimes she thought she saw the black-clad figure watching from a distance; at others she would be startled to find him suddenly at her side in the spring sunshine, talking of all manner of strange things, most of which she did not understand in the slightest, but talking as if it was just part of a long continuing dialogue between them.

'It is important to realize,' he had informed her, 'that while your potential is good, you have still a great deal to learn before you come to the second circle of power. When we get back to the desert, I will teach you – you are a woman, so it will be easier than with many. It has come to me that you have been on the wrong path in the past, and that now you are on no path at all. This must be righted. You must give up what you have been. That is but the mere play of children – dangerous children, like your mother, who is still a child. The path you must follow is the one I have chosen, the right path that leads through the crack in the world to other worlds far surpassing this one. But you must beware of your mother.'

Only this last made any sense to Marie, and that she didn't need to be told.

The gaiety of Carnival, the gaiety of the city, mocked her; in the midst of all the reckless lightheartedness, she felt beset and overwhelmed by her problems. She became moody and depressed.

Nils, sensing the depression, if unaware of the cause, sought means to cheer her up. 'Let's go to a dance – it's time we got out more. Go get yourself a beautiful new ball gown, and we'll have dinner at Antoine's and go on to a dance at the St Louis Hotel. It will be good, *ja*? April twelfth they are having one.'

His eagerness reached out and touched her heart, as it always did, and with the best spirit she could muster, she smiled and agreed.

Dearest Nils, of course he had been right, she thought, as she regarded him mistily over the rim of her cognac glass. Under the warmth of the wine, Antoine's candlelight and Nils's unstinting gallantries, her problems had thawed and melted away. How ridiculous she had been to let herself be so intimidated by an old man who had no place in her life at all! She was enjoying herself, she was enjoying life; *this* was how it was meant to be, and she looked forward to the dance with an eagerness she had not felt in years.

As they crossed the black and white marble foyer of the St Louis Hotel, the excitement of the music and laughter reached out to greet her. The slave block, with its reminder of the auctions that still took place there, had been discreetly

268

removed for this gala occasion, and fashionably dressed couples were strolling up and down its length, cooling themselves off after their activities in the densely packed ballroom. The huge cut-glass chandelier shed the light of a thousand candles on the brilliant and hectic scene, and the ornately liveried slaves, perspiring freely, hurried around with trays laden with glasses and bottles.

With a delighted grin, Nils swept her on to the dance floor and the hectic gaiety engulfed them. For a while she knew only the music and the secure feeling of his arms around her. Then she began to note the elements that made up the kaleidoscope of the background.

How many of the new uniforms there were, she noted, each one more variegated that the last. There were even a few grey ones – those of the new joint army the Confederation of the newly seceded states was trying to form, and these lent a more sober note to the proceedings. Men clad in the customary black and white of yesteryear were few, and she recognized most of those so attired as confreres of Nils – businessmen from the North. The worry started to return, but she shrugged it off. What children men were: Always dressing up and wanting to fight – just as Etienne had been. Again she had come up against a thought from the past she did not like. She hastily switched her thoughts elsewhere.

Many of the black-coated men had greeted them, and some of the gay peacocks had acknowledged their presence civilly enough; only the few Creoles she recognized seemed to draw away, but whether this was on Nils's account or because of her, she was hard put to say. At one point she thought she saw the familiar, ugly face of Aristide Sautelle, who was looking worried, but when they tried to dance towards him in the crowd, he was no longer to be seen.

After a champagne break and a discreet kiss from Nils behind a potted palm, they were just sweeping back into the excitement of a Viennese waltz when there was a slight commotion on the orchestra platform, and the music faltered and scraped into silence. A fair young man in a very flashy light blue uniform with a scarlet sash was up on the platform, waving his hands excitedly and trying to get the attention of the crowd. It took him several minutes to reduce the deafening roar of chatter and laughter to an excited murmuring. Then he called out loudly, 'Silence! Please! I have news, great news! The news most of us have been waiting for. I have the honour to inform you that Brigadier-General Pierre Gustave Toutant Beauregard of the Army of the Confederation, leading troops of our sister state of South Carolina, this day has fired upon and captured Fort Sumter! The Yankee garrison has surrendered. Gentlemen, we are at *war*!'

There was a moment of stunned silence. Then a tremendous roar of cheering rippled and spread through the crowded hall, drowning out the band, which had struck up raggedly the song that everyone had been humming the past few months – 'Dixie'.

Marie looked at the scene in silent disbelief, then up at Nils with panic-stricken eyes. 'War!' she gasped. '*War?* Oh, that *fool* Beauregard!'

The room started to whirl and darken around her, and there was the sound of roaring, cascading waters in her ears. Her vision blurred, and she closed her eyes, trying to steady her mind against the sudden chaos. When she opened them again, her heart almost ceased to beat, for she was looking at an entirely different scene.

She was still in the ballroom, but now there was absolute silence: nobody spoke, nobody moved. The women stood like so many waxen dummies, their arms still raised as if they clasped their partners – but most of them stood clutching at empty air, and those who did so were shrouded in black, their faces draped in black veils. In the middle of the ballroom her father stood beckoning to her. *You see how it is.* His voice sounded in her mind. *There is no path here, no path at all.*

She looked unbelievingly around, her terror rising. 'Nils,' she faltered, 'Nils?' She turned towards the shelter of his arms, but he was no longer by her side; he had disappeared. 'Nils!' she shrieked, and looked down at herself. She, like so many of the others, was shrouded in black. 'Nils!' she screamed, and a new darkness came upon her, blotting out everything as the terror engulfed her.

'Nils!' she cried, and opened her eyes to see his worried face bending over her as she lay in a crumpled heap on the floor of the ballroom.

'I'm here, dearest, right here.' His arms were around her, lifting her up as she clutched him, moaning softly. The few people who had gathered around, seeing that she was all right, drifted off towards the main crowd, which was clustered densely around the young man, who was still giving excited details of the momentous news he bore.

'It's all right, dearest,' Nils assured her in a worried tone. 'You just fainted, that's all. I'll get you out of here; we'll go home. This is no place for us. You will be all right if I set you down?' She nodded and buried her face in his coat, still clinging tightly to him as he set her gently on her feet. 'You all right?' he said again, anxiously.

'Yes ... no ... for God's sake, let's get away from here! Oh, I can't bear it, I can't bear it!' she moaned, writhing in his grasp.

'Marie, for the love of God, get hold of yourself!' His tone was sharp. 'There's no need to get so upset. There have been wars before and people have survived them. It's not the end of the world, you know.'

'Oh, but it *is*,' she whispered, looking up at him with despairing eyes. 'It *is* the end of my world.'

'But it is not the end of mine,' he said firmly. 'So now I make my mind up. No more argument. We go home, pack up, and we go north. We get married and all this is finished.'

She clutched at this straw of hope. 'Oh, yes, yes! Anything you say, so long as you never leave me, never go to this insane war.'

He looked a little uncomfortable. 'A man must do what he has to do, my dearest, but there is plenty of time to talk of that later, when we have taken care of our own affairs.'

They hurried home through streets that were seething with the crowds. On some street corners bonfires were burning on which Marie could see the smouldering remnants of Union flags, as people laughed and danced around them.

Jubilation filled the air, but in Marie's heart there was only cold fear. They must get away, they must escape from the Fate that had been shown to her. Somehow it had to be diverted from its course – there *had* to be a way ... Her mind darted in a dozen different directions like a frightened, trapped animal. But as she turned to go into the house, she saw, outlined against the bonfire at the end of the street, a familiar figure that watched and waited. *There is no path*, it whispered in her mind.

Chapter Twenty-nine

After intoxication comes the hangover; so it was with New Orleans. The wild jubilation and excitement brought forth by the news of Fort Sumter exhausted itself, leaving people ill-tempered and unsure. They were at war – a war they were going to win, certainly – but no one knew exactly where this war was to be fought, or how, or, for that matter, who they were going to be fighting. Lacking clear guidelines to define the enemy, people made up their own rules, which boiled down to the simplistic view that those native to New Orleans were beyond reproach and should stay: those not so blessed were the enemy and should go, bearing with them nothing more than they brought in. This was of small comfort to the divided household on Rampart whose sole thought was escape.

'They are letting Northerners and their families go,' Nils reported unhappily, 'but they tell me I must wind up my affairs and leave by the end of the week, taking with me no more than the trunk and two valises with which I came. Oh, if only we had gone sooner, as I wished, and got married! Then there would be no trouble.'

'It's not much use talking in "ifs",' snapped Marie, whose own fears had not improved her temper. 'We'll just have to get married here, that's all.'

Nils looked at her in astonishment. 'But you told me that was impossible!'

'There is one way,' Marie said slowly. 'I did not mention it before because it is so demeaning, and, in your case, so ridiculous. But it has been done a few times, to my knowledge.'

'What is it, then?' Nils demanded eagerly. 'If we are legally married, they cannot stop us from leaving. Oh, *why* didn't you tell me this before? You know I would do anything in the world to make you mine!'

'White men have married women of colour before by declaring *they* have coloured blood. There is an old story about a man who pricked his wife's finger and sucked the blood so that he would not be lying – whether it's true or not, people have done it since. You would have to say you were coloured.'

Nils grinned weakly. 'Me? Coloured? Of course I will do it, but who will believe it?'

'That's just it – in the present circumstances we would have to find the right man and the right time. But I believe I *might* know someone who would.'

'Then let's go right now.'

'No. The man I have in mind is very old and feeble, but he's not completely stupid, so we'll have to do it at night, when he cannot see you clearly. I'll have to spin him some story – but leave that to me. In the meantime, there is other urgent business I have to take care of; if we are all to get away and start over, we'll have to have money.'

'I have some put away,' Nils said hesitantly.

'But nowhere near enough to see all of us through. We'll have to take Claire and Patty and Jethro with us.'

'All of them? But how on earth would you ever get Patty away? I understand they are keeping a very tight hand on slaves just now – they're afraid there will be wholesale runaways once the slaves realize what is happening.'

'I'm going to free her – that's another thing I'll have to see to.' Marie's voice was heavy with worry. 'I hope that will be enough to get her past any authorities we might run into. Not that I anticipate leaving the city with flags flying and trumpets blaring – we're going to have to rely on Jethro for the getaway.'

'Jethro!'

'Yes, Jethro,' Marie said vexedly. Sometimes she found Nils's naïve astonishment at the world more than a little trying. 'Obviously, I've never made an issue of it, but I know he has been concerned in getting slaves out to the North through the Underground Railroad ever since he's worked for me. If he can do it for them, he can do it for us. He came to me yesterday and said he could not stay here much longer; things are getting too dangerous. I told him to wait just a few days more, because we'd probably need his help. Now that you know, you'd best talk it over with him. I've no idea how he does it, but try and find out how we are to travel and what we'll be able to take with us. I've got to go and see Emile after I've taken care of Patty's manumission papers.'

The interview with Emile was not an easy one. 'Take and sell everything?' he yelled. 'Are you out of your mind? Do you know what you're saying?'

'Everything but the three properties – and I want it in either silver dollars, gold, or jewellery, and as quickly as you can get it. That goes for Claire's money, as well.'

'But, for God's sake, why? Do you realize what a loss you'll take, selling now, when everything is so uncertain?'

'Because I'm leaving, that's why!' Marie exploded. 'And I don't give a damn what losses I take! My life here is finished!'

Emile's pale face had gone a shade paler. 'You're going away with Nils Andersen?' he asked hesitantly.

'I'm leaving for the North with my family,' Marie said grimly, 'and nothing and nobody is going to stop me.'

He picked up a bronze letter-opener he had on the desk and balanced its point delicately on the polished surface. 'You realize you are asking me to connive in what amounts to an act of treason against the South,' he said slowly. 'The South – which is your homeland, after all, and which will need every penny and the support of every man, woman, and child if it is to come through this war at all.'

'I did not ask for this insane war, and I am only asking for what is mine,' she said heatedly. 'And, for the love of God, spare me the usual lecture, Emile. I have neither the time nor the patience to listen to it. It's all very well for you to sit on your high Creole pedestal being patriotic. But just tell me, what can the South honestly expect from people of my kind? Anyway, I don't give a damn about issues. All I want is to get away and be allowed to live a normal life somewhere, preferably as far away from the war as I can get.

275

You've talked a lot about your obligations to me in the past – this is the showdown. Did you mean it, or was this just another polite Creole placebo to the lower orders?'

A dull flush mounted the pale cheeks. 'I am well aware of my obligations to you, Marie,' he said stiffly, 'and against my conscience and against my principles I will try and carry out your orders, though you cannot expect miracles. I will do what I can.'

'That is all I'm asking,' she said. And she got up to leave, but feeling she had been a little harsh, she turned and said in a gentler tone, 'And what about you? What are you going to do?'

'The same as usual.' His tone was bitter, and his eyes, as he looked up at her, were full of frustrated anger. 'Bayard and Lamont have already left to join the Army of the Confederacy. It was decided at a family council that since my father is far from well and is preoccupied elsewhere, it would be my responsibility to look after the families of the absent and to guard the family interests. Justin, too, will probably be leaving shortly – so that will mean looking after Valerie and her family, as well. My father is thinking of offering his services to Jefferson Davis, and will probably go off to Montgomery or Richmond or wherever they decide to locate the Southern capital. I shall remain to keep the home fires burning.'

'Oh, poor Emile, I'm sorry,' Marie said softly.

He looked at her with a face as hard as granite for a moment, then said in a dismissive tone, 'Well, I'll send word when the money is ready. It will probably take a couple of days.' And he turned back to his work.

Later that evening four cloaked figures slipped into the Church of Our Lady of Guadalupe on North Rampart Street and gathered at a dimly lit side altar. The group consisted of Marie and Nils, a girl, Esther Santiago, who had been one of the first group at Maison Blanche, and her coloured husband. She was a girl who Marie knew could keep her mouth shut, and she had agreed to act as a witness to the wedding.

They were presently joined by the shuffling, bent figure of

the priest, Père Jacques, who was inclined to be querulous because of the lateness of the hour. His grumblings were pacified by Esther – who was one of his parishioners – and by the sight of a substantial offering which Marie had promised him earlier that day. So, Nils Andersen, coloured, of North Rampart Street, was united with Marie Laveau, coloured, of 516 Bourbon Street, with a maximum of dispatch and a minimum of ceremony.

As Marie waited in an agony of impatience for the old man to make out the certificate of marriage, which she had insisted they must have, Esther volunteered to sign the church register. She looked at Marie, who nodded and raised a warning finger. Esther sneaked a quick glance at the old man, who was peering closely at his paper as he wrote slowly in the dim candlelight, and then hastily turned over several pages of the old book. She looked at Marie and nodded. And, with a dig in the ribs to Nils, Marie took the quill and wrote firmly: 'Marie Laveau Andersen 15 April 1859,' at the bottom of the page. She pointed the date out to Nils and grimaced at him, and he followed her example, a puzzled frown on his face, and the other two quickly added theirs.

Then Esther stuck the book under Père Jacques's nose. 'Here, Father,' she said cheerfully. 'We're almost done, and you can get to your well-earned rest.'

'I haven't finished this,' he said peevishly, but took the quill and scribbled his signature beneath theirs.

'Oh, you just need the date on the certificate,' Esther said with another meaningful glance at Marie. 'Here, let me help!' And she quickly filled it in for him.

The old man straightened up with a relieved sigh. 'May your marriage be blessed and fruitful,' he muttered automatically, and after handing them the precious slip of paper, he shuffled off to douse the candles on the altar.

'What was that for?' Nils whispered.

'To prevent any queries about Ingrid's baptismal certificate, if we have any run-ins with the authorities,' Marie whispered back. 'There's nothing they can quibble about now.'

She could feel him grinning at her in the darkness. 'You

think of everything, Mrs Andersen,' he said with admiration. 'I have got me a wonderful wife.'

As they made love that night she was almost frantic in her desire for him. Only in that other being could she escape for those few precious moments from the terrors and fears that held her own soul and mind so firmly in their grip. Her needs and demands were so urgent that Nils was moved to unusual reproach.

'Dearest!' he whispered in the darkness. 'No man could ask more of his wedding night, but you are going on as if there will be no tomorrow. Let's rest now – or I will have nothing left for the rest of our lives!'

But long after he had fallen into exhausted slumber, Marie lay awake gazing unhappily at the dim gleam of the silver stars in the *ciel-de-lit* of the great bed. The myriad problems of the escape, the myriad fears, boiled in her mind. The fear that was paramount, that blotted out all the others, was the tremendous feeling inside her that the ties binding her to the Two Waters were so strong that she would be unable to break free . . .

Certain practical matters had been taken care of: she had asked Marie-Philome to keep an eye on Rampart Street and check on Maison Blanche once in a while; Patty's manumission papers had been obtained, albeit with some difficulty; Jethro had informed her that they would need something bigger for the flight than her own small gig, but he had found a carriage they could pick up at the last minute from the livery stable on Governor Nicholl's Street. The mechanics of the escape were now in order, but there was still no sign of the money, and their time was running out.

In desperation she went to the Valdoux counting house on Royal. Emile, grim-faced, greeted her and went to the big iron safe in the corner of his office. He brought forth several leather pouches and plunked them down on the desk before her. 'These are your entire liquid cash assets in silver dollars.'

'How much?'

'In total, two thousand. I'm going to need several more days to collect the rest from your other credits, which are going for just a fraction of what you paid for them. You realize that?'

'But we haven't *got* several more days! Nils must be out of the city the day after tomorrow. Can't you hurry things up? Or, better yet, could you send the money on to me in Chicago?'

Emile snorted. 'Not a hope! Send money into enemy territory? Impossible! I'm doing my damnedest as it is.'

'How much more will there be?'

'At best, around three thousand dollars.'

Marie thought frantically. Two thousand dollars in hand, one of which rightfully belonged to Claire; it was very little. If she had the rest of the money, it would give them a fighting chance in their new life. 'And is there no other way to get it out of Louisiana?' she appealed, with a dreadful sense of helplessness.

'Other than taking it yourself? None,' Emile said sombrely.

'Well, I'll have to think about it – I suppose I could travel separately.'

He did not reply to that.

As she left the office, a well-known figure that had haunted her dreams appeared beside her. 'The time is ripening,' Don Thomé observed. 'It will soon be necessary for me to go. You will, of course, be coming, too. We shall have much to do on our return to Sonora.'

Marie's overstretched nerves snapped. 'Father!' she screamed at him. 'For the last time, I am not going *anywhere* with you! I am leaving New Orleans with my husband and baby, so for God's sake, leave me alone!'

He looked at her and shook his head firmly. She could feel the power behind the black, deep-seated eyes. 'I am afraid I cannot allow that. I will have to stop you, all of you, if need be, though I would hate to spend so much energy on such an unworthy endeavour.'

'You can't! You can't threaten me like that! You wouldn't do that! Not to innocent people!'

'*You* cannot go,' he persisted. 'I do not care about the rest, or the two dead men who go with you.'

His words struck fresh terror in her heart, but they served to make up her divided mind. She would send the others on ahead, get the rest of the money, and then have a final show-down with her father. If it came to a struggle between them, she felt confident enough in her own powers, but she would not risk the others . . .

Her decision, so agonizing to make, was even more agonizing to carry out. 'Come *back* for you!' Jethro had rumbled. 'God knows, it's going to be difficult enough making one trip – but to come *back*? It's damned near suicide!'

'I could meet you away from the city – at Maison Blanche,' she had said desperately. 'There must be ways out through the bayous. Please, Jethro, please, I beg you! I simply can't go with the rest of you!'

Grudgingly, he had said he would try, but that it might take as much as a month, or even longer.

'Anything you say,' she had agreed, 'anything. I will wait at Maison Blanche for however long it takes.'

She had tried to explain to Patty about her new freedom but had made little impression on her. Patty had taken the precious papers with complete indifference. 'Ah ain't free, Miz Marie. Ah belong to this chile, not to ya. Where she go, Ah go 'til mah dyin' day. Ya got no cause to worry 'bout her.'

She had taken Claire aside and given her the thousand dollars. 'Try and keep it intact for your dowry, my dear, but if things get bad, use it – I'll make it up to you some way. And, Claire, though I know Patty will guard Ingrid with her life, if need be, you will have to be *my* eyes and ears with the baby. Promise me that, will you – that you will send word as often as you can, and look after Ingrid, as well, for as long as need be?'

Claire had looked at her with troubled eyes. 'Of course I will – but, Tante Marie, you are talking as if you will not be with us.'

'Oh, of course I will, my dear!' Marie cried in terror, clutching the frail body to her. 'As soon as possible – but, until then, promise me?'

She had promised.

Marie had left the worst until last. '*No!*' Nils exploded. 'I will not leave here without you – never!'

'But you *must*! There is no danger to my staying here, yet much for you. Jethro has promised to return for me. The rest of the money will be important for our future, and there is one other important matter I have to take care of. It will only be for a little while longer,' she pleaded.

They had argued themselves into exhaustion, and it was only after she had burst into hysterical distraught tears that he had finally and grudgingly agreed to accede to her wishes. 'But this is the last time,' he warned. 'From now on *I* say what is to be – I make the decisions for my family.'

'Oh, yes, my darling,' she wept. 'That is all I want of life – that and you.'

The parting was so agonizing that Marie could scarcely believe the heart could feel such pain and still go on beating. After packing the sobbing Claire and Patty into the over-loaded carriage, Nils had turned for a final embrace. 'Oh, God, I do not like this!' he mumbled, as he strained her to him. 'Let it go, my dearest – come with me now! The money does not matter – nothing is more important than us.'

'I know, my dearest, I know – but do not make it any more difficult for me than it is,' she wept.

'We'd best be getting off,' Jethro interrupted. 'It'll be dawn before long, and we'll have to be clear of the city by then.'

'Go, then, go, for pity's sake,' she pleaded.

With a groan, Nils gave her one last, lingering kiss, then climbed up beside Jethro.

Tears streaming down her face, Marie watched everything she held dear go out of sight. Then she stumbled through the green door, kicked it shut, and fell in a dead faint.

Chapter Thirty

She had spent herself with crying and now numbly awaited the message from Emile. There was nothing else to do but wait, for all her heart and mind were on some unknown road heading northward. She still shrank from the final confrontation with her father and was tempted, once the money was in her hands, to run, to hole up, hidden and unseen, until Jethro returned for her.

She was on her way to Emile's when a small troup of horsemen clattered by, all clad in the grey uniform of the Confederacy. As they swept past her, she recognized the long, tight face, the amber eyes blazing, of St Regis. So, her enemy was off to war – she found comfort in that.

She remarked on it with some relief when she saw Emile.

'Yes, since it is out of the question for Dominic to go, St Regis has gone to uphold the honour of the Montals,' he said tightly. 'I imagine he will make an excellent soldier.'

'And it leaves you with an extra burden,' she remarked softly, 'since, from what you have said, I doubt whether Dominic will be capable of looking after the Montal womenfolk.'

Emile shrugged. 'What is one more burden, after all?' But his voice was weary. 'I have liquidated everything I could. The total is just over three thousand: a little in gold, some silver dollars, and one or two choice stones, as you instructed. I can only caution you to conceal it both now and on your journey. With so many of the responsible citizens draining out of the city, there is bound to be an upswing among the lawless elements.'

'Thank you. I'll be careful,' she assured him.

'Then I imagine this is good-bye,' he said stiffly. 'After the war is finished, perhaps you would let me know what you propose to do about the properties. Until then, I will at least collect your share of the Bourbon Street house for you. As to the others, I presume you have made your own arrangements.'

She nodded. 'Yes, I'm afraid it is good-bye, Emile. I will be in the city only a day or so longer. Then I go to Maison Blanche.'

'But I thought you were desperate to go,' he said in surprise.

'The others have gone ahead. There was no other choice. I'll join them later.'

'Then you're alone?' His expression became concerned.

'Being along is not a novelty to me,' she said in a choked voice. 'I have been so before.'

'Well, I wish you'd seriously consider staying either with your mother or one of your relations,' he said worriedly. 'This is no time to be alone.'

'It's good of you to be concerned after all I've put you through, but I'll manage. Good-bye, my dear Emile.' And to her own surprise, she burst into tears.

She had never seen him so upset. He fussed and fumed around her until she had regained her composure, and then he insisted on accompanying her back to Rampart Street with the money. Her sense of the ridiculous overcame her feeling of sadness as he continued to fuss, insisting on searching the house to see no intruder was lurking. checking all the windows and doors, and she only finally got rid of him by promising to get someone in to stay with her – a promise she had no intention of keeping – and to keep all doors barred and windows locked until that mythical someone arrived.

Once the door was barred against him, she busied herself making her little hoard as secure as possible. Removing all the fittings from her grandmother's workbox, she stored the gold and the jewels beneath the red velvet lining, squeezed as many of the silver dollars as she could into the main cavity, and covered them with skeins of embroidery silks. What remained she left in the leather pouches for the moment. This done, she hid them all in a space she had left at the back of her gris-gris cabinet for articles she wished hidden from public view, and then added to the little collection her precious marriage certificate. When she got to Maison Blanche, she would put them all in a safer hiding place she had had constructed under the floor of her bedroom there.

The two valises – all she dared take with her – stood ready, packed with the best of her things. She had told Marie-Philome what to do with the rest, though she had little hope of ever seeing most of it again. Now there was nothing left for her to do but decide, once and for all, what she was going to do about her father . . .

She had almost come to the conclusion that ignominious flight was the best answer when the matter was decided for her. A rapping came on the barred front door. 'Who is it?' she called.

'A message fo' Miz Laveau,' a Negro voice answered.

'Slip it under the door, then.' A rather crumpled piece of paper came into view and she snatched it up. The message, written in a spiky, old-fashioned hand, was brief. It read:

Meet me at Canal and Water Streets. We must talk. I shall be there at six. If you are not there, I must come for you and will not be refused.

Your father
Thomé di Sonora

A feeling of inevitability flooded over her. So let it be; she would answer the summons.

'Tell him I'll be there,' she called through the door.

'Ah'll tell 'im.' And there was the sound of retreating footsteps.

The hours between she used to good purpose, strengthening by every means known to her her own powers. She had a sinking feeling she was going to need them.

When the familiar figure appeared at her side, she was grimly prepared. His face was set in its usual stern expression, but his first utterance verged on the querulous. 'This city presses in upon me,' he said. 'There are too many people. Let us walk along the levee to a spot where we may have some peace. I shall be glad when we are free of it.'

She nodded, and they walked in silence until they had

reached a deserted stretch of the levee. He walked over and gazed moodily down at the muddy river, running swift and swollen with the spring rains. 'There is always a choice of paths,' he observed, 'always a choice. But then there are the times of choice, and these are not frequent. Your time of choice is now, and there is small doubt in my mind what it will be.' He looked at her piercingly. 'Choose well. Aid me now in the sad times that lie ahead for our people, and I will lead you into the second circle of power. Not only will you have the world, but paths to other worlds, other dimensions of being that are beyond your imaginings. The power of the moon and the stars and of light itself will be yours.

'I have found the path and can show the way – it is both the ancient way and the future way. The key to it has been, and will be again, lost and found by a chosen few. I am one of those few; you can be, too. You are free of your encumbrances; you are free of all of this.' He waved a hand at the city behind them that was sinking dimly into dusk. 'You are free to start on the path I have chosen for you. I know you have the power. Choose wisely – come with me.'

Marie looked at him stonily. 'It seems that nothing I have said since you first arrived has made any impression on your mind. I suppose I must say it all again. I am not free – nor do I have any desire to be. My path is chosen and set. It leads to my husband and child, who are safely beyond the reach of your threats. It is no use to threaten me, old man – *I* know I have the power to withstand you if it comes to a contest between us, but I do not wish that to be. I want you to go in peace and leave me in peace. You say you are my father, and I must needs believe you – but you have never been a father to me; I have never had a father. You owe me nothing; I owe you nothing. The powers you talk about and the path you offer have no meaning for me. You, your way of life, your people, and their problems – all mean nothing to me. You have never done anything for me. Why should I do anything at your behest?'

Suddenly he seemed to tower above her. 'You forget quickly,' he thundered, 'I saved you from your mother's evil power – I warned you in time.'

'You warned me, it is true,' she answered quietly, 'but I saved myself – with the aid of the Helper, who has nothing to do with you, but only to do with that part of me that is *from* you. And you did not do it to free me from my mother's bondage, but merely to save me for your own. I do not know which of you is worse, but I do know I owe neither of you anything. I am I. I choose my path and do not follow one chosen for me. If you are still seeking something, old man, I feel sorry for you. I have found what I seek – I have found love and happiness and contentment.'

'Then you are a fool!' he shouted suddenly. 'A fool not to recognize a dream that is but ashes! I *can* bend you to my will! I can *make* you follow the path – the right path. And one day you will know that I am right.' He took a threatening step towards her, his hands lifting, and there was stark tragedy in his eyes.

Marie's patience snapped. 'Oh, get away from me! Leave me be!' she cried. And, hammering with both fists on his chest, she pushed him from her. He was caught off balance, and went reeling back. For a second he hung poised on the brink of the level, his arms flailing. Then he toppled backwards into the river.

The muddy water rose to meet him, and, with the effortlessness of true strength, plucked him away from the bank into the main, swirling current. He rose spluttering to the surface, and from his feeble movements it was evident to the horror-stricken Marie that he could not swim. As the current bore him swiftly seawards, his head turned towards her and the black eyes clamped on hers. He reared almost out of the water, and for a heart-stopping moment she thought he was going to free himself of the currents and come walking towards her. 'You fool!' he called. 'You have killed me, your father, for the sake of a dead man. The path is closed by your own folly. You . . .' But the river plucked at her prey again and he went down, and this time he did not reappear; only the broad-brimmed Spanish hat incongruously remained, sailing on skittishly over the choppy water.

For a second Marie felt a tremendous urge to cast herself

into the water after him; the waters demanded her as the only answer, but she managed to reassert her will and stagger away from the edge to collapse into a sobbing panting heap on the muddy ground. She lay there clutching at the earth with all her strength, her mind overwhelmed with terror. She had killed her own father ...

How long she had lain there she did not know, but now it was quite dark, a few faded stars showing through the river mist. She rose on shaky legs, her mind numbing under the awful reality. She had killed, and there was nothing to be done. She had no recollection afterwards of how she got back to Rampart Street, no recollection of how she did things she had never done before, like hitching the horse up to the gig; no recollection of loading it and setting off towards Maison Blanche. Only upon reaching the bridge to the Duelling Oaks did her conscious mind dimly struggle back to reality. She stopped the gig and sat, shaking uncontrollably, her eyes seeing but not taking in her mud-soaked clothes, the strapped valises, the workbox, the leather pouches containing the money. Part of her had gone on with the escape, but only part ...

When she got to the dark, shuttered house, she barely had strength to free the horse and drag the contents of the gig across the dank, musty-smelling threshold. This done and the door shut, she staggered in the darkness to one of the little cubicle bedrooms, collapsed on the bare bed, and sank from darkness into deeper darkness.

She had no means of knowing how long she had slept, but by the light it seemed to be late afternoon. She was cold and stiff and ravenously hungry – but her mind was working again. She stripped off her mud-soaked clothes, washed and changed, then went off in search of Abraham, a simple-minded old Negro who lived in a shack nearby at the bayou's edge. She begged from him some bread and a little jug of corn liquor – which was all he had – and sent him off in the gig, with a list of necessities and the money to buy them.

When he was dispatched on his errands, she sat down on one of the dusty velvet benches of the salon and tore at the bread like a ravenous wolf, swilling it down her parched, aching throat with great gulps of the fiery liquid. It hit her stomach like a bomb, sending its warmth through her frozen veins and warming her shivering nerves. Her supplies exhausted, she went almost lightheadedly about, putting her house in order. She threw open the shutters, dragged the damp bedding into the spring sunshine to air, dusted, polished – anything to keep her mind and body busy, to fend off their other terrors.

Only when she got to the great bedroom, standing empty and regal, did its bareness recall Rampart Street, which now housed its treasures – and with Rampart Street came other memories and other pain. When she had hidden her store of treasure in the secret hiding place beneath the floor, she walked back into the main salon and sank into her great chair. She had done all she could do. Now there was nothing for it but to wait – wait for the police to come knocking at her door, or wait for Jethro to come and save her. She was caught between past and future, with nothing in between.

When the old man returned from his errands, she was still sitting there gazing into the darkness, her eyes blank, her face set. When he spoke to her and got no reply, with the strange wisdom of the simpleminded he left what he had collected by her side and went on his way.

But in the days that followed nothing happened and though her guilt still bound her, she dared to hope. In the ferment of the preoccupied city, apparently no one had missed one strange old Indian – he had vanished from people's minds as he had vanished in the river, leaving no trace, almost as if he had never been.

From Abraham, who was her sole contact with the outside world, she could get no news that made any sense. But one day, shortly after Marie's flight, Marie-Philome had come driving out in the dusk, concerned and worried at finding the Rampart Street house empty and unlocked, and with no word from her.

'I'm sorry to have worried you,' Marie said, attempting to appear calm. 'My nerves got on top of me, and I just took off without thinking.'

Marie-Philome sympathized but did not probe, and they went on to talk of domestic matters regarding the houses. Before Marie-Philome left, Marie tried to slip in a casual inquiry about any exciting events that had happened in the city. 'Oh, nothing but war fever and more war fever,' Marie-Philome sighed. 'No one has time to think of anything else. Even Jean-Paul seems to be catching it.' She bit her lips and shook her head. 'I do pray he will not go,' she whispered.

'So no juicy scandals or murders or anything like that?' Marie said with a thumping heart.

Again Marie-Philome shook her head. 'Nothing but the war. I do hope it gets over quickly!' When she got up to go, she hesitated. 'Is this good-bye, Marie? I do not wish to pry, but if it is . . .'

'No. It is too soon – I shall be here for a while yet. I have no idea how long, but when I go, I'll send word with Abraham.'

The long days turned into weeks, and then into a month, and still she waited, trying to fill her empty days with work and dreams of the future. She became worn with waiting. She started anxiously at every sound, flew to the window at every strange noise, but still there was nothing.

One day she went to the weeping willow where she and Nils had picnicked in that happy, innocent past. She sat long beneath its sorrowing arms and fondled the rough bark. 'Oh, I wish,' she said aloud, 'how I wish that tomorrow my waiting could be done with. Bring me my wish, oh weeping tree!'

Chapter Thirty-one

She sank into sleep more easily that night than she had for some time, but it was a sleep punctuated by vivid dreams that rolled through her mind like thunderstorms, and she tossed and muttered on the narrow bed. The dreams rose to a gradual climax: she was aware of shouting, muffled by dense vegetation, of dancing, dim lights, and the barking of dogs; the ground beneath her feet squelched and quaked, and she could hear her own harsh breathing. Suddenly a light shone directly into her eyes, blinding her, and from the light came a redder flash that exploded in her mind, bringing darkness and momentary agony. It was then the harsh breathing stopped, and she started into wakefulness, straining to hear the sounds. But there was nothing – nothing but the usual night sounds of the bayou, the croaking of frogs and the cricket chorus, and a full moon shining serenely down at her through the narrow window. She lay feeling curiously empty, as if part of her had been ripped away, and her solitariness overwhelmed her, so that tears welled up and slid silently down her cheeks, bathing her pillow. Quietly, she cried herself back to sleep.

Despite her wish at the willow tree, the day brought no message, and this depressed her spirits, already at a low ebb from her disturbing night. The bright spring vegetation mocked her with its beauty, the bird chorus with its light-heartedness. 'I can't go on like this,' she told herself. 'I must do something or go mad.' But what? An idea, a fear, that had been with her since the dreadful event at the levee came to the front of her mind: Had her deed cost her the Helper?

She felt this was something important to find out, but it would take time if it was anything like her last experience. It was worth a try. At best she could impress on old Abraham that he was to watch the house, and that if anyone came there he was to tell them to find her at the willow tree.

Immobile beneath its shade, she let her mind go gradually blank; time stopped. This time she was far more frightened than the first: aware of things, of forces, in this other dimension that threatened and menaced her. The waiting seemed eternal, but gradually her mind focused on a fallen tree on the other side of the bayou; a thickening in its shadows indicated something was approaching. The bayou sounds stilled, and it was with almost a sense of joy that she glimpsed a flash of gold and saw the tall, shadowy outline of the Indian. He came no nearer and his figure lacked substance, but she was sure in her heart that it was he.

'So you have come – you have not left me.'

'No. I cannot leave.'

'Then help me!'

'With what? No one threatens you.'

'But I am so alone. I need your help, your comfort.'

The figure wavered and seemed to fade. 'I see you have understood and have learned but little. What you ask is not my function. To face what has to be faced, to do what has to be done – that is your task, not mine.'

Then she was looking at a fallen, rotten tree on the opposite bank, and there was desolation in her heart.

She staggered back to Maison Blanche, unaware of how long she had been absent from the world. But when she had satisfied her hunger and thirst and had gone in search of Abraham, it was to find that it mattered little – no messenger, no message, had arrived.

Her efforts had exhausted her, and she spent the next couple of days mostly in sleep. On the third day she was roused by a tapping at the door, and Abraham, looking like a hopeful dog, stood on the threshold. He thrust a grimy and tattered sheet of paper towards her. 'Some man give me dis fo' ya.'

'Who? Where is he?' she demanded eagerly, snatching it from him.

The dim eyes looked blank. 'Ah dunno. Ah never saw 'im befo' 'round here.'

She opened the paper with trembling hands. It was

densely written in a very small hand that she did not recognize, but those first words made her senses swim.

They will hang me in the morning, but if, by some miracle, this gets through to you, I must make one last effort to let you know what has happened. I give this to another prisoner with the last of the money, in the hopes that he can get it to the man who journeyed with us and was not taken.

First, I must ask you, if this comes through, to notify, when you are able, the American Board of Foreign Missions in Boston as to what has become of me. I have a brother and sister who will want to know the manner of my death. I was trained and educated by the board to be a missionary, but, as you have long since guessed, it was felt I could best serve my God and my people by doing what I have been doing for the past ten years. I have no regrets about this, but it is strange that now they are hanging me not for what I did, but for being a Yankee spy, which I am not. Secret are the ways of the Lord.

Second, I must tell you that your family was safe-arrived and well-received in Chicago. You have no cause for worry. Mrs Andersen is a very fine lady . . .

Marie's heart gave an immense leap of joy, but the next sentence set her to trembling again.

I started back as soon as I could, and tried to dissuade Mr Andersen from the venture I knew to be so dangerous. He would come. And also with us was the man who I pray will get this to you – someone who will carry on my work in the city. We kept to the river as much as possible travelling only by night, and got as far as Osceola, which is a little place in Arkansas, not far from the Missouri border. It is here I come to the most difficult part of what I have left to say, which is why I have left it to last. It was full moon, so I was for stopping, but Mr Andersen was so anxious to get to you that he persuaded me and we went on. Being so near Missouri, the Arkansans have many patrols, fearing a federal invasion from there. We had the ill luck to come across one patrol which had a pack of hounds with them. They got wind of us and chased us into a swamp, and there, I deeply sorrow to tell you, a trigger-happy recruit shot Mr Andersen dead. They captured me and . . .

But Marie read no more. The paper slipped from her fingers and she collapsed into blackness.

But even in the blackness there was nothing but terror as she lived over her nightmare of the swamp, the full moon, her sense of obliteration. No! It was impossible, it was too cruel, she could not let it happen, could not have it happen . . . She swam back to consciousness, and this time took up the letter and read doggedly through it.

. . . they captured me and will have it that we were Yankee spies. They have tried to beat the truth out of me, and, indeed, I have told them the truth of our mission – though I did not give your name – but they do not believe. I can write no more. God keep us and save us all, and may you find comfort in Him and His infinite wisdom, as I do.

> *Jethro Jones*

No path at all . . . two dead men . . . you have killed me for a dead man . . . Her father's terrible prophecies ripped through her mind like so many screaming bullets, shattering all that was rational, all that was sane. She could not, would not, believe; it was not true. It was all some ghastly plot to break her down, to make her give up hope. It was not true. Nils would come for her, and she would wait for him. It was not true, it was not true . . .

In the days, weeks, months that followed, Abraham, like some faithful shadow, feeling but not understanding, watched over Marie. He brought food and made her eat, brought water and made her drink, but there was no communication between him and the creature with the dark, wild, tangled hair and the blazing, great inward-looking eyes.

Sometimes she was quite mad: talking and laughing to the

household, as if they were all around her; reliving all the happy, cherished moments. At other times she would wander lost and disconsolate, calling their names to the marshes, and Abraham, following after, would lead her gently home when the fit was spent. One time, her pain being too great, she threw herself into the bayou, and fought the old man as he dragged her out. It made no difference; inexorable as Fate, he forced her to go on living, though he did not know why.

In her few more rational moments, she decided, like her mother before her, that if her love would not come to her, she must summon him. She used all the magic she had been taught, all the rites, all the incantations, and when these failed, she fought against the gods, just as her mother had done. She spent herself railing against the terrible silence of God, and knew at last the face of her enemy, the face of Death . . . Then the madness would come again.

In the world outside this twilight world of the madwoman of the bayou, life and death had been grappling on many fields in many places, and the people of New Orleans were beginning to know the facts of war and the face of the enemy.

In July the first major clash had come at Manassas. In the battle Lamont Valdoux was killed in the first few minutes. And Lieutenant St Regis Montal, fighting with the inspiration of madness, was promoted on the field to Captain for his outstanding bravery. Both sides drew apart, licked their wounds, and realized they were in for a long war.

After the Confederate victory at Antietam in September, Southern hopes ran high, but in that bloody victory there were great losses, among them Bayard Valdoux and Denys Devereux, both wounded and taken prisoner. And Captain St Regis Montal, still fighting like a *condottiere* of old, was promoted from Captain to Major.

New Orleans watched it all from afar. In Louisiana nothing had happened. There had been some action in Kentucky and Tennessee, a Confederate victory in Missouri, which looked as if it would bring that divided state within the Confederacy, but then, in March of '62, a grey-clad army was sent reeling back in Arkansas, and Missouri remained firmly within the Union. The war was coming a little closer, but it was still far from the boundaries of the state, and Justin LeBlanc, home on leave from the frontier that no one apparently cared about was heard to remark to his cronies that war was just about the most boring thing that had been so far invented by man.

Everybody just wished that Lee would get a move on, capture Washington, and be done with it, because – though the war was far away – the economic pinch had come as the mighty river's traffic dried up to a trickle and then stopped altogether. They grumbled about the ineffectiveness of the Confederate Navy in coping with the sea blockade the federals had set up, and they looked woefully at warehouses bursting with merchandise that they could not get to the eager markets of the outer world. All sorts of ingenious schemes were thought up for evading the blockade; few of them worked. And as the warehouses got fuller, the pockets of rich and poor became emptier.

Paul Valdoux, now with Davis in Richmond, wrote long and worried letters to his son, which did nothing to ease his banker's mind. And as Confederate guns boomed victory, the Confederacy sank deeper into an economic quagmire.

Social life continued, but on a muted scale. The balls went on, but now they were all benefits – for guns, for the men, for the wounded. Some families – like the Valdouxs – were already in mourning and had dropped from the social scene, but the gayest of cities could not forget its heritage overnight. The theatres, the gambling houses, the concerts were all open – awash with patriotic themes and melodies, ready with patriotic contributions, and otherwise much as usual. The war was still far away.

But in April 1962 Farragut's blockading fleet suddenly forced past the two pathetic little forts guarding the great city and sailed towards it. It was then that the church bells of the city raised their voice and told it what it most dreaded to hear. The war at last was coming home ...

Chapter Thirty-two

Marie Laveau had saved two of her sons from the war: Jean, on the grounds he was her sole support; and Charles-Louis, because he was the father of two small children and his wife had no other kin. Both claims had raised eyebrows, but she had carried enough weight in certain quarters to bring this about. François she could not save, but had managed to get him into Justin LeBlanc's force in northern Louisiana, which so far had seen no action. Currently, she was wondering whether she had not condemned her remaining sons to a worse fate, as she stalked slowly and majestically towards the flickering, rosy glow that emanated from the dock area and illumined the skyline.

New Orleans was swirling in a frenzy of self-destruction; the bells had tolled and Farragut and the Yankee Navy were on their way. Nothing now could save the city, but its inhabitants were determined that, when the awful moment arrived, the Yankee invaders would find nothing worth having in the bursting storehouses along the levee.

They had started by dragging out the huge stores of cotton and setting them on fire, and the looting fever had spread, so that overexcited crowds of black and white alike jostled Marie Laveau in her path, their arms laden with all manner of barrels, boxes, and sides of meat looted from the ships' provisioners. As she neared the docks, the banquette became gritty from mounds of sugar that lay around like snowdrifts; the gutters ran stickily with molasses oozing slowly out of upturned barrels, and there was a pervading scent of tobacco as the burning tobacco warehouses sent columns of aromatic smoke into the heavy air. When she came out on the clearer dock area, she saw that the ships already loaded with cotton had been set afire, and that some of the steamboats had also suffered the same fate. They had all been cut loose from their moorings and were now drifting slowly out on the surface of the great river, like so many warning beacons, since there was not a single Confederate battery to guard the city.

By the light of the myriad fires, she caught sight of Emile Valdoux, looking most unaristocratic as he toiled in shirt-sleeves, his face grimy with smoke and sweat, to save the two Valdoux warehouses from being consumed by the flames. She made her way to him and raised her voice above the crackling of the flames. 'This is madness! The fools are sacking their own city! Can nothing be done to halt this insanity?'

He threw her a harassed glance. 'They didn't want the cotton and sugar to fall into enemy hands – but it's got completely out of control. We'll be lucky if the whole city does not go up in flames.'

She looked around, her face brooding. 'In a month they will be starving and screaming for help. God knows, after this they can expect little of mercy or consideration from the Yankees. I foresee terrible times ahead – we shall need all the power we can summon if we are to survive this.'

'That is the one thing I am sure of.' He turned and shouted some orders to the men, who were dousing the warehouses with a bucket line and flailing away with sacks at burning embers that settled on the roofs.

She sighed softly. 'I think it is time that Marie returned from her exile – she will be needed.'

'Marie?' He turned back to her with a puzzled frown. 'But Marie went north a year ago with Andersen.'

She looked at him, her eyes veiled. 'Oh, so you did not know, then. I wondered about that.'

'Know what?'

'She never left. She has been out at Maison Blanche all this time.'

'All alone, all this time?' he echoed angrily. 'But why? Did Andersen desert her?'

'Andersen is dead.' Her tone was flat. 'I don't know the whole story, but he was killed, apparently on his way back to get her. The grief of it has turned her mind, so it is said.'

'So it is said!' he exploded. 'You mean you have done nothing to bring her back, nothing to help her?'

Again she gave him a veiled look. 'I have been out there several times, but she wants no part of me. She runs and hides in the bayous when she hears people coming. I have not seen her.'

'But how do you know ... how has she lived ...' He was spluttering with anger.

'My daughter Marie-Philome found a letter about Andersen's death.' She did not elaborate on its contents. 'And there is an old Negro living nearby who has been caring for her. He is dim-witted, so we have been able to learn little of value from him.'

'And you have left her alone and sick in the hands of a dim-witted Negro? In God's name, what kind of a mother are you?'

'Abraham was not always dim-witted,' she returned enigmatically. 'He has done what has to be done.'

'But this can't go on! Not now! She has to be brought back, cared for!' he yelled, trembling with anger.

'Grief must run its course.' Her tone was heavy with her memories. 'But I agree with you. Now it is time – the need for her and what she can do will be great.'

'Then why don't you send your son – Jean, isn't it? – to bring her back – by force, if necessary! She must be cared for,' he repeated.

She shook her head slowly. 'She would not come for us. But I wonder ...' She looked at him with speculation. 'You have always had more influence with her than most. Perhaps if you went – with that doctor she used to work with, Dr Franke, wasn't it? I think you might be able to do something.'

'Well, of course I will.' He was somewhat calmer now, but was still shaking with suppressed anger. 'As soon as I can get away from all this.'

'I thought you might,' she murmured, and a slight smile played around her lips as she moved off into the swirling crowds.

But calamitous events were to prevent Emile Valdoux

from rushing to carry out his errand of mercy. Farragut's fleet anchored off the burning levees that night, but that was not the worst of it. On 1 May, the Army of Occupation arrived. The *Mississippi* drew up at the smoke-blackened levee and fourteen hundred Yankee soldiers poured out and into the Vieux Carré. But even that wasn't the worst of it. Following after the soldiers in stern and solemn state, Major-General Benjamin Butler stepped ashore to take command, and the purgatory of New Orleans began.

The measure of the man was seen on the very first day. Escorting his wife to the St Charles Hotel, he demanded the best suite. The manager, patriotic if not wise, refused. He was hurled bodily off the premises into the street and Butler proceeded to take over the entire hotel.

New Orleans went into a state of shock. Helpless though they might be, however, they were not without immense resourcefulness and pride. Spines stiffened, tempers mounted, as the Union soldiers moved in, taking over the grander houses of the Garden District, dispossessing the occupants with only the clothes on their backs, and proceeding to some systematic looting on their own account.

A few days later the first Yankee died, an officer who, it was said, had overindulged in the contents of the wine cellar of the house he had appropriated. As his funeral went down St Charles Avenue, a lady from the dispossessed family laughed merrily at the sight. She was seized and Butler had her sentenced right away to two years' incarceration in the prison on Ship Island – her guards to be Negroes. To rub added salt into this wound, he issued an order 'that any woman showing any signs of contempt or insult for a member of the Army of Occupation shall be regarded and treated as a whore!'

At the scream of protest that went up from the outraged citizenry, the mayor rushed off to General Butler's headquarters – now moved into one of the grandest houses in the Garden District – to try and reason him out of it. For his pains he was thrown into a military prison, and chained in solitary confinement, where he was to languish for the next three years.

The people of New Orleans became drawn and silent, and fear crept into their hearts as they came to know 'the Beast'. He, wrapped in his own hatred, did not relax his hand of iron for a second; a youth who tore down a Union flag was summarily hanged. And, driven on by his own obsession, Butler had carved ineradicably into the pedestal of the Jackson statue in Lafayette Square the maxim: 'The Union must and shall be preserved' – misquoting that great Southerner's words to serve his private passion.

To Emile Valdoux, already burdened beyond the lot of a normal man, it gave more worry, fresh problems. He had been turned out of his own house, together with his wife and three children, with the clothes they stood up in and precious little else. They had moved back to the Royal Street house, already crowded with Clarisse LeBlanc Valdoux and her two children, Marie-Thérèse LeBlanc Montal, Valerie and her three children, and of, course, Madame Valdoux. In his mother, Emile found a surprising support.

Crisis had wrought great changes in Emilie St Yves Valdoux, whose St Yves blood had risen to challenge. Her hypochondria vanished with the style of life that had brought it forth. Silently sorrowing for years about what her machinations, however well meant, had done to her two eldest children, saddened by Louise's death in the plague of '53 – since she had paid little attention to the quiet girl in her lifetime – her cup ran over when Lamont, her favourite child, was killed at Manassas.

A determination that she would lose no more welled up from an unknown source. Whatever needed to be done to ensure the survival of the rest of her children, that would she do. She could do nothing to help Emile on the outside, but in the inside world of the house on Royal she could and did. She became the complete matriarch, ruling the remaining slaves with an iron hand, smoothing out the quarrels and problems of her daughter and daughters-in-law, and seeing that the children did not kill one another or get on the nerves too much. Emile could scarcely get over the change in her, and wondered what his father would make of it when and if he returned from Richmond.

The many crises had hit his own wife particularly hard, and the dispossession for her had been the final straw. They had no sooner got to Royal Street when she collapsed from nervous exhaustion and became yet another worry on his unending list. He worried about the declining health of Clarisse, who grieved silently for Bayard, of whom no word had been heard since his capture at Antietam. He worried about Marie-Thérèse Montal, whose temperament, never of the best, had been considerably worsened by the fact that her long-separated husband, St Regis, was now something of a war hero and a celebrity. He worried about the impulsive Valerie, who was now trapped in New Orleans by his own well-meant but ill-given advice.

She had wanted to stay at Castle Blanche with the children, but he had vetoed that on the grounds that she would have no protection up at the plantation. Had she followed her own inclinations, she would now be still safely in Confederate territory and in touch with her husband – a fact she was not above pointing out to her brother several times a day. On top of that, she was so furious about the Yankee occupation of her city that Emile went in fear and trembling he would arrive home one day to find she had joined the unfortunate throng of women who had been banished to Ship Island under the infamous 'Woman's Ordinance' of 'Beast' Butler.

Most of all, he worried about his eldest sister, caged up in the Montal house with the two remaining Montal women and a husband who was something worse than useless. No gambling house still open in New Orleans would give Dominic Montal any more credit – for all that, his twin was a war hero. Cut off from his major passion, he had turned increasingly to his minor one, drinking. Seldom in the past year had Emile seen him sober. Yet, in spite of all his own entreaties, his gently obstinate sister had refused to abandon her marriage or the Montals and join the Royal Street *ménage*.

Even the bank was a serious worry, since his father had already siphoned off most of its available resources to Richmond, and he knew how little stood between it and complete insolvency. The mounds of Confederate scrip that now lay in the vault were rapidly becoming of no more value than the paper they were printed on. He thought bleakly that there were few in the city, including himself, who had stashed away gold and silver against a day of want that no one had expected to come. That thought brought him back to one of the few who had: Marie. And with guilt in his heart, he realized that already weeks had passed since his shattering talk with the elder Marie Laveau, and still he had done nothing.

When Emile could tear himself away from all his other worries, he went to see Dr Franke, with whom he was only slightly acquainted. The awkwardness of his task struck him forcibly as he tried to sketch out the situation as he had heard it from the elder Marie.

'And she has been out there all this time alone – with no care of any sort?' Dr Franke said, echoing Emile's words. He nodded, and they eyed one another grimly.

'Then God knows what we are liable to find,' the doctor went on. 'I have always heard that her mother is a very strange woman, but I would have thought at least some other members of the family would have ...' He shook his head and sighed. 'Of course I am willing to go with you, but chances are, if she is not beyond treatment already, she will need extended care, and in the present circumstances here ...' Again he trailed into silence. 'Well' – he shook himself out of his reverie – 'this is not being very positive. Let us go and see what the situation is, and then perhaps we can come up with something sensible. Do you know where the place is?'

'No, I don't, but I'll find out.' And Emile did.

They rode out in the doctor's carriage, both men constrained and silent. Warned that she hid from visitors, they stopped some distance from the house and went the rest of the way on foot, creeping as quietly as a couple of marauding Indians. The house, as they approached it, looked completely dead and deserted – weeds growing up through the long portico in front, and all the shutters closed. They tried the doors but found them locked, so they crept with equal caution around to the rear and there saw that one window stood with its shutters half-open. They peered in and could just make out the form of a woman sitting silently in a great teak chair.

'Marie,' Emile called softly, 'Marie, we've come for you.'

The figure sprang up and with a pitiful cry of joy raced to the window. 'At last! At last! I knew you'd come if I waited long enough!' Marie cried in a voice husky from long disuse.

As daylight fell upon her, they both started back and Emile let out a little moan. They saw a figure gaunt to the point of emaciation, clothed in garments that were ragged and mud-splattered, the long, dark hair dull with dirt and tangled and matted, so that it looked like the head of a Medusa. Only the blazing, dark eyes were recognizable, and as the two men stared in fascinated horror at her, the blaze died out to be replaced by a blank stare, as if a shutter had been dropped, cutting off all light from the brain. Marie began to back away into the darkness. 'You're not the ones. *He* didn't send you for me,' she muttered. 'What do you want of me? Go away!'

Chapter Thirty-three

Perhaps the outcome would have been very different if Emile, for one of the very few times in his long life, had not completely and utterly lost his control and his temper.

They had crawled in through the window like burglars, and he had stood blocking it with his stocky body while Dr Franke soothed and coaxed and wheedled, trying to get some sort of response from Marie. For a long time she just sat in sullen, hostile silence, shooting furtive glances at the window like some trapped animal seeking escape. Then one probe from Dr Franke elicited a sudden response.

'You killed him!' she exploded. 'Damned Southerners killed him in a swamp like a dog!'

He gave an encouraged nod towards Emile and continued to press this line, only to find that Marie had drifted into another of the twilight worlds in which she had found escape. She was now only anxious for them to be gone, lest they should frighten away her rescuers. With endless patience, Dr Franke started anew. The process went on for hours, eliciting responses of shrill vituperation, then anguished pleading, and finally sullen silence.

As he watched, Emile's first feeling of horrified pity gradually gave way to another, more bitter emotion that grew and grew into a boiling anger. How typical of her! How typical of her – always selfish, always! To escape from worry, to escape from pain, to escape from responsibility – as if she weren't in the world at all, as if she were the only one in whatever world she was in. Damn her! Damn her to hell!

As she reached Andersen's death for the sixth or seventh time and was sullenly repeating, 'He's dead and you killed him,' the rage boiled out and Emile could keep silent not a moment longer.

'You're not getting anywhere!' he shouted at the doctor. 'Here, let me at her!' And he plunged towards her. He seized her roughly by the shoulders and shook her so that her teeth rattled, and the matted hair rocked wildly from side to side. 'God damn it!' he cried. 'Do you think you're the only one who ever suffered a loss, a grief? Look at me! Louise is gone; Lamont; probably Bayard, too. Do I sit around living in a never-never-land because I grieve? Damn it, there's a world out there, a world that needs help – but all you can do is snivel and slide out of it . . .'

Dr Franke had made an involuntary movement to stop Emile, but then had stepped back into the shadows and was watching what went on narrowly as Emile continued to rant and rave.

Suddenly Marie screamed at him. 'He *is* coming for me! Go away! I want no part of you!'

'Coming for you?' Emile roared. 'So now we're on that tack again. All right, so he's coming for you. But do you think he'll *want* you when he sees this?' He twisted her savagely towards the mirror that ran along the wall of the tiny bedroom. 'Look at yourself! Look at what you have become – a filthy, ugly slattern! God! Not even on Gallatin Street would you find a customer!'

She turned with a screech of hate and hit him in the face. He slapped her hard back and, as her long, filthy nails came up to claw at him, he went on slapping and yelling, driving her back into a corner with the force of his blows.

Dr Franke again made a move towards them, but checked once more.

Marie made no effort to protect herself, but flailed back at Emile, screaming, 'I hate you! I hate you!' And tears began to stream down the gaunt cheeks.

'And I hate you!' he yelled, beginning to sob in his turn. 'And everything you are!'

They continued to slap and scream at one another until, suddenly, Marie covered her face with her hands and slumped down in the corner, sobbing bitterly. Emile stood over her, his chest heaving, his eyes wild, and Dr Franke finally intervened.

He stepped forward and laid a hand on Emile's shoulder. 'That's enough,' he said gently. 'I can manage now.'

The dazed Emile looked at him, the tears still coursing down the pale cheeks. 'I think I'm going to be sick,' he muttered thickly. And, rushing over to the windowsill, he began to retch.

Dr Franke gently urged Marie to her feet and led her back to the bed, where he sat down, his arm around the skeletal shoulders. He cradled the filthy head against his shoulder and sat rocking her gently as the wild sobbing continued. Since it showed no signs of abating, he gently laid her on the rumpled bed and drew a cover over her.

Then he went over to Emile, who was still at the window shivering violently, his face a pale green, the mild eyes horror-stricken as he gazed at the two of them. 'Are you all right?' Dr Franke asked quietly. He cocked his head towards the bed. 'If it's any comfort to you, I think you may have saved her. Knowing Marie as I do, I doubt whether she has shed a tear since the news came. This may be the release she needed.'

Emile appeared not to hear him. 'I do not know what came over me,' he stammered. And he looked in anguish at the doctor. 'Never in my life have I acted so.'

'In these times we have all been under a great strain,' Dr Franke murmured tactfully.

Emile turned away with a great quivering sigh, and he gripped the windowsill until his knuckles showed white.

Dr Franke looked at the bowed head with compassionate understanding, and he shook his own head slightly. 'I think you may have saved her,' he repeated. 'I'll let this go on for a while and then give her a sedative. I think I'll go look for some light. We may be here a while yet.' And he made a tactful withdrawal.

For a moment Emile stayed by the window in the same position. Then he braced himself with effort and went over to the bed, where he stayed gazing unhappily at the hopeless, sobbing figure on it.

'Ah, I see the dam has broken at last!' a deep voice said at the window, and he jumped back, startled. The tall figure of Marie Laveau was standing at it, gazing in.

'How . . .?' he stammered.

'I followed you here,' Marie Laveau said with dignity. 'I thought you might succeed.'

At the sound of her voice, the figure on the bed went rigid for a second, then whirled around and sprang up. 'God damn you to hell! Stay away from me, and get away from my house!' Marie shrilled, the tears still streaming down her cheeks. But, even as they gazed at her in shock, they saw her eyes were sane and steady, just as they were full of hate. And it was on this tableau that Dr Franke reappeared, bearing light ...

Marie Laveau had withdrawn on Dr Franke's insistence, sedatives had been administered, and now a conference, dimly lit by a couple of tallow dips, was being held in the dusty, deserted salon.

'She can't stay here,' Emile said unhappily. 'And it is obvious she will not go to her mother's. What can we do? I would offer her a room in my house, but we are so crowded, and, anyway, I'm afraid my mother ...' He floundered into silence.

Dr Franke sighed. 'Well, she can't be left alone again until she is fully recovered. There is only one thing to do. I will have to take her back to my house and care for her there. Room will just have to be found, that's all.'

Emile looked at him with evident relief. 'Would you? If there is any expense, I would be only too happy to ...'

The doctor dismissed him with his hand. 'Oh, that is a minor consideration. I owe Marie more than she has ever been paid.' A gentle irony crept into his voice. 'It is just that I will have some explaining to do to my wife, Rachel, about her presence and condition.' He made a wry grimace. 'It is fortunate that she is a woman of rare understanding.'

So Marie was installed in a small, top room of the Franke household, where she slowly found her way back to a new reality under the dark-eyed stares of the Franke children, and the endless mothering and feeding of Rachel Franke.

'You know,' she observed to the doctor one day when she was almost recovered, 'for someone who has worked so much with people, I am very unobservant. During all those years we worked together, it never occurred to me you were Jewish.'

'Didn't it?' Dr Franke returned. 'Would it have made any difference?'

'No, of course not – not to me.' She took a reflective sip of the chicken soup Rachel was always pressing upon her. 'But I have been wondering why you are still here. You could go anywhere – far away from all this ugly mess – and your skills would be needed. Why do you stay?'

He shrugged. 'My family has been here for almost a hundred years – I am as much of a Southerner as you. This is my home; I am needed here.'

'But the Jews have always stood apart. Why be involved in something that is nothing you sought?'

He gazed at her sombrely. 'We do not stand apart – we have always been *set* apart. There is a difference, you know – a difference that you, above all people, should appreciate.'

Marie thought about it. 'Yes, I see that, but I also see that however much you do, however much you help people, in the long run it is the difference they remember, not the kindness or the help.'

'So?' he said with resignation. 'This you live with – this we have always lived with. As long as you are needed, as long as you can help – why not? And I am needed. And, speaking of that, there is a case I could use *your* help on right now.'

A frightened look came into her eyes. 'Oh, I don't know,' she stammered. 'I don't know if I can any more.'

'Of course you can.' His tone was almost rough. 'What you've done before you can do again – *if* you have the will to try. You're needed, Marie.'

He succeeded in convincing her, but her mother had a harder time. Realizing this, she proceeded instantly to the main point of issue between them.' Look, Marie,' she stated flatly, 'if you have any sense left to you at all, you will realize that I am no longer a threat to you. I haven't been for years, but you'd never accept it. I am sixty-five years old, and my powers are fading. Anytime you are ready to take over the rites, they are yours. But that is not the most important thing now. What is important is that we have a mission to fulfil, a mission given us by the people of New Orleans, which between us we can do, but which without you I cannot. We have to get rid of "Beast" Butler.'

'To hell with the people of New Orleans,' Marie said dully. 'And I don't give a damn about "Beast" Butler!'

'Well, then your wits are more addled than I thought,' her mother retorted, 'because what he is doing to this city – what he'll continue to do if he can't be got rid of – affects you just as much as anyone else.' She sighed wearily. 'The same fools who looted the city are beginning to starve now – and soon we'll all start starving right along with them. Do you know that sugar is up to nine dollars a pound? And there is hardly a bite of meat in the whole city! Butler won't care if half the population dies so long as he has the other half to tyrannize.'

'Then why doesn't some brave Southern gentleman shoot him down?' Marie said with bitterness.

Her mother snorted gently. 'Don't think it hasn't been thought of or planned. But it's not the way. Barring some miracle, the Yankees are here to stay for as long as the war lasts – even longer. This is something we've got to accept and learn to live with. Shoot Butler and there'll be reprisals. They may even send someone worse – though that's hard to imagine. No, he's got to be got rid of, out of the city, and have someone milder put in his place. It's the only hope at the moment, and that's where we come in – believe me, the city fathers are right behind us.'

'And how are we supposed to bring about this miracle?'

'You know damn well how,' her mother replied. The two women stared at one another for a moment.

'I don't know that I'm up to it.'

'Well, will you at least try?'

'I suppose so,' Marie returned slowly. 'But I warn you – at the least sign of any funny business, I'm through.'

'You'll have to come back to St Ann Street,' her mother said, and Marie looked instantly suspicious.

'Oh, believe me, no funny business!' Marie Laveau raised a weary hand. 'It's just there is no other choice – I wish there were. The cottage is about to burst with people. But you can't stay here forever, and the Rampart Street house is occupied. Marie-Philome heard that the Yankee soldiers were taking over all unoccupied houses for billets, and rather than have that happen, she let a Negro family that had been burned out move in. She's locked up the front rooms with all the good furniture and let them move into the rest. No, I'm not offering you any bed of roses. The best I can do is to give you Patty's old room. At least it will be some place to have to yourself. And if anyone else turns up, you may even have to move in with me.'

'Who is there?'

'Jean, of course – he's out in the storeroom; Marie-Jeanne and her two children – they conscripted her husband; Marie-Philome and her three – Jean-Paul got out of the city just ahead of the Yankees, and she's let another family have her house on Rampart. They are all in the girls' room. Then Charles-Louis and his wife and children are in the boys' room.'

'My God!' Marie said hollowly.

'Yes, you see how it is.' Her mother was grim. 'Do you have any money at all? There's nothing coming in to speak of, and all I've got left is some jewellery that no one wants or has the money to buy.'

'I have a little money,' Marie admitted cautiously, 'But if the city fathers are backing us, how about them?'

'They'll see we don't starve,' her mother said with sudden impatience, 'but if we don't get moving, it won't be long before we're *all* starving. So – will you come?'

Marie went.

They started to work, operating, in spite of all the handicaps, in the front parlour, and then, after a while, in Crocodile's shack on Bayou Sauvage.

Their campaign did not get under way until August, when the city was sweltering and starving. The grapevine, tattered by many derelictions, but still in operation, told them where they might attack. They did so on two fronts.

Mrs Butler became ailing and fretful – the sultry heat of the city did not suit her northern blood, and the constant threats and rumours against her husband, although nothing

310

concrete ever transpired, were wearing on her nerves. She in turn wore on him.

And in another area his own ruthlessness served against him. His strong-arm tactics had affected not only the indigenous inhabitants of the city but also the foreign colony. The consuls, particularly the French consul, whose charges Butler had been unable to distinguish from the Creoles, became increasingly unhappy. Several unfortunate incidents took place which Butler was puzzled about and unable to account for. The foreign roar reached Washington, already upset by Butler's constant screams for more troops to get on with the occupation of Louisiana and the capture of the Mississippi, still very much in Confederate hands. There were also dark rumours that General Butler had been lining his pockets with the gold of the city.

In December, General Benjamin Butler was duly relieved of his command, and General Nathaniel Banks – yet another of Lincoln's unsuccessful politician generals – took command: perhaps another Massachusetts Yankee, but a man of milder ilk, one with whom the people of New Orleans thought they could at least exist.

The two Maries returned from Bayou Sauvage, tired out but content. They were met by a worried-looking Marie-Philome. 'I didn't want to disturb you,' she whispered, 'but while you were away we have had some additions to the household – Celeste is back with her family. She says she's going to stay.'

The looked wearily at one another. 'Good God!' they said in chorus.

Chapter Thirty-four

The little house was now crowded beyond endurance. Celeste and her three daughters – who obviously had been through a very hard time – temporarily bedded down in the front left parlour. Charles-Louis decided to move his family into the living quarters above the little foundry he and Jean still operated, and the arrangements eased somewhat. Since there was currently no work to be had or done, the fires were out, and so, while not ideal, it gave them a little more breathing space than at the cottage. Celeste and her family moved into the boys' room.

The situation would still have been intolerable had not Celeste been on her very best behaviour. Her husband – as her mother had predicted – had deserted them as soon as the war had started; her little business had foundered, and all she could think of was to return home to New Orleans. Marie privately wondered how she had managed to get back into enemy-occupied territory, but she said nothing.

Her three daughters obviously stood in terror of their mother. All of them were white-skinned, and the youngest, who took after her unsatisfactory father, had a head of carroty-red hair and rather weak-looking blue eyes. They were intensely religious, and soon the front parlour was festooned with holy pictures and echoed with the murmur of the girls saying their rosaries at all hours of the day. Marie found the whole thing somewhat bizarre. All of them were constrained to the point of furtiveness, and they had the maddening habit of whispering into one another's ears, which further frayed Marie's far-from-robust nerves. She contrived to stay out of the house as much as possible, and often found an unexpected sanctuary in the cathedral, where she would sit for long hours in its dusky peace, thinking and worrying on all manner of things.

Dr Franke had convinced her to accept the fact of Nils's

death, which she had found to be almost like accepting her own. The pain when she thought of him was still almost unbearable, and she would look at the statue of the Virgin, wondering how she had been able to bear her burden of grief, and found that thinking along these lines somehow helped. There was nothing in Voodoo that helped like that – Vodun was neither good nor bad, Vodun had no emotions, he was just there, powerful and capricious: a release, perhaps, but not an answer. New ideas burgeoned within her. She had talked long with her mother about the present sad state of the rites – which, under the 'Queens' to whom her mother had delegated her tasks, had deteriorated into little more than general sex orgies. In spite of this, fewer and fewer devotees were attending, and if something was not done soon, there would be nothing of her mother's empire left.

Slavery had been officially abolished while she was still in the twilight of her madness, but, as far as she could see, the fact of freedom had made very little improvement in the lot of the blacks in New Orleans. The younger ones had deserted their former owners, certainly, some lucky ones going to work for the Yankee invaders, others just drifting off out of the city – God knows where. In the households of New Orleans, Creole and Anglo alike, now all that remained were the very old, who were beyond taking advantage of something they had never known and did not rightly understand, or the very young, who were not up to looking after themselves. But there were many others who just stayed and starved in a frightening new-old world in which for them there was still no place.

Though Marie hardly felt the compassion towards them that her mother felt, she realized that they needed help, and that in helping them the debacle of her life and the life of the city might be salvaged. The worship and the power of Vodun melded with the help and hope that the Christian God held out, she thought: something along those lines, an amalgam of the two – new blood, new rites ... She continued to plan as her interest grew.

As it turned out, she was not allowed to give all her mind

313

to this. The city fathers had been grateful, but they had not finished with her. She had been summoned alone to one of the secret conclaves which had become a necessity in a city still under the thumb of martial law, and they had told her quite bluntly what they wanted of her.

'We want you to start your soirées again at Maison Blanche – not for your old clients, but for the Yankee soldiers, the officers mainly, if you can manage it. We need a listening post – one we can trust. There's damn little we can do about them, but the more we know about what they're up to the better off and the better prepared we'll be.' This from old Senator Garonne.

Marie had fought the idea. That part of her life was behind her. To start it again would be like running around in a squirrel's cage. '*No path at all*' echoed in her mind. Besides, she pointed out, there were the practicalities to consider. She had no contact with the Yankee garrison. And where were the supplies to come from, and the help? She had none. They brushed aside her objections and pressed harder. Help would be provided, supplies would be found, and Flo Winfield would see she made the right contacts with the Yankees.

'Flo Winfield bears no love for me,' she protested. 'Why should she do that?'

'Because Flo's a smart businesswoman,' Marie was told. 'She knows the war is not going to last forever, and that when peace comes, if she wants to stay healthy in this city, she'll have to do as she's told now. Sure, she's doing a roaring trade with the enemy at the moment, but she has enough sense to keep her eye on the future, as well. She can even provide the girls you'll need.'

'That won't be necessary,' Marie said with bitterness. 'I know plenty of my own who'd be willing to bury their scruples for the price of a square meal.'

She did not agree at once, but the more she thought about it, the more advantages began to take shape. She had been worrying for some time about how the refugees in the North were faring, and had pinned her hopes on Jethro Jones's assessment of Nils's mother, Mrs Andersen, as a very fine lady. She could not honestly admit to any deep feeling for her absent child, but Ingrid was all she had left of Nils, and she was her responsibility – as indeed were Claire and Patty. With contacts in the Yankee garrison, it might be possible to get word to them, and money and help if they needed it. She no longer thought in terms of escape herself – what, after all, was there to escape to?

Another practical thought came to her. The trade for gris-gris and hexes as a money-making concern was dead in the city, but there was a whole untapped continent out there, full of people with the same needs and desires as the people here – and, more importantly, people with money. If she could but use the Yankee mails, advertise in the Yankee papers ...

She went back to the secret council. 'I'll have to have a free hand,' she informed them. 'And I'll have to pick my own people. And you'll have to back me at the start. It makes no sense just to start the soirées for the Yankees – that in itself would be enough to make them suspicious and defeat your main object. I'll start them again for everyone, but I'll make certain the two groups don't mix. I don't know what information I'm likely to pick up, but there will have to be a contact who will pass the information on to you. It will be better if I have no direct connection with any of you.'

'You use the Valdoux bank, don't you?' someone observed. 'How about Emile Valdoux?'

'No!' Marie said with some violence. 'Definitely not!' She had seen nothing of Emile since her return to normalcy, and she shrank from remembering their last meeting, when too much had been said, too much uncovered.

After some argument, it was settled that the contact should be Aristide Sautelle, who, while not of the secret council, was in the same circle as most of the members, and who, as an old habitué of her soirées, seemed a logical choice.

'We'll not forget you for this service, Marie,' one of the council assured her with hearty warmth.

'I hope not,' she said dryly, 'I most surely hope not.'

So, with an inner weariness, she set about putting Maison Blanche to rights and instituting her new regime. To make certain the Yankee soldiers got no wrong ideas as far as she was concerned, she had a mourning gown of black satin made up, wore a widow's cap, and, as a final touch, borrowed one of the LeGendre Family's many rosaries for her throat.

'I am the widow of a Northern gentleman,' she primly informed the ranking officer at the first of the soirées, 'forced by these ill times into this sad way of life.' She knew he probably would not believe her, but the word went out that she was 'off-limits', and that was all she cared about.

Sitting there in the big chair, fiddling with the rosary beads, she felt like part of a recurring dream – the same naked girls, the same music, the same dancing; only the uniforms were different. And on the Creole nights, with the few middle-aged and elderly men clad in the black evening dress of yesteryear, the illusion of having stepped backwards in time became complete. If only it were possible to bend time like that, she mused, how willingly she would go back to that New Year's eve of 1859 and start anew, and how different would she make the outcome; how very, very different ...

Still, she sat and listened and learned – not only for her hidden backers, but for herself. Within a short while she had singled out two Yankee officers: one, a Captain Foster, from Chicago; the other a Lieutenant Murry, from New York City, who had been a journalist. These she assiduously cultivated until on friendly enough terms to broach her two separate goals.

She showed Captain Foster her precious marriage certificate, told him a carefully edited version of the truth, wept a little on his manly shoulder, and begged for his help in getting a message through to her family in Chicago. Captain Foster became like putty in her hands, volunteering his unstinting services short of treason.

With the young lieutenant, Marie's approach was very different. Despite the fact that he tried to appear swaggeringly confident and hard-boiled among his fellow officers, she surmised that underneath lurked a rather timorous and naïve soul. So she flattered him, told his fortune, predicted all manner of fortunate (and unlikely) events in his future, and got him so convinced of her powers as a soothsayer and as a purveyor of fortunate charms that he in turn agreed with alacrity to advertise her prowess in his old newspaper, and to act as her go-between and junior partner in the proposed mail-order business. And through him she sent the long-delayed news of the manner of Jethro's death to Boston.

The idea of profit acted as a spur. While Marie was awaiting anxiously the outcome of Captain Foster's role of Mercury to Chicago, the first request for gris-gris and hexes started to roll in to the cottage on St Ann Street, together with precious greenback bills that brought a light to the eyes of her two major participants. On Marie's part, she filled the orders with a heavy heart on occasion, for the majority of her requests came from women, and the most common help they sought was 'a charm to bring my loved one safely home from the war'.

The demands grew from a trickle to a stream, which then reached flood proportions, so that the two Maries were hard pressed to keep up with them. Marie-Philome had her hands full with her children, and had undertaken the task of provisioning – no easy one in the present conditions – and cooking for the household. Celeste and her brood were not so burdened, and so Marie suggested rather pointedly that they start to help out and lighten her own load.

Celeste's reaction to this was completely negative. Since her foothold in the house now seemed a great deal more secure, she had reverted to her more normal, shrewish self. 'Certainly not!' she snapped. 'I wouldn't dream of allowing my girls to help in such devil's work! The very idea! I brought them up to be good Christians and ladies, as befits their birth and station, not to cater to blacks steeped in devil worship and superstition!'

'Oh, for God's sake, Celeste!' Marie fumed. 'Who the hell do you think most of the people are who write for the gris-gris, anyway? They're a damned sight whiter than your girls will ever be, and they probably pray just as loud in church, too. If the help they seek from the gris-gris comforts them, it's good – and, I may point out, it's what is putting food in your mouths and clothes on your back just now. You talk a lot about setting up as dressmakers, but New Orleans is crawling with dressmakers who can't find enough work to keep them going because there just plain isn't the money around for it at the moment. If you're too high and mighty to let the girls help me, at least let them either help our mother with her nursing chores – there're plenty of sick folks around – or do what I suggested sometime ago – go out to the households that have lost all their slaves as companion-help. At least the girls know enough to flip a duster and make a pot of coffee!'

'That's no work for white women!' Celeste snarled. 'You just can't – or *won't* – understand!'

'Good God!' You'd think by the way you go on that you're the only coloured who ever had a white husband and white children!' Marie exploded. 'It's addled your brain! I had a white husband and a child far fairer than any of your brood, but I don't let it blind me to the present situation.'

Celeste's eyes narrowed. '*You* had a white husband and child?' Then she gave a sudden laugh. 'I don't believe it! A lover. maybe, and a bastard, but you, *marry*?'

Marie lost her temper. 'It's easy enough to check. Look at the register of Our Lady of Guadalupe for April of '59 – then call me a liar, if you dare!'

The minute the words were out, she regretted them, but it was too late to withdraw, and from behind her came the hiss of an indrawn breath. She turned around to see that her mother had silently entered the room during the heated exchange and was now staring fixedly at her.

'You *married* Nils Andersen?' Marie Laveau said in a curiously flat voice.

There was no drawing back now. 'Yes, I did,' Marie said defiantly, 'just as I said.'

'Then Ingrid was not a love-child,' her mother muttered.

'Ingrid was a child of love,' Marie stated, with another defiant glance at the slit-eyed Celeste, but there was a cold

318

feeling growing around her heart. The news had deeply agitated her mother, she could see – but there was no earthly reason it should have, unless . . . And it was this 'unless' that aroused all her old suspicions, all her old fears . . .

Chapter Thirty-five

Once more she was living her life on several different levels and she had the curious feeling of division within herself. She was Marie Laveau, businesswoman, swamped by cries for help from near and far; she was Marie Laveau, about-to-be Queen of the Voodoos; she was Marie Laveau, procuress-*cum*-spy for the beleaguered South . . .

As the war dragged on and she sat in the great carved chair listening to its sad unfolding, there was little of cheer she had to pass on to the secret council. It did not seem to matter anymore that the South had the best generals and the best officers, and that the southern rank-and-file fought like demons under their aegis. As the North ran through one bumbling general after another, and northern men died by the thousands because of their ineptitude, the northern war machine ground inexorably on; Virginia was a shambles of blood and ruin, and for all his expertise, Lee could not take Washington, could make no inroads into the North.

In New Orleans hope was still high that relief would come. Despite all the Yankee efforts, the Mississippi was still in Confederate hands. They looked hopefully to the north for help that would expel the Yankee garrison in the city, which was like a stopper in the bottle of the great river. But during 1863 these hopes were slowly whittled away; in May, Fort Gibson fell, and in Black July, Marie had the doubly unpleasant task of passing on the news of the southern defeat at Gettysburg and the fall of Vicksburg and Port Hudson, which put the control of the river wholly in Yankee hands. There would be no help from the north, though doggedly the Confederate troops hung on in northern Louisiana – among them, and miraculously unscathed after God knows how many encounters with the enemy, Justin LeBlanc and François Laveau.

Among all the grimness there was other, more personal, news. Word at last had been received from Bayard Valdoux and Denys Devereux, both at least alive, if not well, in a Yankee prison camp. St Regis had continued his meteoric rise, becoming a full colonel after the Chickamauga victory, only to fall victim to a sniper's bullet at the siege of Knoxville. The bullet did not kill, but shattered a hipbone and shattered with it, at the same instant, his hopes and chances of becoming a general. When he was sufficiently recovered, they put him in charge of a prisoner-of-war camp.

'God help the prisoners!' Marie remarked when she heard the news.

Most importantly, from her point of view, Captain Foster had succeeded in his mission shortly after he had been charged with it, and she had news from Chicago.

Claire had written in her schoolgirlish hand:

My dear Aunt Marie,

You can scarcely imagine the sorrow or the joy with which your letter was received here: sorrow to hear of the deaths of dear Mr Andersen and Jethro – though our imaginings had, after so much silence and absence, been even more fearsome than the terrible facts; and joy to hear that at least you are safe and unharmed.

I hasten to say that all is well here. Ingrid is beautiful and happy and well. Patty looks to her with devotion and seems to have forgotten all about New Orleans. Mrs Andersen is a saint, and has loved and cared for us all as well as, if not better than, any mother could have done. Mr Andersen passed away from a heart ailment six months after we arrived here and Mr Nils disappeared.

It has not been easy, but we have managed. With the money Mr Nils left with us and my dowry money, Mrs Andersen has started a small bakery – she makes all kinds of delicious Swedish pastries and has taught me to make them, also. Although times are hard here in Chicago, we are managing to get by, though if prices get higher and flour scarcer I do not know about the future . . .

321

Marie stopped reading and stared long and thoughtfully at the last sentence before continuing.

. . . You say nothing about joining us, dear Aunt, and I fear with this terrible war that it may not be easy to do so. But I miss you so, and pray that one day we may all be together again. Until then be assured that I will devote myself to Ingrid and Patty, and do whatever needs to be done for their welfare.

Mrs Andersen loves Ingrid most tenderly. When she read of Mr Nils's death, she did not cry as I did, but instead took Ingrid on her lap and said, 'Nils is not dead to me, nor will he ever be, for he lives on in this child, and I will cherish her as I did him.' And, indeed, Ingrid is now the spitting image of her father, even to the lock of hair that will flop over her forehead no matter which way I fix it . . .

Marie stopped reading again, her eyes blind with pain. When she started to read once more, there was not much else to the letter.

. . . But I think she has your eyes, because they are now a dark, lustrous brown, with the most amazing pupils. I hope to hear more news of you soon, dear Aunt, and, better still, to see you.

Your loving Claire

Marie thought very hard and very long about the letter, and an idea which had been at the back of her mind began to assert itself. The child was well, happy, and loved – and, more importantly, was beyond her mother's reach. Things would have to remain that way, much as it grieved her to give up this last link to happiness.

She took fifteen hundred dollars of her fast-dwindling hoard and entrusted it to Captain Foster, hoping fervently he was as honest as he seemed. He was shortly to go on leave and agreed without question to deliver the money. She further entrusted him with two letters: one for general consumption in the Andersen household; one for Claire's eyes alone. In that she wrote bluntly:

322

My dear Claire,

I have already put a heavy burden upon you, but I will now put an even heavier one. I will not be joining you. I am what I am, and it is too late to change that. You have entered a new life, a new world, to which you can belong, and Ingrid has a world to which she does belong. It is not my world, and it will be better for her if she remains unaware of me. She is too young now to question, so, for the moment, we can go on as we are. But when she does get old enough to ask questions, well, then it will be best for everyone if I 'die'. Until then I will send money for her and her education when I can. As I explained in the other letter, a thousand dollars of the money Captain Foster will deliver to you is for you and yours alone, and I trust you will one day find a husband as good and as true as you are. After I 'die' I will continue to send money through the Valdoux bank. You can explain it as being money from my estate, but from then on it will be for you to look to Ingrid until such time as she marries. But, be assured, Claire, that as long as I have breath in my body, neither of you will want or go without anything . . .

Claire's letter back was long and chatty and made no mention of this second missive, but at the bottom she added a brief postscript:

I understand and will do everything that you say.

Marie read it and marvelled how two such woolly minded, impractical parents as Jacqueline and Dominic had ever managed to produce such a sensible child.

Marie was now much occupied with another matter. The winter solstice was approaching and her mother was convinced that this was the appropriate time for her to take over as Queen of the Voodoos. 'It is better now, because there is bound to be some opposition from the delegate "Queens" who have been presiding,' the older woman explained. 'And it's best to have this fight over and done with before the great rites of St John's Eve. A lot of the ideas you've told me about I agree with entirely – especially about moving all

323

but the great rite closer to town. Everybody is too busy with his own problems to bother about what we do anymore, and it will simplify matters. As to the rest . . .' – she shrugged – '. . . well, that's up to you now. We've always had our own saints like Makandal, but if you think it's a good idea to make all these other Christian saints part of the rites, you must do it. The old ways do not seem to have much meaning for them anymore; perhaps the new ones will have.'

Marie looked at her mother curiously. 'You have no regrets about any of this?'

Marie Laveau stared back at her. 'It is what was meant to be. I have been Queen for over thirty-five years! A very long time. It is not an easy thing you are taking on, but it is what you have been trained for for the past twenty years.'

There were conferences with Crocodile, Mama Antoine, and a new *hungan*, Dan, a protégé of Crocodile's, who had taken the dead *hungan* Thomas's place and who was very enthusiastic about the proposed changes.

Moving the rites to their new location close to Maison Blanche required a lot of organization, and plans were made also to counteract any opposition that might originate from 'Queen' Eliza and her supporters. In keeping with tradition, Marie had to acquire a snake of her own. This presented problems, since the war had closed the route to Africa. She tried, without success, to get a South American python, but this particular difficulty was overcome when a snake-charmer from a circus was found in the city, stranded by the war and starving, and only too willing to part with his largest python for ready cash.

The scene was set; it was time for the climax. The news that a new Queen was in the making had spread through the New Orleans grapevine, and the crowd that showed up at the new site was larger than any of them had anticipated. This was in their favour, since Queen Eliza and her coterie were greatly outnumbered by newcomers, who were uncommitted, excited, and intensely curious.

Marie had expected to be nervous, but the electric atmosphere, the sense of eager expectation, exhilarated her, and she could feel the power growing within her as the preliminaries of the fire-lighting proceeded. Her mother and she were dressed in identical light blue robes with the heavy indigo cords around their waists, and when they were standing side by side it struck Marie how much her mother had dwindled in both size and stature since they had last done this together. Even her movements, which had always been so sure and strong, had become hesitant and slow.

The drums had started their hypnotic beat, and the dance of the candles was winding around before them as they stood by the leaping fire. Out of the corner of her eye, Marie could see Eliza with a crowd of her supporters standing sullenly at the edge of the centre circle, and wondered at what point, if any, she would make her move and challenge the proceedings. Crocodile decapitated the first rooster and sprayed its blood into the crowd, quickly followed by *Hungan* Dan and two other young men. Still nothing happened. The candles were hurled into the fire and the drums dropped into dramatic silence.

Her mother, who had taken a step forward, slowly raised her arms. 'Hear me!' she called out. 'Hear me for the last time, O children of Vodun!' There were a few scattered groans from the crowd. 'For long I have served you and Vodun as Queen of these rites, but now my day is done. My star wanes and another rises. I present your new Queen. I, Marie Laveau, present Marie Laveau.'

Marie, as rehearsed, took a step up to her side. She was vaguely aware of someone starting to shout, and then she completely blacked out. Afterwards, she was told that she had spun around like a top to crash twitching on the ground. Eliza had started forward into the circle screaming, but no one had paid any attention to her, for from Marie had come a loud, booming voice speaking in a strange tongue that had terrified the crowd, and, at the same time, a sudden squall of wind had sprung up within the circle, causing the great fire to roar skywards with an angry voice. Eliza had reeled away from it back into the crowd, and had collapsed there unnoticed, as Marie rose again to her feet and had stretched her arms out to the flames . . .

At this point her own memory had returned and she was

shouting, 'Hear me, oh, my people ...!' There was not a whisper from the stunned crowd, and she went on with her prepared sermon. 'We are not a house divided, but a house united. Most of you, I know, go to the Christian Church and pray to the Man of Sorrows and the Virgin and the saints as if they were separate and different. I say to you that this is wrong. God has many faces, but in truth they are all part of the One. *We* have our Virgin in Erzulie, we have our St Michael in Dan, we have our St Peter in Legba, who guards the gate of Heaven. When you pray to one, you pray to the other. *But* – and it is a very important "but" – Vodun and his saints have their roots and origins in the same place *you* have your roots and origins. And Vodun, like you, was brought across the seas to comfort and to help you in your time of trials. This still is your time of trial – turn to him and let him help you. Serve him and he will serve you ...' There was not so much as a sigh in the crowd as she elaborated on the theme; it was as if the whole world held its breath, waiting.

Finally, she wound up with the extra garnish she had conceived, but only after much soul-searching. 'To me the *loa* have spoken, and they have shown me a special place for you all – a place where, if you go with a clean heart, your wishes may be granted if it please Vodun. There is a large weeping willow close to the spot, overhanging the bayou; you may recognize it because across the water is another fallen tree – this the *loa* have pointed out to me as the "Wishing Spot"...' It was a place of power, she reflected with bitterness, for there she had seen the Helper, and the only wish she had ever made there had come about all too soon and all too terribly. 'There you may go when there are no rites, for help and for comfort. And may the God grant your wishes and be with you!' She gave a signal and the drums took up a soft beat. 'Let the dancing and celebration begin,' she called.

And the thudding drums were drowned out by a sudden full-throated roar that burst from the crowd. *'Vive la nouvelle Reine!'* it roared. *'Vive la Reine Marie!'*

She mounted the chest which held the sleeping snake and

stood silent as the mad rhythm of the dance began. Would they come to her now, as they had come to her mother? She stood with bowed head and fast-beating heart, but was not left long in doubt. People crowded around, touching her timidly, holding out their arms to her, their anxious black faces shining in the firelight. 'Help me ... Cure me ... Comfort me ...'

A great wave of compassion such as she had never felt before swept over her. She stretched out her arms to them. 'Come!' she said. 'Oh, come!'

Her mother and she had lifted the snake, and the crowd had sunk to its knees. 'Vodun!' it had cried. 'Vodun!'

The rite was ended. She was dreadfully weary, so drained that she could hardly walk erect back to the gig. She was thankful that Maison Blanche – where she intended to spend the night – was near at hand.

The elder Marie also felt the strain, for she sat slumped on the seat beside her daughter, not saying a word, as Crocodile drove them back to the house. Just as they reached it, she slumped heavily against Marie and a curious snoring noise came from her throat.

'Crocodile!' Marie exclaimed in sudden panic. 'Something is wrong! Stop the gig!' She tried to push the heavy, inert body away from her.

'For God's sake, what is it?' He jumped down and held up the lantern to Marie Laveau's face. Her eyes were blank and a small trickle of saliva ran down one side of the flaccid, open mouth.

'Quick!' he commanded. 'We must get her inside. I think your mother has had a stroke ...'

Chapter Thirty-six

The stroke had had no lasting physical effects, but Marie Laveau was greatly changed none the less. She kept almost entirely to her room, and would see only Jean and a few of her old friends and clients. To Marie, when she had recovered her speech, she had said without animosity or any other emotion, 'I am finished with it and with you. Now it is all up to you. Leave me be.'

As 1865 dawned and grew, the problems of the Laveaus mounted. A grey-faced Jean-Paul had slipped through the enemy lines and had come home to Marie-Philome. He had not been wounded, but it was evident that there was something seriously amiss, for he was in constant pain and was wasted away to almost a skeleton. A worried, if eternally optimistic, Marie-Philome had taken him and her family back to South Rampart Street to nurse him back to health.

Marie, having consulted with Dr Franke, was less optimistic. That overworked and harassed man had shaken his head and said, 'Well it could be half a dozen things, but I very much fear it is an incurable tumour of the bowels – only time will tell. He could last for months, or years.'

Not that Marie-Philome's going had eased the pressure much on the St Ann Street house, for Marie-Jeanne and her family were still there, her husband having been conscripted into a federal work force and shipped off. Since Marie had never found her much more compatible than Celeste, this made living conditions more trying now that the peace-keeping Marie-Philome was no longer there to stop the constant feuds. In fact, Celeste even contrived to quarrel with the amiable Jean. She was sorely tempted to move back to Maison Blanche, despite its horrible memories, but the mail-order business that flowed into the cottage was still her main source of income, and she did not trust any of the family sufficiently to leave it in their hands. So, feeling trapped for the moment, she decided to withstand the pressures at the cottage and simply stay out of the house as much as possible.

One day in early spring she was walking in the weak sunshine through Jackson Square, when she saw Emile Valdoux. She had avoided him deliberately ever since her return to the city, for what had passed between them that day at Maison Blanche had altered their friendship, striking at its foundations, and she felt he probably no more wanted to see her than she did him. Now, however, she stopped, shocked by what she saw. There was grey in his coppery locks, his face had fallen away and was lined and thin, and on it was such an expression of abject misery that her heart turned over at the sight. He was sitting at the base of the Jackson statue, gazing unseeingly at the riot of spring flowers in the square. She could not pass by such sorrow, so, nerving herself, she went up to him. 'Emile, what on earth is the matter? What ails you?'

He looked up at her blankly for a second, then said flatly, 'I don't think I can go on. I'm finished, just as the South is finished.'

'Stop it! That's not like you!' she scolded, then sat down beside him. 'Do you want to tell me about it? Can I help? Or is it too private?'

'Private!' he snorted, with a momentary return to his old self. 'Between us? That's a laugh!'

'Well, then, tell me,' she coaxed.

He told. It came pouring out of him like a torrent: Paul Valdoux lay at the point of death in Richmond after suffering a heart attack; the bank's affairs were in chaos; if Bayard could not be exchanged soon, he would not be in time to see Clarisse alive; Marie-Thérèse and Valerie were at one another's throats, and he was worried about his own wife's mental health in consequence, for she had never fully recovered from the shock of their dispossession ... and on and on. Slowly the torrent subsided to a trickle, then dried up altogether. He gave a heavy sigh, then turned and gave her a watery grin. 'Well,' he said, 'what do you say to all that?'

She shrugged and said dryly, 'It sounds just like life in the happy Laveau household. If misery loves company welcome to the growing band!' Then she became more serious. 'There's not much I can do about most of it, but what if I could get Marie-Thérèse and Valerie off your hands? Would that help?'

He looked at her in amazement. 'In the name of Heaven, how?'

'By seeing they got through to Castle Blanche. Let's face it, Emile, the war will soon be over, and there has been no big offensive in the Mississippi valley since Vicksburg. Chances are there won't be now, with the North so close to victory. They'd be safe enough, and Justin will soon be home.'

'But how would they get through the federal lines?'

'At the moment I don't know, but I do know it *can* be done, so I'll find out. Do you want me to try? It would ease things for you, wouldn't it?'

He looked at her for a long moment, then shook his head, a faint smile on his lips. 'No. Since I've gone this far, I think I can keep going just a bit longer. You are right – it is only a matter of months now before our destruction is complete.'

'How is your mother taking all this?'

'Remarkably well. She never ceases to astonish me. When the news arrived about my father, I kept it from her for a while, thinking it would kill her for sure, but when I did nerve myself to tell her, she was a great deal calmer about it than I. In fact, she quite shocked me. All she said was, "If it is your father's time to go, he will go in the knowledge that he has served a cause in which he believed faithfully to the end." I cannot get over the change in her. She, who was nervous about everything, now fears nothing, and is stronger than us all.'

Marie kept quiet, but she felt she understood Madame Valdoux a great deal better than her son did.

Emile got up and smiled down at her. 'Well, I must get back to my labours. Thanks for listening to my woes, Marie. It's good to have you back. It has been a long time – far too long.' And he walked off with something of his old bounce.

330

Why was it, Marie pondered, as she hurried down St Ann Street in the dark that night, that her encounters with the Valdouxs always seemed to happen in pairs? Emile this morning, and now an unexpected and mysterious summons from Claire.

She had been called from the acrimonious atmosphere of the Laveau supper table to find the aged Montal butler waiting for her in the front parlour. He was the same one who had once smugly witnessed her ignominious expulsion by St Regis from the Montal mansion, but he was now in a state of pitiful agitation as he begged her to return to the same house immediately. 'Miz Claire says to tell you she is in most desperate need o' your help, an' would you come right away.'

They entered the dark, shuttered house through the wicket gate, and the old slave led her past the empty slave quarters into the kitchen, where he lighted a candle with shaking hands. Then he led her into the magnificence of the front of the house, which reeked of musty damp and dust, and up the grand staircase, whose balustrade under Marie's fingers was gritty with collected dirt. On the second floor he scratched a gilded door and it opened to reveal Claire Montal.

Marie was as shocked to see her as she had been to see Emile, for, since last sighting, Claire had aged twenty years. She looked at Marie out of reddened, distraught eyes and sighed, 'Thank God you have come! I beg you to help us!' Signalling the old man to leave them, she drew Marie in and closed the door, then leaned against it as if her legs would no longer support her. 'Oh, dear God, I hope you can do something! I am at my wits' end!'

Another one! thought Marie grimly. Aloud she said, 'What is it? What has happened?'

'It's Anne,' Claire said in a whisper. 'Tonight she tried to kill her mother – I fear she has lost her mind.'

Marie's eyebrows shot up. 'Where is she?'

Claire literally wrung her hands. 'She was so violent ... we didn't know what to do ... Dominic and I managed to tie

331

her up, but we can't *keep* her like that. Oh, what shall we do?'

'Well, start by telling me how it came about.'

Claire sighed and looked away from Marie. 'I'm afraid Aunt Margot was taunting her about the usual thing – about being an old maid whom no one had ever wanted. They usually just insult one another until they are exhausted . . .' Her tone was dreary. 'But tonight Anne seemed to go berserk. She snatched up a knife and shouted, "I'll kill you! I'll kill you!" And then she attacked my aunt before Dominic or I could stop her.'

'Was Madame Montal hurt?' Marie said, a cold shiver going up her spine.

'Her arm was cut. I bound it up as well as I could,' Claire faltered. 'But perhaps you'd better have a look.'

'Yes, I probably should,' Marie said grimly. 'Where's Dominic?'

Claire's imploring gaze slid away from hers. 'Out – he went out,' she whispered.

'To get a doctor?'

'Oh, no . . .!' It was almost a moan. 'We couldn't . . . the scandal . . .!'

Marie's exasperation mounted. 'Well, I don't know what I can do. It's obviously a case *for* a doctor, but at least I'll have a look.'

They passed through the dark echoing corridors to the vast master bedroom, where a grey-faced Madame Montal stared icily through Marie and did not say a word, but did submit to having the clumsy bandage removed, the arm bathed, and a more effective bandage put on. The wound was long, but not deep, and Marie thought that, apart from the shock, the old woman was probably in much better shape than her daughter-in-law, who stood so numbly by.

Then there was more echoing corridor and another cavernous bedroom, where a very old black woman crouched over a single candle by the great bed.

'My "mammy",' Claire whispered. 'My mother sent her to me after all our own slaves went – she cooks for us now.'

They tiptoed quietly up to the bed, where Anne Montal,

her wrists tied with knotted rags to the bed-posts, gazed at them with hate-filled eyes. Marie noted with a qualm of revulsion that the fine bed linen which lay crumpled under her was grey with ingrained dirt. She started to talk to the demented woman on the bed, whose body started to writhe and twist but whose eyes she held with a snake-like fascination until the heavy lids drooped into half-slits and finally closed altogether.

'You can untie her now,' Marie whispered to Claire. 'I've put her into a hypnotic sleep. She won't wake up from it until I tell her to.'

Claire looked at her with horrified wonder. 'But how long can you keep her like that? Will she be all right when she wakes up?'

Marie shrugged. 'Probably not. She needs a doctor. All I can do is to keep hypnotizing her – it won't cure her; it will just keep her quiet.'

'A doctor is out of the question.' Claire began to weep quietly. 'What can I do?'

An idea had come to Marie as she had passed all the great, empty rooms of the Montal mansion. Depressing as it undoubtedly was, it was spacious and airy, and it was quiet – none of which could be said for her present circumstances. 'I tell you what I could do, if you were agreeable,' she said cautiously. 'If I could move into a room here, I could keep an eye on the situation, and if she shows signs of violence again, we would be able to control her.'

'Oh, *would* you?' Claire began eagerly. But then her face fell and she stammered, 'But you know we have no help of any kind now ... Everything is such a mess ... It's all Mammy can do to cook a meal a day, and Ephraim is beyond anything but running errands ...'

'That's all right,' Marie pressed quickly. 'I'll bring my own things, and I'll look after myself – it's just the room. However, if you'd rather not ...'

'It would be such a relief to me.' Claire's tone was pleading. 'You could have Yolande's old room, if that would suit you.'

So Marie installed herself in the faded magnificence of

Yolande Montal's bedroom, which, after she had swept and dusted it, thrown wide the shutters, polished the mirrors, and put her own clean linen on the bed, took on something of its old splendour. When she had finished, she looked around at the fine marble mantelpiece, the glittering girandoles, the petit-point chairs, and the dainty Louis XVI bedroom suite, and she laughed to herself ironically. 'So here I am at last – little Marie Laveau, a guest of the mighty Montals. To what giddy heights have you reached, Marie?'

In strict confidence she consulted Dr Franke, who provided her with counsel and sedatives far stronger than anything she could devise. So Anne improved enough and became tractable enough to be allowed free of her bedroom imprisonment.

Marie, on her part, was discreetly self-effacing – coming and going on her many errands through the kitchen entrance, so that Madame Montal was unaware of her presence in the house, and Dominic himself, in his alcoholic fog, only dimly aware. It suited her very well, and, free of the continual bickering and harassment of life at the cottage, her spirits and energy rose despite the worsening of the news from the war fronts.

One bit of news sent her hurrying on another errand of mercy. Bayard Valdoux was at last to be exchanged, but his letter bearing this information also bore the sad tidings of Denys Devereux's death in the camp from exhaustion and dysentery. *Poor Veronique!* was Marie's first thought. *I must go to her and give her what help I can. What a state she'll be in!*

She hurried out to the grand new mansion the Devereuxs had had built out by the old Allard plantation. And she was a little nonplussed to be left cooling her heels for quite a while before Veronique appeared. She was clad in elegant and deep mourning, but appeared very calm and self-possessed. After they had exchanged greetings, Veronique, to Marie's amazement, said coolly and with some condescension. 'And what can I do for you, Marie?'

'Well, I really came to see what *I* could do for *you* – I was so desperately sorry to hear the sad news of Denys.'

'Oh, that was most kind of you. Yes, indeed, it was tragic, a great tragedy,' Veronique murmured, as if she was talking about some sad occurrence that had nothing to do with her. She glanced uneasily at the small gold watch she had pinned to her black bodice.

'Yes ... well ... if I can help in any way,' Marie said, more than a little taken aback.

The door opened suddenly, causing them both to jump, and a distinguished grey head appeared around it. 'Veronique, my dear,' it began, then broke off in mid-sentence on seeing Marie.

'Oh, come in, Monsieur Parise. I was expecting you,' Veronique said smoothly, but she had gone a little pink in the face. An equally distinguished slim figure followed the head, and Monsieur Parise came towards them, an expression of inquiry on the long, well-bred face. 'Monsieur Parise is a lawyer-advocate and has been most kind in helping me with my business affairs,' Veronique explained to Marie. 'Armand, this is Marie Laveau, an old ...' – she stopped – '... friend of mine.'

He bowed politely to Marie and kissed Veronique's hand. 'Your servant, ma'am.'

She swept him an upward glance full of meaning, and then they both looked expectantly at Marie.

She gathered her astonished wits together and said hurriedly, 'Well, I must not keep you, Veronique – but I did want to see that all was well.'

'Most kind,' Veronique murmured again, but she did not press Marie to stay.

'Don't bother to have me shown out. I'll find my way,' Marie said with as much dignity as she could muster. But as she reached the door, she could not resist a backward glance, and she saw that they were so busy gazing at one another that they had already quite forgotten her.

Once outside, her first feeling of annoyance gave way to amusement. First she began to chuckle and then to chortle. 'Well, I'll be double-damned!' It was a little late to realize it, but she should long since have seen that a seventeen-year-old who had stood up to the pressure Veronique had endured, had more to her than met the eye. In fact, when Marie came to think of it, Veronique Grison DuBois Devereux – sure to be Parise as soon as decently possible – had always got exactly what she wanted out of life. 'That should teach you!' she chortled to herself. 'You're getting as bad as Emile, my girl! Next time wait to be asked. If there is one person who does not need your help, it is undoubtedly Veronique Devereux!' And she laughed all the way home to the gloomy purlieus of the Montal mansion.

Chapter Thirty-seven

The war was over; the sad drama of Appomattox had been played out, the South lay open to the victor's thrust. Virginia and Georgia lay in ruins; most of the other Confederate states were scarred and crippled; but Louisiana, rich and tempting, was virtually unscathed – an irresistible morsel for the hungry North.

Marie, for one, did not like to think what that presaged for the future. No prophetic powers were needed to know that the future was unlikely to be good. She already knew from her Yankee soirées that the garrison was going to remain – 'to prevent the danger of civil insurrection', as Captain Foster had informed her blandly. And, she thought with bitterness, the garrison would also help to keep the population subdued when the pillaging began.

Not that such future worries claimed much of her attention; she had enough immediate problems to deal with. The soirées had become a habit, though far less profitable than in the plush days of the past, but now that she could no longer serve a useful function for the powers in the city, she wondered if she could even maintain them at all. The mail-order business, now that the killing had stopped, had fallen off, but it was still her main source of income – and there were still all those hungry mouths to feed at the St Ann Street cottage. In the Montal household it was an uphill battle to deal with Anne Montal, as she retreated further and further into the darkness of her mind. Sometimes, in spite of all Marie's efforts, she would become so violent that they would be forced to lock her up in a small, bare room on the top floor until the fit had passed.

Marie was also becoming increasingly worried about Claire Montal, on whom all the cares of the household fell and who was visibly withering under the strain. Madame Montal had retreated from the realities of poverty, sitting all day in her darkened room, issuing impossible orders and making grandiose plans for the return of her war hero – an eventuality Marie was dreading. Dominic was useless; he was rarely at home, anyway, and when he was, he was usually too drunk to know what was going on. The two old servants were too bewildered and broken to be of any practical help. So it all fell on Claire, and it was a situation for which Marie could see no solution.

So matters stood as one mild May evening she and Claire sat quietly by Anne's bedside. She had been increasingly restless that day, and Marie had put her into a deep hypnotic sleep so that they might all get a small respite. The windows stood wide open, letting in the comforting sound of street noises and some of the balmy air to soften the chill of the vault-like house. They were sitting in the silence of weary companionship when suddenly the great double doors of the bedroom flew open, and St Regis stalked into the room, Dominic shuffling behind him. He was still wearing the uniform of a Confederate colonel, much travel-stained, and he walked with a ferocious limp, but there was nothing of the defeated in his bearing.

His face had thinned out, accentuating the proud beak of the Montal nose and the firm, long line of the Montal jaw, the amber eyes under the hooded lids hard and angry. He looked taut and virile and very, very dangerous. Beside him, Dominic appeared like an obscene caricature, for the drinking had bloated his features to such a degree that the bone structure of his face had disappeared, his eyes being mere slits encased in puffy bags.

St Regis stood in the centre of the room glaring at them. Then he snarled at Claire, 'How dare you let that woman under my roof! How dare you let her lay her dirty hands on a Montal!' Then swinging on Marie, he said, 'I want you out of here, bag and baggage, in the next five minutes, or, by God, I'll take a horse-whip to you!'

Claire sprang to her feet with a little cry, twin spots of colour flaring on the pale cheeks. 'St Regis, you don't know what you are saying! Without Marie we would have been lost, completely lost. Poor Anne is mad, do you hear, quite

338

mad! Marie has been my help, my support. Without her, we'd have been finished. She is here as my guest in my home – you'll not insult her so!'

'*Your* home?' he sneered. 'Since when has it been *your* home? This house is *mine*!'

'And Dominic's,' Claire said firmly. And for the first time, Marie saw the St Yves blood in her. 'And as Dominic's wife, I have been mistress here and have managed this house ever since your mother became incapable.'

'Then I warrant the house is the only thing you have been mistress of,' St Regis said with a cruel laugh. 'Eh, Dominic?'

Claire let out a little gasp of pain, and Marie interrupted hurriedly: 'Claire, it's all right. Maybe it is better that I go. Please don't get yourself upset. St Regis will soon see how it is with Anne, and that she must have proper medical care.'

'*No!*' Claire was angry now. 'If my life is to be bearable here, this must be decided now! You have done more for me than anyone, even my own family. If you go, *I* will go! So if you do not want further scandal, St Regis, it is up to you.'

Marie made a warning gesture, but in vain. St Regis was now regarding his prey with narrowed eyes. 'Oh, no – not up to me,' he said softly, 'up to your husband, surely! What do you say, Dominic? Do you want this unappetizing bag of bones around anymore, or are you finished with her?'

Dominic had slumped down in a chair and apparently had lost interest in the proceedings. 'Eh?' he said blearily. 'Want *her*? No, I've never wanted her – not since the day we were married . . .'

Claire cried out in protest, 'Dominic, please, not now!'

But he ignored her and shouted with the sudden temper of a drunk. 'Yes – you get out, too! Always nagging, always interfering, damned holier-than-thou Valdoux cow – we don't need you anymore! St Regis is back now, and every-thing'll be all right. It will, won't it?' he appealed to his brother, who stood with a satisfied smile on his thin lips.

Claire gave a little moan and covered her face with her

hands. She turned blindly towards Marie. 'I *did* try . . . I've tried so hard,' she said in a broken voice.

'I know.' Marie was boiling with anger. 'But now, perhaps, you'll do what Emile has wanted for years – what, for your own sake, you should have done years ago – leave this cursed family and that drunken sot to their own damnation.' She wheeled on St Regis. 'I'm taking her out of here. We'll be gone in an hour, and you'd better not interfere or stand in our way. And, by God, St Regis, you don't know what a favour you've done us! May you rot with everything else in this house!'

He took a step towards her and she thought for a moment he was going to club her down. Then apparently he changed his mind, for he gave a short, hard laugh and repeated, 'Just get out and stay out. When I come back, I'll expect to find you gone. Come, Dominic, let's go and see Mother and get some order in this damned menagerie . . .'

Marie had collected up the now-sobbing Claire, the old Mammy – whom she was not about to leave in St Regis's clutches – and as many of their things as they could carry, and had shepherded them over to the Valdouxs's Royal Street house. To a grim-faced Emile, she had related what had transpired. At the end of the narration, she looked at him a little hopelessly. 'I know Claire's coming home is something you've wanted for years, but I also know this is not exactly the best time for it to have happened. Can you manage? Is there room for her?'

'Oh, yes, we'll manage,' he assured her, 'even if she has to share her old room with Marie-Thérèse for a while. But how about you, Marie? Where can you go at this time of night?'

'It's all right, Emile,' she said, with more cheerfulness than she felt. 'I'll go back to St Ann Street for the moment. I can always tuck in somewhere.'

'I wish I could offer you something here, but there's nothing. I'm most profoundly grateful to you . . .'

'Oh, for pity's sake, spare me your thanks,' Marie sighed. 'You should know by this time that I wouldn't leave a dog at the mercy of St Regis, let alone someone whom I'm as fond of as your sister.'

But as she tossed in the narrow stuffiness of Patty's old room that night, she thought wistfully of the deserted grandeur of her Montal apartment. It had been a respite from the demands of her family, who had appeared no more glad to see her than she had been to see them. Celeste's eldest girl had had to be dispossessed of even this little room, with much attendant grumbling. The crowding, the poor food, the uncertainties of tomorrow were wearing down everyone's nerves to the breaking point, and even the amiable Jean had become moody and withdrawn. It was intolerable, but for the moment she could see no solution to the problem. There was something else that worried her; in her absence the whole atmosphere of the house had changed – something beyond the hostility of Celeste, the irritability of Marie-Jeanne . . . something which sent cold prickles of unease up her spine, and which threatened . . .

Two days after her return, she found out what it was. She had been out to the Wishing Tree to marvel anew at the miracle she had created. Whenever she had been, it was to find people gathered several ranks deep around it, silent and rapt in their supplications. Word had spread through the black community that this was a place of wonder, a place of power – its success was already an established fact in people's minds. It amazed as much as it heartened her, and she was feeling in consequence almost lighthearted as she came back to the cottage. But the minute she entered the left parlour she became aware of loud, angry voices coming from her mother's sacrosanct domain on the right, the door of which stood wide open. She hurried in on a dramatic scene.

Jean was white with anger and shouting, 'You'd no right to go snooping in there! You might have killed her, you stupid bitch, you and your damned interfering!'

Celeste, also livid, faced him, her arms akimbo and her lips drawn back in a snarl. Her daughters, like a battery of scared hens, huddled in one corner of the room. Marie-Jeanne and her howling children crouched in another '*I!*' she screamed. 'If harm comes to her, it will be the Devil taking his due, for Devil's work she's been at – and you've been helping her! You and that cursed Voodoo Marie!'

'What *is* all this?' Marie cried above the din.

Celeste wheeled on her and pointed a shaking finger. 'You're part of it!' she accused. 'Don't deny this is you and your Devil's work!'

'Part of *what*? I have no idea what all this is about, I've been back only a couple of days. What is it? Has something happened to Mother?' she appealed to Jean.

'Yes!' he shouted. 'She's had another attack, and it's all Celeste's fault! Snooping in Mother's bedroom, where she had no business to be, when Mother was busy with a client in here.'

'*My* fault!' Celeste shrilled. '*Mine!* Her own evil doings caused it. Faced with those unspeakable things I found, her sins came home to her and God smote her down. Those things *you* must have brought to her – don't deny it!'

'*What* things?' Marie cried.

'I'll show you,' Celeste hissed. 'But I think you know full well what I'm talking about. Come!'

She scuttled into the darkened bedroom, Marie close behind, and threw wide the doors of the big armoire. '*That's* what!' she said triumphantly.

Marie recoiled in horror. A mummified black baby, its tiny eyes and mouth gaping open in ghastly semblance of life, looked out at her. In a small bath of noisome-smelling liquid, another small black body floated sluggishly, and a third small body, looking like a bit of shrivelled, petrified stone, sat propped against the back of the cabinet. 'Oh, dear God!' she whispered, as the full import of what she was seeing flooded over her, and she felt her senses darken.

When Marie's vision cleared, Celeste was looking at her uncertainly. 'You *didn't* know?' She shook her head numbly and made a move towards the prone figure on the bed, but Celeste sprang in front of her. 'No!' she shrilled. 'None of your Devil's tricks. *I* will look to her and save her immortal soul, even if I can't save her body. I have sent for the priest, who will help me. But I want you both out of here now, or I'll call the police, as well. You and that Devil's assistant!' She shot a look of hatred at Jean.

'Yes, I cannot stay now,' Marie murmured, her thoughts in a whirling chaos. So her mother had not given up; her mother must all along have been working on the same lines that she herself so many years ago ... She glanced at Jean, whose panic-stricken eyes told her that at least part of Celeste's surmise had been correct; he must have brought those babies to her mother ... 'For the present you had better come, too,' she said quietly, 'at least until we can straighten some things out.'

In the clearer air of the front parlour, Marie collected herself and turned on Celeste, who had been following on her heels like an avenging Fate. 'Now, look,' she said with firmness, 'I do not know what all this is about, but for reasons of my own I no longer wish to remain here. But let me make things very clear to you. You are living here on *my* charity. Mother's money is gone; her properties are bringing in nothing because no one has money to pay anymore. So it is *my* money that is keeping this place and you going. The mail-order business has to go on from here, and I shall be coming by constantly to collect and check on it. And woe betide you if you try to hinder or cheat me, because for all I care, you and your family can starve. Is *that* clear?'

Celeste, taken aback by this sudden change, nodded dumbly.

'Now, I'm relying on you to bring Mother around from this spell, and until she is better, Jean will stay away, but when she is recovered, she will certainly want to see him, and when she does, he will be allowed to. Is *that* clear?'

Celeste started to protest, but Marie cut her short. 'It will be as *we* say – Mother and I – or out you go! The only rights you have here are the ones we give you – don't forget that. But do right by Mother and play fair with me, and I will leave you a clear field. Marie-Jeanne will soon be going back to her own place, so you'll have it all to yourself. Think about that.'

Celeste grudgingly agreed to her terms, and Marie tugged the unwilling Jean away. For the second time in a week she had lost the roof over her head, but this roof now held for her nothing but old terrors. She would have to go back to Maison Blanche, with its own remembered horrors, but at least, she thought as she looked at Jean, numb with misery at her side, this time she would have a companion who knew how to suffer, too.

Chapter Thirty-eight

'I hear they're closing the Valdoux bank . . .'

The casually spoken words made Marie prick up her ears and sit up straighter in her great chair to listen in on the two federal officers who were gossiping idly behind her. 'They've disenfranchised the Creole who owns it, and maybe it'll be a matter of confiscation and prison for him, too, so I understand – a lucky windfall for someone. I wish I had a few friends in the right places . . .' They drifted off out of earshot.

'Reconstruction' in New Orleans was in full swing, and all Aristide's fears of the long-ago were being realized beyond even his wildest imaginings. The streets were flooded with hard-faced men from the North, and with rednecks from the country areas of Louisiana – people who had been overseers or foremen and just a little less ignorant than the slaves they had lorded over – all carrying the inevitable carpetbag, and all eager to carry off whatever spoils could be found in the helpless city.

It was not unusual these days to see Creole ladies walking in the narrow streets with heavy shopping baskets on their arms, being splashed with mud from the smart phaetons and gigs driven by flashily dressed Negroes – in some cases their own ex-slaves. It was a hard time, a make-or-break time; and while there were many who were making, there were many also who were breaking . . .

Marie found she was gripping the arms of her chair with painful intensity. Something had to be done – they couldn't do that to the Valdouxs! But what could she do?

The next day she hurried into the city and to the shuttered bank on Royal. Though his face was still drawn and careworn, for a man facing the prospect of prison and ultimate disaster, Emile appeared in excellent spirits, a sparkle in his eyes she had not seen for a very long time. Without even bothering with a greeting, she burst out, 'I've heard they're closing the bank and talking of confiscation. Is it true?'

'Oh, yes,' he said quite cheerfully. 'It's true enough – the bank *is* closed. As to the confiscation, well, that's still up in the air.'

'But *why*? You haven't done anything wrong. Why you?'

'Does there have to be a reason these days?' He looked at her quizzically. 'Actually, I'm afraid it is not so much what I've done as "the sins of the fathers" – mine, after all, was a pretty important part of the Confederate government, and examples have to be made, apparently – a rampant case of *pour encourager les autres*, you know.'

Paul Valdoux had succumbed to his heart ailment in Richmond shortly before Appomattox, and Emile had not helped his present position by moving hell and high water to get to his dying father's bedside. He had not succeeded, but the very fact he had tried had tainted him in the eyes of the authorities and was now being held against him.

'But what are you going to *do*?' Marie almost wailed.

'Well, if I can't be a banker, I'll have to do something else – that is, if they don't put me in prison. I have one or two ideas.'

'Such as?'

'The banana business.'

Marie gasped. *'What?'*

He grinned at her. 'The banana business. People still have to eat. Even if they confiscate everything else, I've still got the two warehouses on the levee. I put them in my wife's name some time ago – it was an idea Dr Franke gave me – and they won't confiscate *her* property. I did the same with a couple of steamboats we managed to save. And part of Clarisse's dowry was a LeBlanc banana plantation down in Nicaragua or some such God-forsaken spot. I plan to turn the warehouses – or at least one of them – into banana-processing plants. There'll be no problem about labour; I've had half our old slaves from the upstate plantations here at my door begging for work of any kind. In fact, the boats are making their first trip right at this moment. We should go into business as soon as they arrive.'

'But what if they put you in prison?'

He became a little more serious. 'In that case, Bayard will have to carry on alone. Even they would scarcely stoop to picking on a crippled ex-soldier who has been in the hell of a prison camp for all those years.'

'Speaking of which – why don't they pick on people who *did* do them harm, instead of people like you, who never lifted a finger against them? It's so unfair! Why don't they pick on someone like St Regis? Talk of hell – I warrant some of the Union soldiers under his tender care could tell some tales!' Marie fumed.

'Oh, I don't think they'll do anything to St Regis.' There was a curious note in his voice.

'Why not? I bet he's as guilty as hell of all sorts of war crimes.'

'You've heard of a "scalawag"?' Emile inquired.

She shook her head.

'Well, it's a term that's been coined for a Southerner who's helping with the so-called "reconstruction"; one who's aiding and abetting the new powers that be in anything they choose to do. St Regis has become a scalawag.'

'How typical!' she snorted, then brightened. 'But maybe he can help you – particularly if he's "in" with the new group.'

'In view of past events, I scarcely think so,' he murmured with a wry smile. 'But I don't blame him for what he is doing. St Regis intends to survive – as I do,' he added quietly.

'This is no time to be saintly,' she snapped.

'Not saintly, merely realistic. I don't see what else St Regis could have done in his circumstances. I just happen to be more fortunate than he.'

'The code of Creole gentlemen!' Marie snorted again, but her mind was furiously at work, 'What about this house? What'll happen to the family if they confiscate this, as well?'

For the first time Emile looked downcast. 'They've already taken my own house,' he sighed. 'I rather am hoping they'll be satisfied with that. If not . . .' He gave a hopeless little shrug.

'What if this place didn't belong to you anymore?' she said eagerly. 'They couldn't take it then, could they?'

He looked at her, puzzled, and shook his head. 'No – but it *does* belong to me. It's too late to transfer it to my wife.'

'But you could sell it to *me*!'

He looked astonished. 'But you don't have any money! And, anyway, why would you want it?'

'Oh, not a *real* sale, you idiot – only on *paper*! I'd set up a hairdresser business – I've been toying with that idea for some time. And I could live behind the shop in your old office. I really do need a place in town, since I don't trust Celeste an inch, and it's hard to check on things while I'm out at Maison Blanche. I'd sign a paper saying I'd sell it back to you if things change for the same price I bought it at – which is nothing! – and that should cover everything.' Her tone was eager.

He looked dubious. 'I doubt whether they'd accept a sale at this late date.'

'Well then, back-date it! Who's to know?'

'That's illegal,' he said with horror.

She burst out laughing. 'Oh, Emile, you're *hopeless*, really hopeless! We're trying to save your ancestral home from the worst kind of carpetbaggers, and you talk about legality? Come on, now!'

He started to chuckle, too. 'Marie, I believe you're right. It's worth a try! Why not, indeed!'

She was privately determined that if anyone was going to jail, it would not be Emile. She pestered the few people she knew who still held positions of power in the city, but to little avail. It came as no surprise to her that so far as gratitude for past services went, their memories were woefully short, and they were far too concerned about their own survival and future prospects to worry about one of their number who had fallen prey to the new order. Only by making a thorough nuisance of herself, by veiled threats, and a little covert blackmail, was she able to stir up any action at all. It did not endear her to her victims, but at least there was no further talk of imprisonment, and although the bank remained closed, it was not confiscated. One of her contacts had asked viciously, 'What's so all-fired important to you about the Valdoux bank? There are plenty of other banks in the city.'

'Because one of these days I'm going to need it,' she had informed him. 'And I'm going to need it open.'

But, for the moment, they had to carry out their original plan, and she opened up her hairdressing salon in the old counting house and established her new foothold in the city in Emile's old office. At least, she reflected, I'm not likely to be kicked out of this one.

Her own hairdressing skills were so woefully rusty that she quickly imported one of her 'girls', who had also had training in the art. Marie confined her own activities to chatting with the customers and taking in the money. The minute she was back in the city, the mail-order gris-gris business immediately picked up, confirming her suspicions that Celeste had been siphoning off a portion of the spoils, but she did not make an issue of it, since, as far as her mother and Jean were concerned, Celeste appeared to be living up to her part of their bargain.

What exactly her mother had been up to at the time of her second stroke still puzzled Marie. The only thing she had been able to get out of Jean on the subject was that the babies had all been illegitimate ones that nobody wanted, least of all the mothers. But what for? Her mother could not still be after Ingrid, who was now well beyond the baby stage, though Marie had the uneasy feeling that it was in some way connected with her growing daughter. Baffled, she put it at the back of her mind and turned to more practical matters.

Between the hairdressing shop, her salons, the mail-order business, and her position as a successful Voodoo Queen, financially she was getting by, though every penny she could scrape together as surplus went north to support the needs of the Andersen household. Claire was a faithful correspondent, and, reading between the lines, Marie could tell that the widow Andersen was having every bit as hard a time in the battle of survival as she was having herself; the little extra she could send them made the difference between poverty and a passable existence.

Inevitably, though Marie tried to keep her business activities as far removed from them as possible, she saw a lot of the Valdouxs.

Valerie, radiant that she had Justin home safe and sound, despite the horrendous problems they still had to face, had gone with him back to Castle Blanche to see what could be salvaged of their former mode of existence. They left without Marie-Thérèse, who had rather surprisingly opted to stay behind to nurse her dying sister.

Clarisse had rallied briefly on Bayard's return, but everyone except the invalid herself knew that it was just a matter of time; the consumption was too far along for recovery. Of Bayard. Marie found there was very little of the devil-may-care gallant left. His left arm shattered and useless, he was silent, somewhat bitter, obsessed with his dying wife, but ready, if not particularly able, to assist Emile in the new life he was building for the Valdouxs. In that, Emile was getting more help than he had ever expected from the distaff side: from Claire, who had turned up with a totally unexpected flair for bookkeeping; and from his mother, who not only continued to run the household, but also had efficiently organized her farflung St Yves relatives into a distributing network for the new banana business. That she did not care for having her home used as a hairdressing establishment was evident, but she appreciated the necessity which had brought it about, and, in typical St Yves fashion, came to terms with the situation by completely ignoring its existence. This was a great relief to Marie.

As it turned out, she did not have to utilize her makeshift headquarters for very long. The Negro family that had been staying at Rampart Street decided to try its luck in the north, and moved out. At long last she was mistress of her own house again, and the joy of having so much space and so much peace all to herself overrode the more poignant memories her return brought forth.

The neighbourhood had greatly changed. Now, nearly all

350

the little houses contained black families – and blacks, for the most part, of the 'new' kind, with which Marie had little in common. These were the new government 'officials' who connived with and were exploited by the real rulers of the city, the new Anglos, who used them as a weapon against the Creoles and the 'old' Anglos. Their 'power' was a shadow without substance, but they acted out the charade in return for heretofore undreamed-of material comforts and benefits. They tended to be loud, flashy, and aggressive, and they regarded Marie with a mixture of hostility and fear – for, though few of them were Voodoos, they knew full well who she was. Emile, for one, was very nervous about her going back into these changed circumstances, but the prospect of so much personal freedom after the years of confinement overrode her own fears, though she was cautious about locking up the house and of ascertaining who was at her door before opening up.

Then one Sunday morning, as she was sitting peacefully surveying the fading splendours of her parlour, a knocking came at the front door. She opened it cautiously on the chain she had had Jean install, and she peered through the crack to see a tall, gaunt Negro in very shabby clothes standing on the step. 'What is it? What do you want?' she called.

'It's me, Miz Marie. Can Ah talk to ya?'

For a moment she did not recognize either the voice or the man. Then he turned in profile and the LeBlanc likeness – blurred but evident – leaped out at her and she gasped, 'Billy Boy!'

A weak grin slashed across the dark face. 'Yes'm, Ah'm back sho' enough.'

She unlatched the door and let him in. He was thin to the point of emaciation, and his first words were: 'Ah ain't et in three days, Miz Marie. Can ya spare a bite o' food?'

All she had in the house was some bread and milk, and after he had wolfed that down it was clear that it had not even touched his great hunger, for he was still trembling with weakness. She had sent off every penny she had to Claire the day before, so there was no money to buy anything else. She sat looking at him with helpless sympathy.

'You look like a corpse warmed up, Billy Boy. Things have been really that bad for you, eh?'

'Dey sho' have!' he agreed fervently. 'Dis freedom sho' ain't what Ah expected. Leastways, when Ah was a slave, Ah et reg'lar, but now! Ah cain't find work, Ah got no money – Ah's desperate ...' His eyes roamed hungrily around. 'Ain't there anythin' else?'

She shook her head. Then, looking at him, an idea came to her and she began to laugh. 'Can you hold your breath, Billy?'

He looked popeyed. 'Sho' – but why?'

She explained and he began to laugh weakly, too. 'If we can get some money in, we can buy some more food for you,' she chuckled, as she spread a sheet on the parlour floor, stuck some lighted candles around it, and he stretched out on it, while she covered him up to the neck with another sheet. She closed the shutters and said, 'I'll cough before I come in and then you stop breathing. I'll make sure they don't stay long.'

This done, she went out on the front steps, sat down, and began to wail loudly, rocking to and fro. Rampart Street was thronged as usual, and before many minutes had passed, she had a solemn and curious crowd of black faces around her. 'Oh, that poor young man! known him since he was a baby!' she wailed. 'Tottered to my door to die, he did – and me with not a penny to bury him with. Oh, those damned whities left him to die like a dog, and be buried like one.' There was a sympathetic murmur from the crowd. She lamented on in this vein for a while and at the perfect psychological moment said to those nearest her, 'Would you, perhaps, care to see him and say a prayer for his poor, tormented soul? Oh, the pity of it! The shame of it!' She led the way into the darkened room and they obediently formed a line and shuffled after her.

Billy Boy made an impressive corpse. It was only a moment or two before she heard the welcome clinking of coins in the large brass bowl she had thoughtfully placed at his feet. She kept wailing all the while, pushing people ahead of her, to give Billy breathing space, until the pile in the bowl had reached substantial proportions. Then she brought the act to an end. 'Oh, I can stand no more,' she moaned. 'Bless you all for your Christian charity – may the Lord always bless you. Now, please, leave me with my dead!'

They shuffled out, murmuring embarrassed sympathy. And the minute the front door was locked and barred against the last of them, she collected up the money, hopped out the back door, and sped off to buy enough food for a feast.

As he ploughed steadily through the food she had garnered, Billy Boy began to chuckle. 'Ah always did think ya was somethin' special, Miz Marie. Now Ah knows it fo' sho'. Can Ah stay on with ya? It sho' beats workin' fo' white folks.'

Chapter Thirty-nine

'Whatever happened to Geneviève?' It was several days before Marie got around to asking this burning question. Billy Boy had moved in. It meant another mouth to feed, but there were also some advantages to having him around. The neighbourhood had changed so, and there had been such a general upswing in lawlessness of all kinds that it was no longer particularly safe to stay in the Rampart Street house by herself. Billy Boy was smart, strong, and the right colour for the new circumstances. What was more, after the hardships he had undergone – which he had recounted in some detail – he was willing to settle for his keep and nothing else. 'If things get better for me again, I'll do better by you.' And Marie meant what she said.

His newfound security had made him loquacious and bluntly candid. 'Oh, Geneviève!' He rolled expressive eyes heavenward. 'She was too much of a woman fo' me, Ah can tell ya – wowee! Last Ah seen her, she was workin' in a whorehouse in St Louis. An', ma'am, did she ever *enjoy* her work! Ah never seen anythin' lak it – two at a time, she wanted, one at each end! She could stuff all night long an' still come back fo' mo'! Probably runnin' the house by this time, she was that popular – Ah dunno, 'cause they chased me off. Didn' want no black pimp hangin' 'round, they said, an' long as she was gittin' what she wanted reg'lar as clock-work, she couldn't care less 'bout me.'

'Poor Geneviève,' Marie murmured, with fascinated horror.

'Po' Geneviève!' he mocked, 'she was the happiest gal Ah ever did see, bar none, once she got into the swing o' things. No call to waste yo' sympathy on that one. An' Ah'll tell ya somethin' else.' He leaned forward confidentially. 'Ah wasn't the first one into her, lak we thought – no, ma'am, she wasn't no virgin when Ah got to her that night. Someone got there ahead o' me!'

Marie frowned. 'I wonder who,' she said softly. 'But I suppose that's something we'll never know.' She was wrong.

In 1872 the federal troops finally moved out of New Orleans. It was not an occasion for universal rejoicing. Far from indicating a return to normalcy, it merely underlined the fact that the people of the city were now helplessly in the grip of the Reconstructionists and no longer had to be kept there by force. This helplessness was underlined when Lincoln's one truly successful general became President that year, and during his drunken presidency the powers of graft and greed rode paramount in the land. People thought there could be no further depths of misery to plunge into. Again they were wrong.

Everything has its compensation, and with the departure of the troops, some of the older Creole elements had rallied. They needed a man they could trust to handle their fading affairs. Pressure was brought to bear, and the Valdoux bank reopened for business. Emile accepted this with more resignation than delight. He had enjoyed the banana business as his own creation, which he had built into a going and growing concern in spite of all the obstacles, and which he now, perforce, had to turn over to Bayard's less capable hands.

It also meant less to Marie now than it would have at another time. With Emile's connivance, she had 'died' several years before, at the time when Ingrid had started to ask questions. And it was through him that the pipeline to the faithful Claire was kept open.

The spring of the year had brought a letter from her that had given a rare moment of pure happiness. It was a radiant letter. Claire had written:

My dear Marie,
I am so happy that my heart is bursting. I am to be married to a most wonderful man at Easter. His name is Vittorio Agnelli, and he is an Italian from Sicily. He runs

355

*a restaurant here in the city, and we met through the
bakery. He is quite rich and is a widower with two young
daughters, and such a dear, great-hearted man. When we
are wed, he says Mama Andersen must come and live
with us, and Ingrid and Patty, also. We will be living in a
beautiful house in a new part of town called Oak Park,
and there is a very good convent school there where his
daughters go and which Ingrid can attend. So things will
be much easier for us, and we will, I pray, be less of a
burden to you than we have been. He loves me and I love
him with all my heart – I cannot believe there is so much
happiness in the whole world.*

> *Your loving and devoted Claire.*

There had been a revealing and pathetic postscript:

*He does not know about me, but I do not think it will
matter, so I shall say nothing – he is darker than I am.*

Marie had read and reread the letter with a feeling of
savage triumph. Dear, plain Claire had found love and happiness and security; her beautiful ill-starred mother could
rest in peace, and her own task was done – the last of the
Montals had found a new world.

When the wedding photograph had arrived, she had
looked at it long and hard. Its formal stiffness was dominated by the burly figure of Vittorio Agnelli, with his sweeping handlebar moustache and the tight black curly hair
parted starkly in the middle. He looked what he was – a man
of substance. The small figure of Claire by his side was
almost swamped by her ornate dress and veil, but Marie
could make out the beaky outline of the Montal nose and
one eye, bright with happiness, peering out of the elaborate
draperies. The slim, long-haired, solemn-faced bridesmaid
by her side was Ingrid, in whom, despite all Claire's as-
sertions, Marie could see little of Nils, but much of the
handsome, heavy-bodied woman who stood behind her, one
hand resting on the slim shoulder. Marie tried to feel something, but there was nothing. 'Yes, she is all yours,' she
confided to the picture, 'all . . .' And she wept.

A year later another picture arrived, this time with a beaming Claire holding a small, black-eyed bundle up to the camera, a looming and delighted-looking Vittorio in the background. Claire wrote in ecstasy:

> *My son is so beautiful! And Vittorio is so proud to have a son at last. We are naming him after V's father, Ernesto, and Delambe after Grandpapa, and Vittorio has opened two new restaurants in his honour.*

It was shortly after receiving this that Marie had a prophetic encounter on South Rampart Street. She was hurrying home very late from Marie-Philome's, where Jean-Paul lay at long and agonizing last on his deathbed, and saw, staggering towards her, a drunk, quavering a song she recognized vaguely as a favourite dance tune of her own youth. As he came within the circle of the guttering gas streetlight, she saw it was Dominic Montal, dirty and extremely shabby. She was about to cross over to the other side of the street to avoid him, when he called out, 'Marie? Is that you, Marie?' She hesitated and he wobbled up to her, clasping one of the cast-iron hitching posts to keep his balance, and he peered at her out of bleary, misery-stricken eyes. He waved a hand vaguely around. 'Came back to see the old place,' he confided. 'Often come here, y'know. Come to be near my Jackie – my dearest, beloved Jackie. I loved her, y'know, loved her more'n anything in the whole world.'

'Did you, Dominic?' Marie's tone was icy. 'Is that why you left her to die?' She gathered up her skirts and went to pass on, but he put out a restraining hand.

'Wait a second, ol' friend. Owe you an apology.' Tears were now trickling down the bloated cheeks. 'My dear brother,' he enunciated carefully, 'my dear brother was kind enough to tell me the truth of the matter the other day, when he was angry 'bout something. Guess the joke was on me, eh, ol' friend?' His face puckered in agony. 'All those years hating her, loving her, needing her. And it was as you said all along – it was St Regis. Oh, dear *God*!'

Marie felt sick. So St Regis's cruelty had not even spared his mirror image the ultimate pain. 'Well, it is all long past, and too late for mending.' This was all she could think of to say, and she went to move on, but again he put out a restraining hand.

'Don't you want to know why?' he said in a choked voice. 'Don't you at least want to know that?'

Looking at the hell in his eyes, Marie stayed where she was, and his grasp on her sleeve tightened. 'No one was good enough for the Montals, y'see. Only the Montals were good enough for the Montals. Oh, what times we had up on that top floor! St Regis and me and Anne and Yolande, and even little Geneviève – yes, even little Geneviève!' He hiccupped and shuddered convulsively. 'Oh, what games we had up there! Such wicked, funny games my brother did devise! And then . . . and then I met my Jackie, and suddenly all the world was different . . .' He gazed owlishly at Marie. 'I wouldn't play St Regis's games anymore – not with him, not with any of them. And he didn't like that. But I never knew quite how much he didn't like that . . .' The tears began to flow again. 'D'you know what I mean?'

Marie, feeling even sicker, nodded dumbly. It did indeed explain so much. He let out a weird, strangled laugh. 'And I'll tell you another thing, ol' Voodoo Marie, ol' friend; it wasn't your curse that did us in at all – we did ourselves in. Joke's on you – we did it ourselves!' The ghastly laughter continued and then stopped abruptly as the hand tightened again. 'But watch out, Marie! He'll get you one day, for sure, just as he got the rest of us. He never forgets, never . . .' His voice trailed off and his head drooped.

Like hell he will! Marie thought. But she said quietly, 'Go home, Dominic, go home and sleep it off. It's late to be out walking around.'

'Home!' he echoed hollowly. 'I have no home.' And he staggered off into the darkness.

Jean-Paul died the next day, and in all the turmoil of coping with the grief-stricken Marie-Philome and her family and of trying to straighten out the tangled state of affairs he had left, other events in the city passed by Marie unnoticed. When she did hear of it, it was already old news. The body of Dominic Montal had been fished out of the river by a crab boat returning home.

Since St Regis stood high with the new powers, and the fact of Dominic's drunkenness was well known, the death was recorded as an accidental drowning, and he was buried with all due pomp in the Montal vault. Marie put fresh flowers on Jacqueline's grave and wondered, after all the torments he had suffered, if Dominic was once again united with his hapless love; she doubted it.

But his words stuck with her, and sometime later, when she thought she saw St Regis watching the house, she decided it was time to make changes again.

With the departure of the federal garrison, her soirées had perforce been altered – and, like everything else in the city, not for the better. The clientele in the happy days of yore had come by invitation only, but this was something the new breed in the city did not understand, and her salon was now often crowded with gamblers and toughs of all sorts who mingled uneasily with the older-style Anglos and the few faithful and solvent Creoles, like Aristide Sautelle, who still attended. Jean, mild as he was, was of no help to her in keeping order, either in the salon or behind the scenes with the equally new breed of servants. On top of this, he had struck up a surprising alliance with one of her regular girls, who declared him a 'sweet' of the first order, and had been pressing him to move into the city with her. So he, too, had been muttering for some time about being marooned out in the bayou, and that he would like to be closer to town to see his mother.

It had long since occurred to Marie that St Regis may have discovered more about Geneviève's disappearance than he had ever let on, and although Billy Boy had changed greatly, there was always the risk of his being recognized. He could be useful to her out at Maison Blanche to keep an eye on the servants, who were always getting into the liquor, and as an additional bouncer to the two huge plug-uglies she had had to hire to keep even a semblance of order in the place. These looked impressive but were of dubious worth: one a 'poor white' river rat, the other a light mulatto who had been an unsuccessful prize-fighter. But both tended to like their liquor a bit too much and often stirred up, rather than stopped, trouble. So the switch of Billy for Jean was made to everyone's satisfaction, and Marie congratulated herself on nipping trouble in the bud. She should not have been so complacent, for the trouble came, anyway.

It was a crowded Saturday night, the noise level so high that the Voodoo drums were scarcely more than a muffled counterpoint to the din. Marie was seated as usual in the great chair, a table with the open cashbox at her elbow – for the gracious days, when the gentlemen had quietly paid their contribution to her ahead of time, were long gone. On one side of her chair was one of the plug-uglies on guard duty, and on the other was Aristide Sautelle, with whom she was chatting as quietly as the circumstances permitted. Aristide was entertaining, as always, and she was quite engrossed in what he was saying and unmindful of her surroundings, when he suddenly stopped in mid-sentence and a startled look came into his face. Marie looked up to see a trio of smartly dressed men coming towards her. Two of them were of the new breed of Anglo, one a city councilman, the other a ward boss – the third was St Regis.

To her lasting credit, her first thought was for Billy Boy, and she hastily gave a message to the plug-ugly to tell him to stay out of sight. By the bright spots of colour on the high cheekbones and the glitter in his eyes, she could see St Regis had been drinking heavily, so she braced herself.

The two Anglos, oblivious to the electric undercurrents around them, came up, greeted her politely enough, and dropped their contributions into the box. St Regis limped up, supporting himself on the gold-topped ebony sword-cane he now habitually carried. His contemptuous glance flicked over Aristide and dismissed him. Then he gazed down at Marie. 'So this is where you go to ground,' he said softly. His feverish eyes strayed over the scene and clamped on hers again. 'How I have long awaited this most-talked-about experience!'

'This is my house,' Marie said warningly, 'my roof. You

were not invited to it, but I want no trouble from you here, St Regis, and I will make none.'

He hefted his cane and lightly ran the gold knob along the line of her cheek. 'Trouble!' he mocked. 'What trouble? I came here to enjoy the delights you offer. What a handsome woman you still are, Marie Laveau!'

At this rather opportune moment, the plug-ugly returned to her side, his errand accomplished, and as St Regis took in his considerable girth Marie noticed his knuckles whiten on the cane. 'How much are you?' he rapped out.

She kept her voice and her temper level. 'The contribution to the house is five dollars; that covers drinks, refeshments, and the dancing. Any other arrangement you make with the girls here is your business.'

With a contemptuous gesture, he flung the money into the box, and one of the silver dollars bounced out and rolled on the floor. The plug-ugly, keeping a cold eye on St Regis, stooped, picked it up, and placed it with exaggerated care in the box. He hitched his chin towards the back wall. 'The bar's over there, Mister,' he said. 'Make yourself at home.'

St Regis hovered undecidedly for a moment. Then he murmured so that only Marie could hear: 'Later, perhaps – no need to rush things. Later.' And he moved off into the crowd.

'I don't like this, I don't like this at all,' Aristide hissed at her. 'Not only is St Regis drunk, but he's really looking for trouble. Shall I get hold of those two he came with and tell them to get him out of here?'

'No – not yet!' Marie had a horrible feeling of calamity closing in on her. 'Don't you get involved, Aristide. Let's just keep a careful eye on him and hope for the best. If we make an issue of it, he may stir up real trouble.'

They watched and waited tensely, but St Regis kept away from them. 'Isn't that Jim Warner's girl he's making a play for?' Marie said sometime later, as they saw a small and very young 'high-yellow' girl stroll past on his arm, clinging to and laughing up at him. 'Yes, that's Nicole Martins,' Aristide muttered, 'and she's drunk already by the looks of her.

It's just as well Jim's involved in a big poker game at the St Charles tonight – he's as jealous as hell over her.'

'She looks terribly young to tangle with the likes of St Regis,' Marie said in a worried tone. 'Can you pass the word to one of the other girls to tell her to beg off if he gets any ideas?'

'Yes, indeed I will,' Aristide said. And he made off into the crowd.

He reappeared sometime later looking worried. 'Well, I've passed the word, but I can't seem to see her anywhere. Have you seen her?'

They searched, but they did not find her. Nicole and St Regis had disappeared into the night.

'At least he has gone – and without trouble,' Marie said with relief. But, all the same, she did not know whether to laugh or to cry about it, for the terrible feeling of calamity remained.

Chapter Forty

Four days later the body of Nicole Martins was found floating in the bayou. Though the crabs had already been at work, there was enough of the body left to show that she had been mutilated and murdered; her throat was cut, and a Voodoo symbol was carved into one of her young breasts. The murder occasioned little comment in the city, for which this type of thing had become almost commonplace. Only the Voodoo symbol offered any kind of novelty.

A very sick-looking Aristide sought Marie out. 'Do you think it was St Regis?' he demanded.

'Almost positive of it,' Marie said grimly. 'Not only is it part of his sickening pattern, but I think this one was intended as a warning to me.'

'He's got to be stopped.' Aristide was white to the lips. 'He's got to be punished for it.'

'Oh, yes, he has got to be stopped,' Marie agreed, thinking of herself, 'but bringing it about is something else.'

'This time will be the last.' There was something in his tone that made her look up in surprise.

'Why, Aristide! What upsets you so about this murder in particular? As I've told you before, I don't think it's the first one by a long shot. Were you involved with the girl?'

He looked away. 'Not with her, no. But I was very fond of her mother – for all I know, Nicole could have been mine. No one ever knew because her mother died in the birth, but I've always kept an eye on her. Anyway, it has gone on too long – someone's got to stop him.'

'Well, it is nothing for a Creole gentleman to get involved in,' Marie said dryly. 'That's more my line. You better keep out of it.'

'I've been keeping out of things all my life,' he said with

sudden passion, 'standing on the sidelines making sarcastic observations to which no one listened. And what the hell has it all been for?'

'You've nearly always been right,' Marie pointed out, 'about everything. It's not your fault if we were all too foolish to profit from your wisdom.'

'And what good was that?' He looked at her haggardly. 'I'll tell you, Marie, another gem of wisdom I have learned from my long misspent life. There is only one thing in the long run that counts: not love, not money – only power. Without power the rest is nothing. One can be as wise as Socrates, as all-knowing as Jesus, but without the power to back it, the world will crush and crucify you. No, power is the only thing to seek, the only path to follow. I used to long for the future, thinking it would be different. But now I see that too was foolishness, for I would still be I, a man without the power for power.' He laughed mirthlessly. 'Look at the two of us right now! We bashed our brains out during the war trying to help the power structure here, and yet, if we went to them with our suspicions, where do you think we'd end up? Right out on the street on our backsides!'

'There are all kinds of power,' Marie murmured.

'Oh, I know!' He waved a dismissive hand. 'Queen of the Voodoos and all that – but what does that mean, other than that you reign over a lot of people a hell of a lot worse off than yourself, and of no account to anyone?'

'I didn't mean that exactly.' She was thoughtful.

'Well, perhaps there is still some hope for you – you've got a lot of years ahead,' he conceded. 'But I'm certain you are no match for the St Regises of this world – strong though you are.'

'Unless I change sex or become a blue-eyed blonde, eh?' She smiled grimly.

'An *aristocratic* blue-eyed blonde.' He rejoined with a momentary return to his old debonair manner, but then sighed heavily. 'Still, the point is: What the hell are we going to do about him? How can we bring it home to him?'

While they were still debating this unanswerable question, the police found their own murderer. Three days after the body was found, they arrested James Warner for the murder of his mistress, Nicole Martins. Though the case against him was purely circumstantial, they felt it was a good one. He and Nicole had been heard quarrelling furiously on the weekend she had disappeared. He was known to be reckless and extremely jealous of her. He had attended the *'Fe Chauffé* dances out at the lake with her, so was well acquainted with Voodoo symbols. And, most unfortunately, he had remarked to his cronies at the Saturday night poker game that, if she attended any more of the soirées at Maison Blanche, he was going to wring her neck. Furthermore, since no one could say exactly when the murder had taken place, he had no alibi.

'I think you've got the wrong man,' Marie said to the police sergeant who had come to question her concerning the Voodoo symbol on the body. He was an old acquaintance, though very much of the 'new' party, but a man she had always found reasonable and straightforward in his dealings.

'Oh?' He cocked an eyebrow at her. 'Why do you say that?'

'Because you haven't got a scrap of positive evidence against him, and because I'm pretty sure I know who did do it.'

'I'm listening. Name a name.'

She debated with herself, then plunged on. 'She was here that Saturday night, and when she left, I think the man who left with her killed her. It was St Regis Montal.'

His mouth set in a grim line. 'You've just said the wrong name. That one's too well connected with the right people. You should have picked on some smaller fish in the sea. Unless you can prove it to the hilt?' He looked at her questioningly.

'St Regis was drunk and in an ugly mood. He carries a sword-cane, which could easily have been the murder weapon. As to the Voodoo symbol, well, every person in New Orleans probably knows that. *And* he was last seen going with the girl in the direction of the Wishing Tree. Her body was found not far from there, wasn't it?'

'You can produce a witness to face him with that?' It was more of a challenge than a question.

She hesitated. The witness had been Billy Boy, who had been lurking outside in the dark until the coast was clear, and who had seen St Regis come out with the giggling girl and head off into the darkness. A confrontation between him and St Regis was the last thing Marie wanted. 'No – I don't think so.'

'Why not?' he rapped out.

'Because it's a nigger witness – and what good would that be against the word of a white man?' she said with sudden bitterness.

'Then you ain't got a thing, not a blasted thing – nothing but happenstance.'

'That's all you've got against Warner,' she retaliated.

'Not quite. Motive, means, opportunity – they all fit him like a made-to-order glove. No, you'll have to do better than that, Marie.' He got up to go. 'I'm going to forget this conversation, and if I were you, I wouldn't say a word to anyone about Montal – he's no one to tangle with,' he counselled.

'But Warner didn't do it!' Marie protested.

'That's for a jury to decide,' he said. 'We've got our case.'

A jury of his peers decided in very short order that James Warner was guilty as charged. He did not help himself much throughout the trial by alternating between truculent bluster and sobbing self-pity, so the verdict came as no surprise to anybody, and he was sentenced to be hanged, despite his agonized plea of innocence.

Marie was in the midst of a dilemma. She had already decided there was only one solution to her problem – that, dangerous though it was, she would have to use the Voodoo death ritual against St Regis. She had tried it once before and failed, but that was when she was young and inexperienced; now she knew she would succeed, even at cost to herself. But this was only part of the problem – to kill St Regis would be to rid the world of a scourge, but it would not save an innocent man from being hanged. She tried to tell herself that it did not matter, that James Warner was nothing to her, not much loss to the world – but in her heart she knew this was not so, and the thought kept her tossing restlessly night after night.

While she still hovered in indecision, time ticked methodically towards the execution. Then, suddenly, two things happened: St Regis disappeared, and she received an urgent summons from Aristide.

She hurried to the Chartres Street house where he was in lodgings with a coloured woman, and to the large room on the first floor that was his. Though it was furnished with some lovely antique pieces, it still had the air of gloom and shabbiness that had settled on the houses of the Vieux Carré like a blight. Aristide was sitting at an exquisite Louis XVI writing table as she let herself in, and she was surprised to see that his lined, ugly little face was serene, his eyes bright with happy purpose.

'Sit down, Marie,' he commanded. 'We have much to talk about, and I have a mission for you. I have solved our problem.'

'You have! How?'

He fingered a fat white envelope on the desk and looked across at her. 'St Regis is dead – I killed him. Here is my confession.'

She gasped in dismay. 'Oh, Aristide, how *could* you? *I* would have taken care of St Regis – that was but part of the problem. Now nothing in this world can save James Warner.'

'You don't understand,' he said gently, tapping the envelope. 'This is not a confession to the killing of St Regis; this is a confession to the murder of Nicole Martins.'

This completely took her breath away. 'But you *can't*!' she gasped out at length. 'Think of what that will mean! The shame, the disgrace – for something you did not do! It's insane!'

He shook his head. 'It is the only way. I am, after all, a murderer, and in my system of belief murder should not go unpunished – even if it was the murder of someone so unworthy of life as St Regis.' He held up a hand as she started to gasp out another protest. 'Oh, believe me, I did not plan it this way! I tried to have it out with him – tried to force a confession out of him.'

'And did you?'

'Oh, yes. He laughed about it – said it was just preliminary to better things he had in mind.'

'And then you struggled with him and he was killed in the fight!' she said eagerly. 'Why, that's self-defence! We could go to the police with that – it might save Warner.'

He shook his head again and smiled with wry amusement. 'It wasn't like that at all, I'm afraid. After he'd admitted it to me – boasted, in fact – he laughed, told me there wasn't a damned thing I could do about it, and walked away. I shot him through the back as he went.'

Marie looked at him aghast. 'Where's the body?'

'Where no one will ever find it. I do not think St Regis and hallowed ground would go easily together, so I have denied him that, too. Only you will ever know the truth of the matter; but where he rests, or, more likely, does not rest, will go with me to the grave.'

'But the disappearance – surely that would be enough to make them doubt . . .' she said wretchedly.

'No, believe me' – his tone was firm – 'this is the only way. Do not take this from me, Marie – the one good deed, the only definite thing I have done in my whole life. You know, some time ago I read a book by an English writer named Dickens. I don't suppose . . . no, of course not, you don't clutter up your mind with books . . . Anyway, it was about a man named Sydney Carton, a man very much like me, who had never done a thing with his life. It impressed me very much.'

'Well?' Marie was mystified.

'Oh – in the end he gets executed in place of a friend – redemption in a single and singular act. I wonder if it really works that way,' he added thoughtfully.

'But Warner is no friend of yours!' she cried. 'I tell you what. You get out of the city, and then I'll take the confession to the authorities. Go west. They'd never find you out there.'

He seemed not to hear her. 'Have you ever noticed that

when the twilight comes, the flowers fade and lose their colour, how even their scent seems less?' he mused. 'My world has become like that – without either scent or colour – and yet it was once a very fair one.' He sighed and waved an explanatory hand around the shabby room. 'Once, the Sautelle plantations were the fairest in Louisiana, and we lived that vivid, feckless Creole life to the extreme. This is all that is left of it. And when a dream dies, why should the dreamer linger? There is no one to come after me, no one to inherit the taint or the shame, no one even to mourn. So, bear with me, and take this to the prison governor of the parish prison beyond Congo Square. That will stay the execution. When you have done that, you can bring the police back here, and I will confirm verbally what I have written.' He smiled faintly. 'It is a masterpiece of literary invention and should convince them.'

'Oh, Aristide!' Marie muttered wretchedly. 'Why won't you at least *try* to save yourself?'

'I've just told you, so please!' he said with gentleness. 'Please do as I say!'

Marie went on her mission, and after much wrangling got to see the governor. After more wrangling with him over the bombshell she had dropped into the municipal lap, she ascertained that a stay of execution had indeed been authorized by telegraph from the governor of the state, and only then would she agree to accompany the police officers back to Aristide's lodging.

He greeted them, still sitting at the Louis XVI writing table. The minute Marie set eyes on him, she realized that the last of the Sautelles would not swing from any gallows; there was a greyness to his skin and a bluish tinge around his mouth that told her Aristide had indeed thought of everything.

He held up a restraining hand to the two policemen who were advancing towards him, their hands on their guns. 'Gentlemen,' he said, 'there is no need for violence of any kind. I regret I cannot rise to greet you, but half of me is already dead. I have taken enough hemlock to kill an ox – and though the bane of Socrates does take an uncommon

while to kill, I should not take up much more of your time.'
As they stopped uncertainly, he went on. 'I merely want to
confirm what I wrote in the confession this good friend
brought to you – that I, Aristide Sautelle, did wilfully
murder Nicole Martins – I and no one else. And, I may add,
I have also saved the state the expense of a trial.'

'I'll get a doctor,' one of the policemen said, then rushed
out.

Aristide looked at Marie and smiled faintly. 'Good-bye,
my dear, and my eternal thanks. May you find your own
pathway to power – sometime, somewhere . . .'

By the time the breathless policeman had returned with a
doctor, Aristide was already dead, an embittered Marie
clinging to one of the dead hands.

Dazed and thankful, James Warner was released from the
parish prison that night. Eighteen months later he was shot
dead on the waterfront in a gamblers' brawl over a ten-
dollar bet.

Chapter Forty-one

The disappearance of St Regis remained a mystery. No sign of him was ever found, and eventually the head of the St Yves family came to take reluctant charge of his sister. It was said – though nothing was known for sure – that Anne Montal had been found in an indescribable condition in a barred room upstairs. She was hopelessly mad, and what the St Yves family did with her no one knew. The Montal house once more stood shuttered and empty, but occupied – so it was said – by sundry sad shades that stirred its echoes with their cries. Since no buyer for it could be found, it was torn down to make way for a new hotel, and the city passed on by and forgot the Montals.

New Orleans was slowly coming to life again; a new kind of life, it was true, but the great river was pumping its riches once again into the withered veins, and the city rose and breathed and swirled into a new kaleidoscope of groups and colours. Creole society had closed its ranks and was beginning to fight back against the brash encroachments of the newcomers. The pre-war society for Carnival of Comus was the first rallying point, and it had been followed by other 'krewes' formed by those old families that had managed to cling to some of their wealth – first Rex, then Momus, eventually others. Revolving around them the city became gay again, forgetting its sad past.

But not all were so lucky. For every family that survived in this new world, there were three that did not, wiped out either physically or financially by the war, and their going left an indelible change on the Vieux Carré.

There were bordellos now in the plush mansions on Basin Street, and other parts of the quarter not so well fed by easy money were fast degenerating into slums. Many of the remaining old families moved out to new mansions in the Garden District or beyond, not wishing this constant reminder of decay; among them were Emile Valdoux and his family.

His mother was obstinate and would not leave the Royal Street house, and Claire stayed on with her. Although, in keeping with the times, he had built a larger bank in the business district for old times' sake, Emile kept the counting house open and just as it was. Marie was glad of that, and she remembered fondly how they had laughed and drunk champagne on the day when she had solemnly handed back the fake deed that had made her for a happy while the owner of its glories.

She was finding it increasingly hard to come to terms with this new world, in which for her there was still no real place. Part of it was middle age, she supposed; she had already seen its hand at work on her sisters, and now it was her turn. With Marie-Philome, it had taken the form of a surge into fatness and a sudden and unexpected burst of late blooming, social energy. She had formed two societies, both for coloured people: one basically social, called the 'Ladies with Tignons'; the other devoted to good works. In the process she had lost a lot of her serenity and had become dogmatic and domineering, which had caused problems for the youngest of her children, the adolescent Georgina. In reaction, Georgina had turned to Marie and what Marie stood for; she yearned to become a Voodoo. And Marie, after much doubt, consulted with her elder sister, who was surprisingly indifferent and offered no objections. Thus, Georgina was quietly training to be a Mambo, and though she showed no sign of great powers, Marie wondered if eventually Georgina could not take her own place as Queen. Already she was delegating a lot of the rites to the lesser Queens, including the deposed Eliza and another very promising Mambo. Malvina Latour. She still maintained overall control and presided at the great rites, but this 'divide and rule' system she had instituted was working very well and was far less wearing on herself.

Celeste in middle age had become even thinner and even more vinegary. Two of her daughters had married white men, and, buoyed up by this fact, she strove to keep the rest of the Glapions as far away from the St Ann Street house as she could. Increasingly pious, if correspondingly less Christian, she had banished all signs of Voodoo from the house, even the altar to Saint Makandal, and now her mother's room was as festooned with holy pictures and general Christian bric-à-brac as the rest of the house. The old lady rarely left her room.

Just as her maturity had been late, so was her menopause, but Marie, at this time, found herself swept by unpredictable moods and sudden rages, during which she would do petty meannesses that subsequently bewildered her and caused her regret. She had chased out by a series of mean little intimidations an Irish family that had settled in a house on Rampart opposite hers, and afterwards she had found no rationale for it, other than that they had a tall, fair daughter who reminded her constantly of her own shortcomings as a mother.

Physically, she was still an extremely handsome woman, her only sign of years being in a slight thickening of her waistline, but inside she had begun to feel mean and ugly and, somehow, lost.

In a strange way she missed St Regis. His enmity had been a continuing theme in her life, almost an anchor, and without it she felt herself drifting without direction. She even dreamed strange dreams in which she and St Regis were twin-souled lovers conquering an unknown world. Mad though he had been, vicious and evil, he had also been a man of power, just as she was a woman of power: Had that been the source of their conflict and not the obvious externals? Or had the source of it lain even deeper than that? Now she would never know.

She felt much the same way about her mother. On the few occasions she could get past Celeste's external vigilance, she found it hard to equate the shrunken, white-haired old lady sitting in her chair in the semi-darkened room with the figure that had dominated so much of her life. She scarcely seemed the same person, though, on occasion, Marie had felt her eyes upon her, and in their dark glance she felt still a power and a purpose that gave her pause. Was her mother as frail and subdued as she seemed, or was this another of her elaborate charades? Yet there was no visible sign, nothing anymore to stir her own will to combat – nothing anymore to give her purpose.

On the surface hers was a success story; not only had she survived the bad times, but she was even moderately prosperous again. She was still someone to be reckoned with, someone to ask favours of, in the power structure of New Orleans. And yet she realized how little any of it meant, that it was all more shadow than substance; she had no real power, no real goal – and it was not likely to change if she continued to drift on this path that was no path.

A sense of coming change came to her when Marie LeBeau died and Marie became full owner of 516 Bourbon Street. Although they had never reached the stage of friendship, they had come to an understanding of one another, and during the bad times Marie had helped her 'almost' namesake to keep the place going. Marie LeBeau, a businesswoman to the end, had appreciated this – though she had never said so – and on her death Marie was surprised to find that she had willed her the other half of the boarding house 'in appreciation of our long and profitable business association, and in the hopes you will continue the fine tradition I have maintained'.

To run a boardinghouse was about the last thing in the world Marie wanted, but she realized its worth, and the sense of its being somehow important in the change that was to come stayed with her. As a temporary stopgap, she put in one of her former 'girls', who she knew was a good cook, as manager, until she made up her mind what to do about the situation. She knew the house, like all the rest of the Quarter, was run down, and would need extensive redecorating if she was to keep the kind of clientele who were paying propositions, but it was some time before she could nerve herself sufficiently to go there and look the place over.

When she did so, it was with inner dread. Though the scars of her brief happiness had long since healed over, she was afraid that the poignant memories the house would bring would rip open the wounds – and she had had enough of pain. 'No, you don't need to come with me,' she almost snapped at her manager. 'I know my way around and can see for myself what needs to be done.'

She spent a long time dallying on the first floor, then the second, until she got up enough nerve to face the narrow staircase leading to the third floor. Every step of it tore her heart, and she tried to focus her thoughts on inconsequential things, like how much narrower the skirts were nowadays, how much handier than the bulky crinolines for getting around . . .

Once there, she spent a long time looking over the other third-floor rooms, but finally could no longer put off the moment and stood before the door of Nils's old room. She knocked and, receiving no answer, opened it slowly and went in.

The wallpaper was shabby but different; the cracks in the ceiling many but different. The carpet had been changed but was worn in patches, and was scattered with an amorphous mixture of a man's clothing, books, and papers that filtered in an untidy cascade from a small writing table that stood by the window. The table was similarly piled up with a mixture of papers, books, steel pens, and ink bottles. Only the chest of drawers, the wardrobe, and the small round table by the easy chair were recognizable: a little more worn, a little more scarred, but the same. Marie moved like a sleep-walker over to the chest of drawers and stood fingering its scratched surface, gazing at herself in the wavy outlines of the mirror that hung above it. As remembrance flooded over her, she half-expected to see Nils's face appear behind her in its hazy surface, and feel again his hands clasping her breasts. Automatically, she leaned back against his solid warmth and, closing her eyes, gave herself up to the sweet flood of memories that engulfed her. It bore her up on its tide, swirling her into that other being she had once so wonderfully become. She was free, she was happy, she was at peace . . .

'What the devil are you doing in here?' a man's voice demanded, and Marie's dream shattered.

She swung around and for a breath-stopping moment

thought that the ghost of Aristide Sautelle stood before her. But as her tear-blurred vision cleared, she saw it was no ghost, but a real man – slight of stature like Aristide, dark-haired like him, but there the resemblance ended. Aristide had been ugly, but this man was grotesque: his left eye blind and slitted, his right, as if to compensate, twice the size of a normal eye, which gave his monkey-like countenance the semblance of a lopsided Cyclops. Marie gasped as he scowled at her and advanced towards her with purposeful menace. 'What the hell are you doing in my room, messing with my things?' he demanded again.

With an effort, Marie gathered herself together, and drew herself up so that she topped him by several inches. '*M'sieu*,' she said in a commanding tone, 'I happen to be the new owner of this building and I am taking inventory of things that need to be done. As to messing your things ...' – she swept the room with a withering, contemptuous glance – '... I scarcely think it would be possible to improve on the mess you have made yourself. I am Marie Laveau. And who might you be?'

He stopped uncertainly and the great eye blinked rapidly several times. 'Oh!' he said in a flat voice. 'Come to think of it, Eugenie did say something about the owner coming today. My apologies, *Madame*. The name is Hearn – Lafcadio Hearn.' He gave her a sudden smile and it transformed the grotesque face into the appealing ugliness of a Greek comic mask. He peered around as if seeing the room for the first time. 'Um ... I suppose it is a bit messy, but I'm a writer, you see.' He waved an explanatory hand at the cluttered tables. 'I write for the *Item* for my bread, and for myself for the glory of the world.' He said it with pride, and as if it excused all errors and omissions of the flesh.

'Oh, a writer!' Marie replied, her voice edged with contempt. 'Well, *M'sieu*, I sincerely hope your thoughts are less cluttered than your papers, or you will be hard put to it to find the rent money for even this.'

She had evidently touched a sore spot, for he flinched and muttered defensively, 'I explained to Eugenie it was just a temporary shortage of funds; I'll settle in full next week.'

He looked so hangdog and contrite that Marie felt a twinge of amusement at his obvious discomfiture. Thinking she had won the honours and could leave the field with banners flying and her adversary sufficiently trampled, she took another swift look around the room and made as if to leave. He immediately shot out a restraining hand.

'Don't go!' he appealed. 'Don't go just yet. Now I've remembered who you are, and we have so much to talk about; there are so many things I want to find out from you and about you.'

The touch of his hand electrified her. Whether it was the atmosphere of the room or the memories it had engendered, a sensual desire flooded over her such as she had not felt in years.

For a long time after Nils's death, Marie had felt cold and dead, with no desire at all, though her power to attract men had in no way diminished. It was an attraction which she had continued to use cold-bloodedly for her purpose without ever taking the final step. Then, during the worst part of the early '70s, there had been a brief, violent affair with a local judge – sweet for a while, but they had both quickly come to their senses and drawn apart. Of late, however, with the dying of her womanhood, she had been aware of a restless urge inside her, and only the memory of her mother clasped in the dark embrace of Christophe had kept her from similar indulgence. Now, looking down at the ugly face of the young Lafcadio, she realized, despite the incongruities of the situation, that she relished him, she wanted him, she would have him.

She widened her eyes and gently placed her hand over his. 'And what do you want to find out about me?' she murmured.

He became very still, and she wondered if he could be feeling the stormy tide that was sweeping through her own veins. He cocked his strange head to one side and regarded her soberly. 'I had no idea quite how much I had to talk to you about, how much I *wanted* to find out until now.' His voice was husky. 'My thoughts are not in order; there is so much I want to say. Perhaps you would dine with me this evening and we can talk then?'

'That would be delightful,' she murmured.

They dined at Antoine's, and they talked and talked, and kept talking all the way back to the small shabby room on the third floor. And for a brief while in his arms, Marie reached out to the past and became whole once again.

Chapter Forty-two

He was impossible, insufferable, self-obsessed, vain, prickly as a porcupine, boorish, and bad-mannered – but she needed him. Despite the fact that they quarrelled constantly, he fascinated her, for he was unlike any man she had ever known.

His insensitivity to others and his general ignorance never ceased to amaze her, and she was always slapping him down in an effort to make him realize his shortcomings. In the main, the effort was a vain one.

'You speak English remarkably well for a Creole,' he remarked patronizingly one day.

'Why not? I've been speaking it most of my life, and with people a lot better bred and better educated than you,' she snapped.

He remained unruffled. 'And do you speak French equally well?' he persisted.

'Of course!'

But, as usual, he had found a sore spot, for though she spoke her native tongue well enough, she had never managed to master the elegant niceties of the aristocratic tongue spoken by the Valdouxs and their ilk – a fact that had always rankled her. Since Lafcadio spoke only an execrable type of French himself, he was luckily unaware of this – he would not have been slow to harp on it had he noticed it.

He was an Anglo, and that, to her, explained a lot about him; but he was an Anglo who did not fit into any category of her previous knowledge. Part Irish, part Greek, English educated – or semi-educated, she would have said – and thrown into the vast melting pot of America at the age of nineteen, he belonged nowhere, and yet was at home anywhere, functioning in a little cocoon-like world of his own making, from which he peered out at the real world with unquenchable curiosity. He baffled her.

She still found it hard to adjust to the fact that he had

been born the year after the great flood of New Orleans and her first climactic clash with her mother. Yet, despite his youth, there was something about him that was timeless, and she strove to discover the source of this something, feeling it to be important.

Did it lie in his passion for writing – a passion which she did not pretend to understand? His writing for the newspaper was comprehensible, for that at least he got paid. But what drove him hour after hour, day after day, to sit cramped at his desk, scribbling, tearing up, scribbling again – more often than not to throw out everything he had done, only to start all over again?

'Why,' she exclaimed in exasperation, 'do you spend so much of yourself on these things that nobody buys or is even interested in? Why don't you do something useful for a change?'

He looked at her in amazement. 'Because I am a writer – a good writer; maybe one day a *great* writer. I write because I can and must. I write not for present glory, though that would be nice,' he muttered in a wistful aside, 'but so that a hundred years from now, two hundred, three . . . people will read what I have written and say, "Yes, *that* is how it was, how it must have been, because the writing is true and good. That Lafcadio Hearn was a *writer*." '

'A form of immortality,' she murmured thoughtfully, 'but surely one without substance.' Yet, seeing his many shortcomings as a man, she could not help but think that they would somehow stand in the way of the very goal he sought. His boorishness and unpleasantness were already legend in the city, and she kept her own association with him as quiet as possible, being none too proud of it herself. Inevitably, however, it became known, and while many turned their heads away in discretion or disgust, Emile had tackled her directly about it.

'Why, in the name of Heaven, Marie,' he had said, more in sorrow than in anger, 'have you taken up with such a man? He's a hack journalist of the worst sort, and a thoroughly unpleasant character, as well. What on earth can you see in the fellow?'

Marie had not argued with him. 'You just wouldn't understand, Emile,' she had soothed, 'so let's not discuss it.' And indeed he would not understand, she thought. How could he, since she didn't understand it herself?

Lafcadio had not an ounce of gratitude or consideration in his makeup. Knowing how he was usually in dire financial straits, Marie had quietly passed the word to Eugenie not to pressure him on his rent money, and he fell further and further behind in his sporadic payments. She was therefore infuriated when one day he calmly informed her that he was moving out of 'this dump' and into an old mansion on St Louis Street.

He rhapsodized about his find. 'I've been looking for a room like that for months – only three dollars a week, too! It's huge and gorgeous, five windows looking out on the courtyard, and the most enormous bed you've ever seen. Come and see it!' He was as enthusiastic as a small boy.

When they got to the mansion, Marie recognized it as one belonging to a family destroyed by the war, but she had known it well in its glory during her hairdressing days. As they passed up the grand staircase and through the empty, echoing corridors to his 'palace on the third floor', he continued to rave enthusiastically about everything, and she could see in her mind's eye how it had once been, and in her heart was only pain for all that had been so irretrievably lost. When they got to the great room, his exuberance burst out anew.

'Look, Marie! A white marble fireplace, and I believe that's a real Venetian mirror above it. It's as good as something in a Venetian palace – better, even. And look at the bed! Have you ever seen such a beauty? Let's baptize it here and now ...' He turned from the great Seignouret bed to her, his good eye bright with desire, his face flushed. 'Let's make love.'

'No!' she said sharply. Somehow the idea revolted her. It was one thing to lie in his arms in the room that held for her such dear memories, but the idea of doing it here was a desecration, something almost obscene. This room, that bed, represented to her something to which she had always aspired, never gained, but which she still thought of as something fine and wonderful: the Creole way of life, which had been killed – just as surely as the ancient family that had sired its sons in that great bed – by the Anglos' terrible war. To make love in it with this insensitive clod of an Anglo, who had never known that world, could never understand it, was an impossibility.

'Why not?' he pouted. 'It would be wonderful in that bed, and I feel like it.'

'Well I don't,' she snapped. 'Nor will I ever in this tomb – so if you're so set on this move, you can forget about me!' They quarrelled again, separating in a fury, only to be driven back into one another's arms a few weeks later by the strange need, the strange bond, that would not let them go. But she persisted in her refusal to come to the house on St Louis, and so their affair continued in the almost-as-great Seignouret bed at Rampart Street.

Even his lovemaking infuriated her, since it never occurred to him for one moment to cater to her pleasure while gratifying his. One night, angered by some love-play that hurt her, she bit him so hard on the neck that blood began to flow. He sprang up from the bed, clapping a hand to his injury, and screamed, 'You damned vampire! What did you do that for? I'm sick of you and your whims! Get out!'

'This is my house and my bed!' Marie screamed back in her frustration. 'Just because you're a man, you think you can do what you like! But get a little of the same treatment back, and you scream like a wounded alley cat. *You* get out, you undersized little vermin!'

Grabbing up his clothes, he rushed out swearing, and it was the last she saw of him for a month.

His size was the most constant in his litany of complaints against the world; on his lack of inches he blamed practically every other failing, setback, and mishap. His constant moaning about it so exasperated Marie that one day she snarled back, 'Oh, for God's sake, if it concerns you so, why don't you *do* something about it instead of moaning all the time?'

'Do? What the hell can a pygmy do in a land of giants?' he yelled.

'It's obvious. Go to some place where there are other pygmies, where *you* can be a giant.'

The thought appeared to surprise him. 'And where would that be?' he demanded.

'How do I know? You're the world traveller. I've never been beyond the two waters, remember? But there must be somewhere,' she returned. 'How about China? Those little yellow men who run all the laundries these days are a lot smaller than you are.'

'Hmm,' he said, sinking deeper into thought, 'the mystic Orient – the land of the lotus, eh? That's quite a thought. They say there's a lot in Buddhism for a mystic and occultist like me. When I'm finished with this place, I might even try it sometime.'

When I'm finished with ... It was one of his typical phrases – he used everything and everybody, Marie reflected, including herself. Everything and everyone had to be ingested, devoured, only to be spewed out again in ink on endless reams of paper, reshaped by his imagination. As to being a mystic! She snorted inwardly. He was about as mystic as a bedpost.

He pestered her constantly about Voodoo, for his interest in all things arcane was a dominant one. Not trusting him, Marie told him only the obvious and the unimportant, and she warned others to do the same. He had struck up an ardent friendship with *Hungan* Dan, only to quarrel with him. And then he had turned his attentions towards the aging Crocodile. Indeed, he seemed more at ease with the blacks and coloureds than with his own kind, and he constantly sought them out for their company.

His friendship with Crocodile worried Marie. The old man was so far gone in age that he was semi-senile and very garrulous, and Marie was concerned that he would tell Lafcadio more than was good for him to know. She took her worries to Dan, with whom she had become quite close since a singular happening a couple of years back. She had found that old Abraham had disappeared from his shack. Knowing that Dan had been friendly with the simpleminded Negro, she had enlisted his help in a search, but they had found no trace. It had upset her and made her feel guilty, being well aware of her debt to the old man.

Seeing this and meaning to comfort her, Dan had said something that had upset her even more. 'I should not worry or grieve, Marie. I think poor old Abraham has finally escaped from your mother's clutches.'

She had been startled. 'What do you mean?'

'Oh, don't you know about him and your mother? It was Crocodile who told me when I was in training.'

'Told you what?'

'Abraham was a *hungan* at one time – oh, years ago, before I was ever born, and you must have been quite small. He and your mother had some falling-out over Voodoo business, something she wanted and he didn't, I guess. Anyway, as Crocodile told it, they had a power battle and, well, she zombified him. Leastways, that's what Crocodile said.'

She had believed him, and while it did not really surprise her, it had concerned her – and still did. But ever since she had felt close to Dan and had consulted him on many an occasion.

On Crocodile, he again was soothing. 'His powers are gone and most of his memory, too. I don't think Lafcadio will get much sense out of him or make much sense out of what he does get told. But if it'll set your mind at rest, I'll try to keep him out of the way as much as possible.'

Lafcadio was intelligent enough to realize he was not being told the whole story on many matters and often grumbled about it, but Marie was not about to expose anything meaningful, either, to him or to the seedy circle of journalists that formed the bulk of his white acquaintances and whom she could not tolerate.

There was one exception to this: a man named George Cable, whom she rather liked. Although he was several years older than Lafcadio, and had already not only had articles printed in national magazines but also had produced his first book, Lafcadio treated him patronizingly, as if he were a young fledgling of no particular worth or merit.

'Why on earth do you tolerate it, George?' Marie fumed one day when Lafcadio had been particularly obnoxious. 'Why don't you tell him off? Put him in his place. It would do him a world of good. After all, you *are* a success and he isn't; nor, as far as I can see, is he ever likely to be.'

George had cocked a mild eyebrow at her. 'Because I am a mere teller of tales, but Lafcadio is a *writer*. I admit he can be more than trying, but the fact remains that he *does* have talent. One day, if he can ever find himself, I think he will have the potential for greatness – it's a rare power, Marie, and one that most of us lack. So I suppose that's why I put up with more from him than I would from anyone else.'

Was that why she stuck with him, too? she wondered. Somehow she did not think so – there was something else, something that still had to come to fruition.

That happened as the year turned and the sorrowful '70s became a new and more hopeful decade. Lafcadio summoned her to dine with him, with a conspiratorial air of great excitement. 'There's someone you've simply got to meet. George found him and he's the *real* McCoy. You've given me the run-around on Voodoo long enough, but this man makes everything you get up to look like a bunch of cheap conjurer's tricks! I'm going to get the real story from him.'

Intrigued and somewhat alarmed at who this viper in the nest could be, Marie obeyed the summons. When they got to the restaurant, however, it was to find George Cable sitting by himself at a side table.

'Where is he?' Lafcadio demanded eagerly.

'He'll be along later. He said to go ahead and have dinner because he won't be eating tonight. He'll join us after.'

They dined and had got to the coffee-and-liqueur stage when Marie felt, rather than saw, the stranger's presence. She glanced quickly behind her, and for a moment her senses swam – the Helper, in solid flesh, was standing behind her chair. The men were on their feet, shaking hands, and through her agitation she was vaguely aware of an introduction being made.

'Marie, I'd like you to meet Jim Alexander, who has just moved into town.'

The proud young Indian face looked down at her, the eyes sharp and hard as an eagle's. Almost involuntarily she looked for the gold ornament at his throat and the long braided hair, but his hair was cut in the current fashion and he was clad in sober evening wear. *This is a man*, she told herself desperately, *a likeness, a deluding likeness – nothing more.*

But as he took her hand and bowed over it, he looked deep into her eyes and she knew there was much more to it than that. 'I have waited long for this meeting, Marie Laveau,' he said.

And she knew beyond question that a climax, a moment of decision, had just been reached.

Chapter Forty-three

Who was he? And what was his purpose? These questions continued to torment Marie in the time that followed. Some facts about himself he was prodigal with – there were at least three different stories about his origins circulating in the city, all apparently started by himself. Others were self-evident, like his white wife, Clemence, born and bred in Haiti and herself a Mambo. It was also true that he had been in Mississippi for several years before moving to the city. He had practised there as a healer and was by all accounts a very good one. But all the vital things about him were veiled in mystery, and it was a mystery she had to penetrate, for of one thing she was certain – she was now face to face with an enmity far surpassing anything that had ever existed between St Regis and herself. But what was its reason or its source?

When the confusion of her senses had passed after that first meeting, she realized that he was not the Helper at all; the fact that he was young and an Indian of power, together with her own unfulfilled yearning for the Helper, had misted her mind. Jim Alexander sought her out, and she found she had more in common with him than with anyone she had ever known – and yet she knew it was all wrong.

Her feelings of doubt were widely shared by the Negro community. While the mixed bloods and the whites were flocking excitedly to the 'services' he held in his Orleans Street house, the blacks were divided in their minds about him. Billy Boy, who had taken a mulatto wife and was now raising a growing family and becoming a man of substance, voiced the prevailing opinion succinctly. 'Folks say he sho' is a good healer, but Ah just don' know 'bout 'im. There's somethin' Ah jus' don' trust. He's after somethin', that's fo' sho'.'

Marie tried not to let it worry her; afer all, in the present growing prosperity of the city, there was plenty for both of them, and she had more business than she could comfortably handle. But where was everything heading? To what end? There had been some dropping-off in her own clientele, although her Voodoo Negroes stood firm and would have little to do with either Alexander or his wife, who also held services of her own. Marie's delegate Queens were almost as uneasy about the situation as she was.

'I just don't like the pair of them,' Malvina Latour had declared. 'I think we ought to get together and run them out of town.'

But Marie was not ready for that; there was too much she had to find out first, and an old sense of guilt bound her as she took stock of herself.

Looking at all the busy movement and growth around her, she began to feel like a hothouse plant, seeing the rest of the hothouse plants growing and stretching arms out to the sun while remaining stunted herself. So much was happening, so much was developing, yet she stayed the same.

Among the Laveaus, the new spirit of restlessness was very evident. Charles-Louis, François, and Marie-Jeanne and her husband had all moved away from the city to start up their iron-working business in Baton Rouge, which – so it was rumoured – would shortly become the state capital again and which was booming in consequence. Only the ever-faithful Jean remained, doing very little business but seemingly content to potter around after his coloured mistress, who now ran a small boardinghouse on the Esplanade. Celeste reigned supreme at the St Ann Street cottage, which had become the centre for her daughters, now all married, and where she guarded the aged Marie like a dragon. George Cable, who had been very intrigued by Marie's stories of her mother, had actually gained access to the old woman for an interview, but had reported wryly that her mother had sat in silence while Celeste had done all the talking.

As to others, it came as no surprise to Marie that Veronique Parise, as the wife of one of the city's leading advocates, was now a leader in New Orleans society. The Valdouxs, on the other hand, though once more prosperous, remained leaders only within the select group of old Creole families that wanted no part of the new order. Marie was happy to see that most of the changes within the Valdoux family had been for the good. St Regis had finally been proclaimed legally dead, and Marie-Thérèse Montal had become *de facto* what she had been for years in secret, the wife of Bayard Valdoux and the fond step-mother of her dead sister's children. Claire and her mother, with the return of prosperity, had contrived to turn back the clock in the Royal Street house, and there lived the comfortable serene, and indolent life of the ante-bellum years. Only Valerie had not improved with the prospering times. The hard fight she and Justin had had to save Castle Blanche had left an indelible mark on her. She was brittle in her bitterness, sharp of tongue, and imperious of manner, reminding Marie uncomfortably of her late Montal aunt; there was little left of her childhood friend. And Emile was the rock to which she could always cling in times of tempest, her anchor point in a fast-changing world.

But there was little she could ask of him in the case of Jim Alexander. What lay between 'Dr Jim' and her was a problem she had to solve for herself.

When, however, he started his own dances out at the lake, Marie decided he was going too far and that something had to be done. She tackled him directly. 'Look, the authorities have left us alone for years now because I cleaned up our own dances and turned our people's minds in other directions. The things you're running are little better than sex orgies, serving no good purpose but, I suppose, to line your pockets. For the good of us all, I'm asking you to stop.'

He had given her an unfathomable look. 'I'm sorry, but my dances will go on.' And he would not be budged.

'Then you will bring on yourself nothing but trouble!' she exclaimed grimly. And to make sure this was so, she quietly contacted friends on the police force. His dances were raided and he was imprisoned for a short while, but when he came out they started up again as if nothing had happened. Again she put on pressure in the right places, and again he went to jail, but, apart from growing hostility between them, it made no difference; his dances went on.

Meeting him face to face one day on Johnson Street near his house, Marie's temper got the better of her and she began to shout at him. 'What is it with you? Have you no sense? Do you want to spend your life going to jail? Why must you thwart me so?'

Usually he met her tirades with maddening impassivity, but this time his own anger suddenly erupted. 'Because you have thwarted *me*! Because you have taken from me the one thing in life that mattered, the one chance I had – somehow, somewhere, you took from me Don Thomé, and, by the powers, one day I will find out how.' He towered over her, his eyes blazing, his fists clenched.

She shrank from him as if he had struck her; the old guilt washed over her like a tide. 'I don't know what you mean,' she stammered.

'You deny you are the daughter of Don Thomé, the one he left me to seek?' he roared.

'No, I don't deny that . . .' – she was more frightened than she had ever been in her life – '. . . but . . . you are not his, also?' she gasped.

'His son? No, I had not that good fortune.' There was pain in his eyes. 'But I was his apprentice – the most gifted one he had ever had. In another year, young though I was, I would have been ready, he said: ready to seek the path to the second circle, ready to find the crack between the worlds. And then . . . and then he had to go to seek *you*' – he spat out the word with venom – 'because *you* were flesh of his flesh.' He seized her by the wrist. 'He never returned. What did you do to him? Why did you destroy him? For I know in my heart that this is so.'

As Marie looked at him in terror, a voice over her shoulder broke in: 'This man giving you trouble, Marie? You, there, let go of her. You're under arrest.' Marie wheeled to see a policeman she knew well glaring at Dr Jim, his hand hovering near his gun. 'Got a message that there was a disturbance going on here,' he went on. 'What do you want to charge him with, Marie?'

Gathering her scattered wits together, she realized that to have him temporarily out of the way would be no solution to anything. So she managed to say, 'No . . . no charges. Just a little business misunderstanding, officer. Nothing that we cannot straighten out.' She gazed meaningfully at Dr Jim. 'I'm sorry we created a disturbance.'

'Well, if you say so,' he said grudgingly. 'Be off with you, then, and don't bother her again. I'll walk you home, Marie.'

He would have to be got rid of; she could not kill him, but she had to get him away – out of the city, out of her life, for as long as he was around, she would know no peace. Her thoughts were panic-stricken as she made her preparations. Now she knew the way of it. But what was his aim? To destroy her? Or merely to find out the truth? He had to be stopped in either case, but did she have sufficient power?

She started the ritual in old Abraham's deserted shack on the bayou's edge. She needed to be near the waters, which were not his element and which would give her the power of that other stream in her blood, the one that he lacked.

It began well and she could feel the power in her grow and take on direction, and that gave her a sense of triumph. Then it was as if an invisible wall arose around her, blocking her, sending the streams of energy deep into her own body like knives, and as she twisted in agony, she was aware that the Helper was there, his shadowy form taking on definition against the wooden wall of the dusty shack. 'Help me!' she managed to gasp out, and the pain began to fade. When it was gone, she crouched on the floor looking up at the form with dread in her heart for what might come next.

'You will not succeed – this is not the path,' the Helper said in the voice so like, yet unlike, the voice of her enemy.

'I must – he will destroy me.'

'No.'

'But he is my enemy.'

'Yes – but he will not destroy you unless you cause him to.'

'Then what must I do?'

'Seek him out and make your peace. He is part of the path you have lost. You must learn.'

'But *he* doesn't know!' she cried. 'That is where the hate lies!'

'You still do not understand, but you will learn,' the Helper said, then was gone.

Defeated, and still sadly troubled, Marie made her way back to the city. After much thought, she summoned Jim Alexander for a meeting on neutral ground. She had decided to tell him all but the final truth; and to prevent him from fathoming that, she built up a firm mental image of her father walking away from their last fatal meeting, of him leaving the city by boat and then being overwhelmed by a storm at sea, sinking, sinking to his death in the waters. She hoped this image, so near to the truth, would serve to block any powers Dr Jim might have in reading her mind.

It seemed to work. At the meeting, Dr Jim was his usual impassive self, hearing Marie out in silence. At the end she held out her ultimate peace offering. 'It is senseless,' she said, 'for the two of us, with so much in common, to be in competition. Why do we not compromise and work together, instead? There is plenty here for us both.'

Somewhat to her surprise, he had not opposed her, and they had worked out a compromise. He agreed to hold his dances in private, and to join her in the public ones. And they charted their areas of activities so as to get in one another's way as little as possible. From then on they were seen so much together that it occasioned public comment and not a little criticism from her own people, but on the surface it worked well enough. Under the surface Marie was not so sure. It had all been a little too easy, and the fear remained that a hate nourished for so long could not be dispelled by a glib story and a business partnership. In her heart she felt that the struggle, far from being over, might not even have begun.

This series of events left her drained to a point where she began to doubt her own powers. Thinking that her affair with Lafcadio might be too much of a strain on her at her age, she separated from him for a while. She found it made little difference, and so they drifted back together again in the same uneasy necessity.

Not that it was as turbulent as it had been. They were used to one another now, and she found that with this new major enemy to face, Lafcadio's human failings were not half as important as they had once been. In fact, his short-comings provided an almost blessed counter-irritant to the chief worry that obsessed her. He also was in a milder mood. He had shifted over to the *Times-Democrat*, having quarrelled with everyone at the *Item*, and was currently full of plans for writing for the New York magazines, an idea instigated by George Cable, who had already broken through into that magic circle.

As Marie kept a close eye on Dr Jim, she could not but admire his showmanship and his skill. He had installed a pool in his Orleans Street home and stocked it with swamp alligators, which he had trained to answer his call – a fact that mightily impressed his more credulous clients. A magnificent dancer himself, his organized dances were spectacular. Though people still flocked to Marie for personal counsel of all kinds, when they started to hurt anywhere, increasing numbers of them sought out Dr Jim; nor could she blame them, for he was a great healer.

But in her heart she knew that he stalked her still. With the uncanny patience of the Indian, he was watching and waiting for his moment – a moment of weakness on her part, a mistake, and she knew she would be finished. Somehow she had to put herself beyond his reach, but try as she might, she could not see the path. So she waited for a sign, a sign that had to come.

Chapter Forty-four

Claire wrote:

My dear Marie,

*I do not know if you will find this news joyful or sad,
but Ingrid is about to be married. She has fallen in love
with a man named Charles Ballou, a businessman from
the east, who is part-owner of a jewellery factory in
Rhode Island. I confess to mixed feelings about it myself,
since he is not a Catholic, and he will only be here in
Chicago for a few years while he establishes a branch of
his business here. After that he plans to return to Rhode
Island, and that will take her far away from us all. Vittorio also shares my doubts. He has investigated Mr
Ballou thoroughly, and finds nothing against him, but I
know he had hoped she would marry his nephew, Dom-
enico, who runs several of his restaurants for him. However, she is very much in love, and since she is now of age,
we do not feel we can stand in her way. Mrs Andersen is
very fond of Mr Ballou and approves of the match, since
she has never liked Ingrid being raised as a Catholic. But
if you have any objections, I will do what I can . . .*

What right had she to have any objections? What right to
dictate anything to this daughter, who was a stranger in all
but blood? She wrote soothingly to the troubled Claire:

*Let her follow her heart; in these matters no one can
ever know what is for the best, and it is her life and her
destiny. Your task is finished, my dear, that heavy task I
laid upon you so long ago and which you have done so
magnificently. Be quiet in your mind, knowing that, and
devote yourself now to your own family, of whom you
may be equally proud.*

But the responsibility so long borne was not so lightly

discarded, and, in a series of letters, Claire worried her way through the brief engagement, the wedding, the honeymoon trip – which was a lengthy one and which spoke well for Mr Ballou's resources, Marie reflected – the settling into their new home, and, not too long after this, the news of Ingrid's pregnancy.

This news that she was to be a grandmother stirred in Marie old ideas, old ambitions, that had long remained dormant. Her present life was at a dangerous impasse, but could she still, should she, reach out into the future – as she had done once long ago – that future where, if Aristide had been a true prophet, she could really have power? Here she had reached her limit and she saw what a narrow one it was, but there, in that future time, what might she not do?

She had turned her back on the path her father had offered, so that was closed to her. But the one that her mother had so treacherously embarked on – was that for her, also? It was dangerous, she knew; she might destroy or be destroyed in the process, but it was a path, an aim – something to give her life direction once more. She must waste no more time, for there would be much to learn, much to strive after. Before, except for the idea itself, she had not done anything, and her one true happiness had intervened and prevented it. But now there was nothing to waylay her – no happiness, no grief; her heart had died with Nils, and there could be no other.

Afire with this new purpose, Marie sought out Mama Antoine in her tiny cottage. The old Mambo was far gone in years, but she had been spared her own mother's physical afflictions. She was frail in body but still alert in her mind, and she was willing, even strangely eager, to tell Marie all she knew. Marie soon realized that, though valuable, this was not enough. She looked for help elsewhere and found a strange ally in George Cable.

'*Books* on Voodoo?' he said with some surprise. 'Well, yes, I'll see what I can find for you. But may I ask what you, of all people, should want them for?'

'I thought I might find something more in them to help my people, who are having such a hard time just now,' she lied glibly, knowing full well this particular chink in George's armour.

Southerner though he was, he had a vast empathy with and sympathy for the Negroes – stemming, she surmised, no doubt, from his mother's Yankee blood – and he had been horrified by the recent developments in the South. The brief honeymoon between the freed Negro and the white man had long been over. The white Reconstructionists, safe in their newly built kingdoms, no longer needed Negro front-men, and they were now only interested in them as cheap labour, and the Ku Klux Klan had been spawned and spread like a blight that kept the Negro in his place – at the very bottom of the human pile. The days of the slave block, the brand, and the lash might indeed have gone forever, but the Negro was free in name only; his lot was still to suffer.

All this George Cable saw and was horrified by, and he had become highly unpopular in certain quarters for voicing his outrage, so Marie knew an appeal along these lines was sure of success. It was. Books he found, and she, who had never opened one since her youth, now strained her eyes and mind over the printed page. Her head ached, her mind whirled, but she kept doggedly on at this unaccustomed activity, and she learned how much she had to learn and where she must look for more . . .

Claire's worryings meanwhile culminated in a joyful outburst. She wrote exultantly:

You are the grandmother of a fine baby girl, and she is beautiful, even more so than her mother, if that be possible. She is so fair and, at the moment, has blue eyes like her father, but they are darkening rapidly and will, I think, be either green or hazel. As soon as Ingrid is recovered enough, I shall insist they be photographed and will send you a copy. Although I cannot be her godmother, since she is to be raised a Baptist like her father, they are going to name her after me. I am so proud of that. And for her middle name they are calling her for Mr Ballou's mother, Jacqueline. Is not that a rare coincidence? I am so happy!

But her next letter, sent but a scant ten days later, was again troubled. She wrote:

I have some strange news to relate, news which I fear will cause you pain. Let me say hastily that all is very well with Ingrid and baby Claire, but it is about Patty that I write.

Ingrid has been so looking forward to having her look after the baby, for, since the marriage, Patty has been subject to moody spells and has not been her usual self at all. Knowing how devoted she has always been to 'her chile', I think it was mostly jealousy and the feeling Ingrid no longer needed her as much. So Ingrid thought, sensibly, that the new baby would give her a whole new interest in life. But when the baby came, Patty would not even hold it and said it was not 'her chile', and she did not want anything to do with it.

Now comes the really strange part. Last night Patty arrived at our house. She had walked clear across town in the pouring rain, and when we let her in she was quite wild and rambling. Not only has she turned against the baby, but against Ingrid, as well. She keeps saying that she wants to go home to New Orleans and to you – though, as you know, to her, as well as to Ingrid, you have been dead these many years. I fear the soaking she got has given her a severe chill, and perhaps even a brain fever. We have put her to bed and have sent for a doctor.

In haste,
Claire

Poor little singleminded Patty. Marie felt Patty's pain as if it were her own. She sat down to compose a reply to Claire, saying that when the little slave had recovered sufficiently she should be sent home to New Orleans. It was the least she could do, she reflected, after so many years of devotion, to bring her back to where she belonged and to look after her. Her own resurrection could be easily passed over in Patty's blurred mind, and a suitable cover story could be thought up for Ingrid's benefit.

Before Marie's letter had even reached its destination, she received another one from Claire.

I sorrow to tell you that Patty is dead, but it is a blessed release after the torments I witnessed her suffer. The fever came on her, and in her delirium she screamed all manner of terrible things – all about a sister (I never knew she had one), and a wicked 'Missus' (not your mother), and then on and on about your mother – oh, things that I shall never recount to anyone, but which I'll not forget until my dying day. After that she went into a succession of fits, and only at the very end did calm come to her. She seemed to lapse into what looked like a trance; she was so stiff and rigid. Suddenly she spoke very clearly. She said, 'Tell Miss Marie I always did what she said, but I can't anymore. I could not keep her away.' Then she died. May her poor soul rest in peace. We will see to the burying, and I shall keep everything from Ingrid.

Marie read the letter with tear-blurred eyes. At the end Patty's memory had unblocked – she wished she could have spared her that. But how strange that she had rejected the new child – almost as if she knew . . .

This was at the end of May. Towards the end of June, the widow Paris had another stroke and Celeste sent word of it to Marie. 'I think this one may well kill her,' she said briefly, 'coming so soon after the last. So if you wish to see her alive, you'd better come.'

Marie went, though there had been many other summonses of the same kind. There was really nothing to be done. She had called in Dr Franke over Celeste's strenuous objections some time before. After the examination he had said, 'The amazing thing is that she is still alive – at her great age, and having suffered enough strokes to have killed off half a dozen normal people. She must have the constitution of a whole herd of oxen, not to mention a fantastic will to live. Make her as comfortable as possible, and one of these days the end will just come quietly. In your mother's case, it is impossible to predict when.'

Six months ago she had had a stroke that left her speechless and, for the first time, bedridden, her limbs refusing to support her, though she was not paralysed. To Celeste's eternal credit, now that her mother had become entirely helpless, she cared for her most tenderly and well, with none of her former impatience. She was even half-way decent to the remaining members of the family when they visited her mother, so that going to the St Ann Street cottage was no longer quite the trial it had been.

This time Marie found Celeste in her mother's parlour, surrounded by her usual coterie of daughters and pallid grandchildren. 'How is she?' Marie demanded.

Celeste shrugged wearily. 'I don't know. Lately she has been restless. Then last night she had a little convulsion and I thought she was going then and there, but she came out of it and has been lying like a statue ever since, scarcely breathing. Jean and Marie-Philome are in there with her. I've sent for a priest. You'd better go on in and see for yourself.'

She led the way into the darkened room and then stood aside. Marie-Philome loomed, hugely fat by her mother's chair, which was pulled up to the bedside. She nodded briefly at Marie. Jean was kneeling on the other side of the bed, holding his mother's left hand, his head buried in the covers as he cried quietly.

'I sent a telegram to the lot up in Baton Rouge,' Celeste whispered with some of her old venom. 'But doubtless they'll be too busy to come!' She tiptoed up to the bed, looked down at the still figure in it, and beckoned Marie to join her. There was a murmur of voices from the outer room, and Celeste's head went up like that of a hunting dog. 'That will be the priest,' she whispered excitedly. 'I must go and greet him. It is good of him to come so quickly – such a dear man!' And she bustled out of the room.

Marie went up to the bed. For some reason Marie-Philome's presence in her mother's chair irked her; it was a violation of some kind. Looking down, she marvelled anew at how small her mother had become. Every time she saw her, she appeared to have shrivelled a little more, as if she were gradually drying up from within and would finally just blow away. Even her features had altered to the point where she was no longer recognizable as Marie Laveau; they had sharpened and thinned, as had the heavy hair, which now lay starkly white, neatly arranged on the immaculate pillow by Celeste's untiring hand. Her mother lay with her eyes closed, her breathing barely perceptible. Marie took her right hand, which lay blanched and almost weightless on top of the covers, and gave it some of her own warmth.

To come to this at last, after so much life and living. Her mind went back over the struggles and the triumphs; she thought of their battles side by side against the world, and of their battles with one another. Such an appetite for life – only to fail at last – as always, she thought.

Marie was dimly aware that her older sister and the priest had entered the room, and she was jerked out of her reverie by Celeste's sudden horrified gasp. She glanced up to see that her mother's head was slowly turning towards her, the great dark eyes, still brilliant in their deep, sunken sockets, gradually opening. The hand in hers moved, and the mouth worked and then opened, as life flooded back into the empty face and Marie saw her mother as she had always been. Clear as a bell in the startled silence of the room, her mother's voice rang out, deep and strong, as if in answer to her own last thought.

'I HAVE NOT FAILED!' said Marie Laveau in triumph. Then the eyes became fixed, the head fell back, and Celeste sprang towards the bed with an inarticulate cry, pushing Marie aside.

Marie Laveau lay, smiling in death. And Marie, still clasping the dead hand, knew that it was no longer her mother's hand she held, but that of a stranger.

Chapter Forty-five

The word had spread in the city, and vast crowds followed the closed coffin of the widow Paris from the cottage on St Ann Street to the mortuary chapel of Our Lady of Guadalupe and then to the old cemetery of St Louis beyond. The cortege passed with difficulty through the massed crowds at the Basin Street gate of the cemetery, and police had to be called in to clear a way through the narrow gravel pathway that ran beside the old wall, the few short yards to the whitewashed tomb, which proclaimed from its lintel the final resting place of the family of the widow Paris.

'Her remains will soon mingle with Papa's – the only man she ever loved,' Celeste sobbed in lugubrious satisfaction. 'And I pray they may be reunited in Heaven.'

Marie, numb at Celeste's side, said nothing. Whoever or whatever had been carried to the vault in that strangely light coffin had nothing to do with the Marie Laveau she had known. Her thoughts ran wildly around like rats in a cage. Where was she? Who was she? There was fear in her and hope. If her mother's dying boast was true, it had been done. It could be done. *She* could do it, once she found the key – the key, the key . . .

A strong voice lifted in the crowd with a mourning chant that stemmed from the dark jungles half a world away, and reduced the white vestments of the priest and the glittering gold of the cross going before the coffin to pallid insignificance. The chant was taken up by a brass trumpet that carried the mournful note way beyond the range of human voice, its brazen voice screaming its grief into the hot, clear sky. A drum answered somewhere, and then the crowd in myriad voice took up the minor, plaintive theme, twining and intertwining the patterns of their grief and loss. They sang the sorrow of their life; it had nothing to do with Marie Laveau, nothing to do with her . . . Marie did not wait to see the coffin lowered into the dank recesses of the vault. She turned and pushed blindly through the pressing crowd until she was free of it and halfway back to her own oasis of peace on Rampart Street. The key, the key: Who was she? Where was she?

The press of New Orleans wrote paeans of praise in honour of the dead woman. They talked of her work with the sick, her work in the prisons, and, in veiled terms, of her great contribution to 'the Southern Cause'. They linked her, in varying stages of improbability, with every person of note who had ever been connected with the city – with a naïve disregard for either chronology or plausibility. Only one lone dissenter touched on the one most important facet of her life, which nobody else had mentioned, and that in a derogatory fashion. A reporter for the *New Orleans Democrat*, revolted by his colleagues' attempts to make a saint out of her, called it as he saw it.

'She was no saint,' he wrote. 'She was a Voodoo Queen, and the prime mover in all their indecent orgies – *that* is what was important to her and about her. She probably induced more virtuous women – many of them white – to fall from grace than anyone else in the history of the South. So don't talk to me of saintly Marie – even if she did have some good points!' And for that burst of honesty, he was all but hounded out of town.

Celeste, who had culled all the 'saintly' articles with great avidity, was furious. 'I've a good mind to sue!' she fumed. 'All the other reporters were so *nice. Maman* was so different when she put all that terrible business behind her, and now to have it all dragged up again! As if it wasn't bad enough to have those terrible Voodoo people marking things on her grave – and all those beautiful flowers trampled and dead because of them! It's all Marie's fault – no wonder she dared not show her face! Where *is* she? When she shows up here, I'm going to give her a good piece of my mind. She's finished as far as this house is concerned. Voodoo Queen, indeed!'

There was no trace of Marie in any of her usual haunts. and only a very few knew her whereabouts. After the funeral a terrible sense of urgency had seized her and would not let her rest. St John's Eve was only a few days away, that time of great power. She felt that this was above all a propitious time to make the first attempt – she must know, she must do. She spent long hours with Mama Antoine, who alone had any idea of what she was aiming for.

The old woman was nervous. 'It is too soon,' she had warned. But with the resignation of old age, she had allowed herself to be overridden.

Marie had sent for Malvina Latour. 'I want you to preside over the great rites this year as Queen,' she announced.

Malvina, glad to seize this edge of power over the other 'Queens', had accepted with alacrity. After they had gone over the organization and arrangements, Malvina muttered with heavy tact, 'I understand – so soon after your mother's death and all. It must be a great blow to you. You can depend on me. I won't make trouble for you like some of the others might.'

At other times her transparency would have amused Marie, but now she was too self-absorbed even to notice. With Malvina disposed of, Marie sent for *Hungan* Dan, who was the only one in the inner circle of power in whom she had any trust.

'I want you to do something for me,' she said when he arrived. 'Two days after the rites, I want you to come to old Abraham's shack on the bayou. Whatever you find there and however you find me, I want you to take care of it. If you need help of any kind, go to Billy Boy, but don't tell any of the others. I wish I could tell you more, but I don't know what to expect myself, so I'm depending on your own good sense.'

He agreed uneasily, but was so intimidated by this new and forbidding Marie, stern of face and of eyes that pierced, that he forbore probing further and made haste to leave.

At the door she called him back. 'Oh, there's one other thing, Dan. Where's Dr Jim? Do you know if he plans to go on St John's Eve?'

He shook his head. 'I've no idea. Haven't seen him in over a week – his wife, either. Went by his place the other day and it seemed to be all closed up – maybe they're out of town. Want me to let you know?'

'No. It doesn't matter that much – just as long as he doesn't know that I won't be there, or where I am. You won't fail me, Dan, will you?'

'Of course not,' he said gruffly. 'Since Crocodile went, you're the only true friend I've had. You can trust me.'

St John's Eve dawned as fair a day as could be wished for in the middle of summer. A cool breeze blew off the lake, cutting the searing heat to a pleasant warmth, and crowds began to gather early at the lakeside. There was almost a joyous atmosphere of Carnival in the air, as if the recent funeral of the dead Queen had been a catharsis of accumulated grief which was now spent. But as the afternoon light deepened into the forerunner of dusk, great black clouds from the north swept across the lake, thunder crashed, the heavens opened up with purple bolts of lightning, and the rains began – not gentle, but in sheets, whipping with the winds the placid surface of the waters into answering frenzies. The crowds fled before the battering elements, and that year no fire to Vodun was lit, no cry to him was raised. Terrified and trembling, they fled to whatever shelter they could find against the strange wrath, and there they cowered for a night and a day until the glutted storm growled off into silence, and the sun reasserted its serene power over the wreckage of its going.

Dan, much troubled, went slowly towards his appointed rendezvous. Had Marie been the cause of this strange event, which had shown up so clearly the weakness and helplessness of the followers of Vodun? Had that been her purpose – that, and to demonstrate her own great powers?

Dan reached the bayou's edge and threaded his way through the mountainous debris left by the storm at its swollen edge to the old shack. When he came to it, he stopped, appalled, doubting his own senses. In frantic haste he began to run farther along the bank of the bayou, casting around like a hunting dog after a scent, but when his path had taken him far beyond what his mind told him was the place, he

stopped dead and, with a shudder, began to retrace his steps
to his first discovery. There he stayed gazing down, his eyes
wide with fear. Where old Abraham's shack had stood was
now but a pool of still, dark water, an inlet of the bayou, as
if some giant hand had scooped up whatever had been there
and had thrown its pulverized powder to the winds; not a
board, not a bit of floating jetsam, remained, not a trace of
Marie Laveau. He stayed long gazing down at the waters,
trying to come to terms with what his eyes told him. When
he did leave, he was certain only of one thing – Marie
Laveau had not been the cause of the great storm; she had
been its victim.

Dan said nothing about his discovery, but in the strange
subconscious of the city a murmur grew and a rumour
spread. Marie Laveau was dead; with the mother had also
passed the daughter – the two great Queens were gone.
Tales, each one wilder than the last, came into being. She
had led her people during the rites into the water and had
been swallowed up; she had been snatched up by a giant
whirlwind and had been taken away from the very midst of
the crowd; she had been walking on the water – as many had
seen her do – and the waters had risen and covered her. No
matter how wild the tales, they all had one thing in common
– she was drowned and she was dead; many grieved, some
rejoiced.

Two days later a young girl was taking a walk along the
bayou to see what manner of havoc the storm had caused to
her favourite fishing place. There were willows thick around
it, and as she entered their tangled shade the first thing she
saw was a huge dead snake, its flaccid coils emerging from
a large chest that lay half-in half-out of the water. Then she
saw the body of a woman. It lay across the chest, tied to it by
a thick blue cord, its light blue dress and the veil over the
head soaked with mud. In horrified fascination she tiptoed
closer, just in time to catch a faint moan – the woman still
lived! Not knowing what to do, the girl stooped down and
shook the sopping shoulder. 'Here – get up! Can I help you?
Can you hear me?' The shake had dislodged the veil and

revealed a chiselled face of startling pallor, but as she looked the eyelids fluttered and opened to reveal piercing dark eyes.

The lips of the woman moved. 'Help me!' she whispered. 'Help me, my child!'

Somehow the girl managed to drag her clear of the water and prop her against a tree. The woman began to shake until her whole body was quivering violently, but the strange dark eyes clamped mesmerizingly on to the scared blue ones of the child. 'Is your home close by?'

The young girl nodded.

'Then take me there quickly. I need something hot to drink and some dry clothes. It is important that no one see me like this. Do you understand?'

With difficulty the girl got an arm around the woman's shoulders and managed to get her on her feet, and they staggered back to the small house not far from the bayou. The woman seemed to gain strength with every step. As they reached the door, she stopped and asked, 'Who is in there?'

'No one,' the girl panted. 'There's just me and my mother – my papa died – and she works in the city.'

'Good.' The woman looked down at her and smiled. 'There's no need to be frightened. I'm going to be all right now – thanks to you. And that is something I shall never forget.'

Later, when she was wrapped in blankets, her own clothes steaming and drying in the hot sun outside, she looked at the girl over the rim of a cup of hot soup and demanded, 'What's your name?'

'Louise – Louise Walters.'

'A pretty name for a pretty, fair-haired, blue-eyed girl.' There was a hint of pain in the dark eyes. 'Well, Louise, do you know who I am?'

She shook her head.

'I am Marie Laveau.'

Louise gasped and almost dropped the cup she was holding. 'But they say you're dead!' she stammered. 'It's all over the city!'

'I expect so, but Marie Laveau has been dead before – and

probably will be times again,' Marie said strangely, then began to laugh. 'Don't be scared. As you can see, I'm very much alive. I'm a strong woman – it will take a lot more than this to kill me. Do you know what I am?'

The girl hesitated, then muttered, 'They say you're a Voodoo.'

Marie nodded. 'But you know there are many things a Voodoo knows about, things that would be very useful even to a white girl like you. Would you like to know how to read people's fortunes and how to help them? I could teach you, if you like, and since I am much in your debt, I would very much like to. Would you?'

'Oh, yes!' Louise was eager.

'Good. Then that's settled. Now you can help me back to my Maison Blanche. It's not far, so you can see where I live and where you'll come for your lessons. I don't like a great many people, but I've taken a fancy to you. Friends, Louise?'

'Friends,' the white girl agreed.

When she appeared, as majestic and elegant as ever, and apparently out of nowhere, the resurrection of Marie Laveau caused as much of a furore as her disappearance had caused. She would say nothing of where she had been or what she had been doing but merely smiled enigmatically and parried all queries, anxious or furious, with bland dexterity.

Only with Dan and Mama Antoine was she less guarded. The shock to him upon seeing her was so great that he burst out, 'I saw that place: trees on either side without so much as a twig snapped, and yet the shack was destroyed – gone! No one could have survived that – no one! What happened to you?'

Marie looked at him, her eyes opaque. 'I do not know – I wish I did. Things were going well, and then, suddenly, I was nothing and nowhere. I have no recollection of anything until I opened my eyes to see a white child bending over me. I don't know what happened or what went wrong. I do know one thing: whatever it was had been directed, and directed at me – and I think I know by whom.'

Chapter Forty-six

'I heard you were dead.' A smile on the handsome face of the Indian appeared to rob the words of their sting. But Marie, gazing deep into the dark eyes, sensed his baffled anger. 'You heard of the death of my mother,' she countered. 'There has often been such a confusion between us. As you can see, I am not only alive, but have never been better.'

Dr Jim shifted ground. 'There was trouble with the rites at the lake, I gather.'

'You were there?'

'No. I was busy elsewhere.'

Their eyes clashed, then held. A sense of desperation seized Marie. She must deflect or destroy this terrible enmity that lay between them. He was so much younger, so much stronger, perhaps, even now, as powerful as she; his powers could only grow, and hers fade – if only he would leave her this one thing.

'Look, Jim' – her voice was grimly earnest – 'for years now I have not tried to block you. In fact, it's been quite the opposite – you have my patients, my clients, your own dances. If it were in my power to give you the rites as well, I'd do that, too, but you know that is impossible. You can have it all, as far as I am concerned, but leave me just this one thing. It is nothing of yours. Do not block me in this, I beg you. I may not even succeed, but at least leave me alone to try.'

His smile widened and hardened. 'I can't imagine what you're talking about,' he said in mock surprise. 'In what am I supposed to be interfering?'

'Oh, you know quite well!' she cried. 'Please!'

The smile died. 'If the path is closed to me,' he said with quiet venom, 'why should it be opened to you?' He bowed ironically. 'I am glad to see you so well, but I must be about my own business. Until our next meeting, Marie Laveau!'

'You still do not understand. Why should we waste our powers fighting one another? It can only lead to trouble for us both!' she cried, appealing to his retreating figure. 'There must be an ending!'

'Indeed,' the quiet voice floated back. 'Oh, yes, indeed – there must.'

She had to escape him. But how? The question haunted her. She resigned herself to not making any sudden moves – Mama Antoine had been right: the first attempt had been too precipitate; she must move slowly, plan calmly. There had to be a way.

In the time that followed, though her life followed the same pattern as before – the soirées, the rites, Lafcadio – Marie's main objective was never far from her thoughts. *The dying speak truly* hammered at her – her mother had claimed victory, and she had believed her. If this were so, in her mother's life must be found clues to guide her on her way.

She proceeded to go over her mother's last years step by step for these signposts to the future, and she was surprised by what she found.

Her mother had died a poor woman. Marie knew that she had lost much in the war, but even the actual properties she had owned were all gone, sold, and the money apparently given away. It had been a deliberate stripping of all worldly goods. And, on top of this, she learned from Jean and Marie-Philome some facts that had been carefully kept from her on her mother's orders. During the last years of her life, the old Marie had practised all manner of physical austerities on herself – forswearing all flesh, fasting for weeks at a time – to the hysterical distraction of Celeste – and drinking only sparingly of water and some of her own herbal concoctions. *No wonder she grew so light* was Marie's first thought, and a doubt about her mother's sanity came to her. What if she had lost her mind and her 'success' was all a senile delusion?

From Celeste. Marie learned nothing. Since the funeral, the door of the St Ann Street cottage had been firmly closed against her, as Celeste pursued with singleminded determination the task of whitewashing her mother's image. She was even talking about having her mother's body removed from the tomb and secretly interred elsewhere, in an effort to stamp out the Voodoo signs and symbols which she was constantly finding inscribed on the grave and which she just as constantly scrubbed off. She blamed it all on Marie and refused even to mention her name anymore; not that this was of much concern to the latter, who was just as thankful not to have to cope with her older sister's hostility.

The thought of imitating her mother's austerities came hard to Marie. She had always so enjoyed the material things that it was painful to imagine life without them, and so she kept postponing any definite step in that direction. She knew that this had always been a basic difference between them, but her vigorously fought-for security and comfort meant so much to her that she was not sure she could ever completely give them up.

Two things finally prodded her into action. The first was her break-up with Lafcadio. The beginnings of success had mellowed him considerably. They had settled into an almost humdrum, amiable marital relationship when she found out he was secretly involved with a bevy of black beauties. It had not roused in her any deep sense of hurt or jealousy, but it was a signal. Her life with Lafcadio had been a dying turbulence; now it was over and there would be no other man. They parted amiably, and he confided to her that, if the piece he was currently writing was any success, he was going to implement her advice of long ago and set off for the Orient. 'It will be the right path for you, my dear,' she said, and knew that it was so.

The second was more traumatic. She was presiding over the St John's Eve rites two years after the great storm; everything was going along normally and she was receiving petitioners as the dance whirled around her. She was standing, as always, on the chest in which the python – imported from Africa this time to replace the one lost in the storm –

slept. A Negro man tugging a small child by the hand came up to her with a routine request: his son was not quite right in the head and had the most terrible pains in it – could she help? She looked deep into the child's dull eyes and put her hands on his head; immediately there came the most terrible feeling of all the power draining out of her. The child gave a single squeal and fell senseless at her feet, and she stood swaying with weakness, hard put to it to keep from falling into unconsciousness herself. After a brief commotion the child revived and all seemed well, but the whole episode had shaken her to the roots of her being. As she had feared for some time, her powers were waning and becoming more uncontrollable. She would have to make her move soon, and she would have to move fast.

After the rites she went into seclusion and there thought over the plans that she had been slowly maturing one more time. To escape from Dr Jim she would have to disappear – to put herself out of his reach and knowledge. She thought she knew how to achieve this. When she was certain of it, she made her last move – she sent for Emile.

He came immediately – so resplendent in his black banker's garb, neat cravat, and shiny silk top hat that she felt impelled to apologize for dragging him through the sad shabbiness of Rampart Street, which was fast becoming a slum.

'I really am sorry for asking you here, but this is a matter of vital importance to me, and . . . well . . . I find your new office building so grand as to be intimidating, and for this I want all my thoughts crystal-clear.'

He smiled gravely at her. 'No problem. And I know what you mean. I find the new building somewhat intimidating myself. I still much prefer the old counting house on Royal. I wanted to bring my old desk to the new office, but Gaston – that's my eldest, who is in the business now – would have none of it; bad for my "image" he said. So I'm stuck with a monstrosity of a desk so big I can hardly see over the top of it!'

'Well, do sit down, Emile. This is going to take quite a while, so at least make yourself comfortable.'

He went out into the little hallway and put his hat, stick and gloves neatly on the small table, then came back in, smoothing the sides of his grizzled red hair into place. 'If you don't mind, I'll just wander around for a bit,' he said, 'I spend so much of my life sitting down – either at my desk or at the head of a boardroom table – that it's a treat to be able to wander free for a change. Besides, I've always liked this room so, such pretty things ...' He pottered happily, touching everything, setting straight things crooked and crooked things straight. Marie watched him with an ache in her heart. He had not been in this room more than three times in his life, and yet he acted as if he had lived in it always.

'That's something new, isn't it?' he demanded, pointing a finger at Nils's watercolour hanging beside the fireplace.

'Not particularly.' She was amused in spite of her pain.

He peered closely at it. 'Hmm – very pretty. The Wishing Tree, isn't it?'

'You know about that?' She was surprised.

'Everyone knows about that.' He smiled. His gaze moved on to the carpet. 'It's getting a bit worn, isn't it? But a lovely colour, still.'

They both gazed in gloomy silence for a moment at the faded glories of the rose Aubusson. 'Yes,' she agreed absently. 'I was going to replace it, but now ...' Then she gave herself an impatient shake. 'Oh, Emile, for heaven's sake, *do* sit down! I can't think with you wandering about like that, and I've so much on my mind.'

'Oh, all right!' he grumbled, and settled himself with a comfortable squirm into the pale blue cushions of the couch, his head still swivelling to see any detail of the room he might have missed. He looked across at her with a slight frown. 'Oh, by the way, who's the little mulatto boy who let me in?' he asked in a too-casual voice.

She smiled back at him and shook her head in reproof. 'That's little Billy – Billy Boy's eldest. And if you want to be technical, he's a quadroon – his mother's a mulatto like Billy. They are living here now – one of the many things I want to talk to you about.'

He looked relieved. 'Oh! Well, fire away, then.'

Marie picked up two fat white envelopes that lay on the little pie-crust table beside her armchair. 'The detailed instructions for everything I'm going to tell you are in these two packets, which you can look at later at your leisure. But, since you are going to find their contents strange, I must explain at least some of it. First, I want you to sell Maison Blanche and the Bourbon Street house for me and add the proceeds to what I already have with you, and I want you to have this house deeded over to Billy Boy and his family. In the first packet is my full power of attorney.'

His eyebrows rose. 'Planning another flight?' he said carefully.

'Not in the sense you mean, no – but it is imperative that I disappear. I shall probably never leave the two waters, but still I must and will be unseen. Sometime in the future I may have to cross the waters to Santo Domingo or Haiti – I just don't know yet, but that, too, I have provided for with a contingency fund, the details of which are in the second packet.'

'Are you in some kind of trouble? Because, if so, you know anything within my power, I . . .'

She interrupted him. 'Not the kind of trouble you would either understand or could possibly do anything about; otherwise, you would have been my first thought. I have but one great aim left in my life, and to accomplish it the only means will be to cut myself off completely from everything that has gone before.'

There was pain in his eyes. 'Has your life become so unbearable, then? I know times have been very hard, but they are becoming easier again – they could be better for you, you know. You have only to say the word.'

'And what would lie ahead would be exactly the same as what was before – and for me that is nothing, or nothing that means anything anymore.' She looked at him with defiance. 'When you build, you build *something*, something that will last, but for me that road is closed. It is the difference that has always existed, probably always will exist, between one born on Royal Street and one born on Rampart.'

'I see – I do not understand, but I see.' His tone was flat. 'Well, continue with what you want me to do.'

Marie made a helpless gesture. 'This is far more difficult than I thought. Perhaps you had better read the contents of that first packet before I go on. Then I can make myself clearer.'

'Very well.' He drew out the thick sheaf of papers, gazing curiously at the object that fell out from the middle of them before beginning his reading. He had not got very far, however, when he stopped and looked up at her with incredulous amazement. 'What *is* all this, Marie? It reads like something out of a French melodrama by Dumas.' He held up the object, which proved to be one half of a Spanish doubloon, carefully sawed, with a complicated serrated edge. 'I, and I alone, am to give money in the amount stated to the person who comes bearing the other half of this, so long as he bears a piece of paper with your signature? In Heaven's name, why?'

'Believe me, it is *necessary*.' She leaned forward in her earnestness. 'You know, once, when I was very young, my mother said a very wise thing to me. She said we could only look for true friendship – for the kind of friendship that asks no questions but will always help – among the Negroes and our own people. I would go further than that, for in my own case I would not trust my own people, *only* the Negroes – that is, with one exception, and you are it. You are vital to me, and you I trust with my very life, but in order to succeed in what I must do, there can never be any other meeting between us after this. I must disappear without a trace, and let the black world close around and over me so that I cannot be found. Since it will be black people who will be coming for the money – different ones all the time – this scheme is the only safe one I could devise. You must spread word around the bank that anyone bearing this token' – she held up the matching half – 'must be admitted to see you, but *no one* must know its meaning, save you.'

Emile continued to stare at her in blank astonishment as she went on. 'When I say you, I'm afraid I must also ask you to pass the burden on eventually to your son Gaston in exactly the same way, for I fear, my dear, that my task may take long and that I must needs outlive you. In addition, I must ask for your solemn oath that after today you will not seek me out or try to contact me, no matter *what* – hear me now – no matter *what* happens. Will you do this for me? Swear to it! I beg you!'

He came to with a start. 'I swear,' he said gruffly, then went on with his reading. In a moment he said in a pained voice, 'You can't be serious about this amount, Marie – it's so small! How will you ever manage on it?'

She smiled faintly. 'In the first place, what funds I do possess may have to last a very long time, and there will be no more coming in. And in the second place, it is the only way I will ever have strength enough to discipline myself – if I had more, I'd live higher.'

'But what if the cost of living goes up – as it is almost bound to do?' he asked. 'What then?'

'Then my standard of living will have to go down,' she replied matter-of-factly. 'There can be no other way.'

Another thought struck Emile. 'I don't doubt for a moment that you will outlive me by many years. But when you *do* go, what instructions should I pass on to Gaston about the disposal of your ... er ... estate?'

She burst out laughing. 'Oh, my dear, what the devil do I care? Tell him to give it to his favourite charity!'

He looked shocked. 'It really is most irregular!' he said in a pained voice. 'Surely you should make a will. There is your daughter, after all – and other members of your family.'

Marie sobered. 'My daughter is married, with children of her own, and so far away that she has no longer any need of me or anything of mine. You forget that to her I have been dead these many years. As to the rest, they have had much from me in life; let us leave it like that.'

He shook his head sadly and carefully folded up the paper. 'Well, if this is what you really wish,' he sighed, then got up. 'If there is anything that is unclear, I'll contact you about it here.'

'*No!* After today I shall not even be here,' Marie said. 'Already you forget your solemn oath, Emile. This must be our *final* meeting.'

He stood looking at her, saying nothing. To break the almost unbearable tension that was building, she spoke in a carefully controlled voice. 'It was very good of you to come, Emile. How are all the family?'

'Oh fine, fine,' he muttered. Then, with a sudden shy smile, he added, 'My youngest daughter is to be Queen of Comus this year.'

'Oh, she will love that.'

'Yes – they seem to set great store by such things,' he agreed absently. Another heavy silence fell.

'And how is Marie?'

He looked at her with blank astonishment. 'Your wife,' she prompted gently. 'How is your wife?'

'Oh!' His face cleared. 'Fine, too, thank you.' With a visible effort, he gathered himself together. 'Well, I suppose I had better be on my way. Please don't bother to come to the door.' He crossed the room slowly, but when he had his hand on the doorknob he stopped, his head bent so that his words came out muffled. 'I expect you thought me extremely stupid just now – about the name, I mean. But the sad fact is that for me, in all my life, there has been only one Marie.'

'I know, my dear, I know,' she said softly.

'Have you always known?' He was still facing the door.

'No, not always – but, then, I have been blind about many things in my life.'

'Would it have made a difference if you had known?' His tone was wistful.

'I don't know. Perhaps. But don't you think, all things considered, that we may have had, may still have, the best of it, after all?' she said with difficulty, her throat pained her so.

'I don't know. Perhaps you're right,' he said. And he turned to face her for the last time. 'I just don't know.'

They looked at one another for a final moment. 'Good-bye, my dearest Marie. May you find what you seek,' he said, and there were tears in the hazel eyes.

'Good-bye, my dearest Emile,' she whispered, and there were answering tears in her eyes.

Chapter Forty-seven

The years surged to high tide, ebbed, and faded imperceptibly into the endless sea of Time; and with them surged the city. In 1885 it hosted the International Cotton Exhibition – cotton was king again; the bad times were gone. The city grew upwards and outwards: bigger hotels, bigger theatres, bigger gambling houses, bigger brothels – everything bigger and better. People began to talk of the pleasures and gaiety of yesteryear – that they had returned, were even surpassed. The city, bursting in its new pride, spread out towards the lake, gulped in the old towns to the east and west, even spread its tentacles across the river. There was no stopping this New Orleans – and no one had even heard of the boll weevil.

Emile did not fight change; he accepted it as he had accepted all things in his life, but he did not necessarily like it. He had been one of the last to adopt gas-lighting into his houses – he hated the hissing – yet was one of the first to put in electricity when it arrived. Like every other successful businessman, he was constantly building and rebuilding, adding storey to topping storey, developing always onwards, but his heart was not in it. To him the world had become full of meaningless noise: the endless clang and rattle of trolley cars; the peevish whistle of steamships; the shrill insistence of the newfangled telephones, whose utility he recognized but which he personally detested. Even people's voices seemed to have taken on a harsher, more aggressive note as he attended the endless succession of dinners, balls, and parties his social position demanded of him.

With relief, and more and more frequently as the years slipped by, he would retreat to the refuge of quiet and solitude his mother and Claire had preserved on Royal Street. Here, where soft-voiced and soft-footed servants still trimmed the endless tapers in the great chandeliers, which spread cool circles of quiet light through the great rooms; here, where sounds were muted so that the tinkling fountain in the courtyard could still be heard, he could relax and permit himself to dream a little, to creep back into a past which could be recaptured only in these surroundings.

To him, in spite of all the vibrant life encircling him, it was a time of death. Bayard went first, a pale shadow of the laughing, reckless boy who had somehow lost the talent for living. Then it was Valerie – poor, shrill-voiced, hard-eyed Valerie, who had never come to terms with the post-bellum world. The Valdouxs, it seemed, were to die in the inverse order of their birth. Then his mother died – she, the 'delicate' one, had outlived all the St Yveses of her generation. On her deathbed she had looked at her one remaining son. 'You've been so good, Emile,' she said. 'I'm so sorry. Forgive me!' They both had known what she meant.

But one death, one life, was never far from his thoughts. At the outset, his strange order, that anyone bearing the split doubloon be admitted immediately into his presence no matter what, had occasioned much excited comment and speculation in the bank, but even this mystery Time and custom had worn down to a commonplace. The messengers came irregularly and in an endless variety: some neatly dressed and hostile of eye; some shabby and furtively downcast; but all black and all bearing the talisman and the familiar signature scrawled on scraps of paper. Each time it happened, Emile was conscious of a feeling of exquisite relief.

There were times when he was sorely tempted to break his vow. One came in 1897, when the rumour reached him that a Marie Glapion had died dramatically. Since he could not conceive of Marie dying other than dramatically, he was in an agony of suspense until cautious inquiry revealed that it was Marie-Philome, whose obesity had finally caught up with her and who had succumbed to a heart attack in the middle of a ball. At her going, the two coloured 'societies' on which she had lavished all her energies since the death of Jean-Paul split up into warring factions and disintegrated without a trace.

A similar thing had happened to the Voodoos. Malvina Latour had kept things going for a time after Marie's disappearance. But without either the personality or the powers of the 'Queen of Queens,' she was soon battling with other ambitious Mambos, to the detriment of the rites. The worshippers drifted away. The time of Vodun was past, it was whispered. There was no place for an African god in this new world of electricity and the internal combustion engine; only in small backrooms in decaying houses of the French Quarter was his name heard, or by con men who culled the tourist in his name.

A further blow to the Voodoos had come with the strange death of Dr Jim, to whom many had still turned. He had been attacked by a dim-witted Negro boy, a regular at the rites since the great days of Marie Laveau. The youth had cracked him over the head with a rock. An abscess had formed in the brain and he had died of it. For all his powers, Vodun had not saved him. There was no power in Vodun, went the whisper.

That same year a strange occurrence out at the lake had again set Emile's pulses jumping. There had been another freak storm like that of '84, where a tornado had come up out of nowhere and had caused great havoc along the lake's edge. Five days later a woman had been found clinging to the remnants of a shanty which still floated. She had fought off her rescuers. 'Again I have failed!' she had screamed. 'I want to die, I want to die . . .' The rumour once more spread around that this was Marie Laveau, that she had been holding a secret Voodoo rite with several others, all drowned, and that the Devil had come for her. Though it certainly did not sound to him like Marie, he again checked, only to find that the woman had been rescued in spite of herself, had recovered, and had disappeared.

Once, there had been a break of two years after the contingency fund had been called upon suddenly. Had she crossed the sea for good? he had worried. But then the talisman reappeared with yet another messenger, and things went on as before.

Sometimes he would brave the raucous atmosphere of

Storyville, with its continuous array of bawdy houses, each one larger and flashier than the last, to get to the quieter slum of Rampart Street, just to walk past her house on his way to Royal. Occasionally he would see a black face at the window, a black child playing on the steps – but of her, no sign. There were one or two occasions when, going home from the Royal Street house late at night, he could have sworn he had seen her tall figure in the light of the carriage lamps. But when he stopped the coachman and had tried to follow the dim form, it was only to find it had vanished, and he had put it down to his aging faculties and fancies.

In 1903 the cottage on St Ann, far gone in neglect and decrepitude, was torn down, and two new white frame houses crowded on to its site. Celeste had never entirely won the fight to whitewash her mother's name. No matter what she did or said, writers, reporters, and those who simply wanted to gawk had come to the cottage – prying, asking questions, always, about Voodoo Marie. In the late '90s, in a fit of pique, she sold the cottage and went to live with one of her married daughters. There was no one left who cared enough to stop her. Jean and Marie-Philome were dead, the rest far away. And Marie? Well, who knew about Marie?

There were strange tales circulating about a great python that lived in Bayou St John. Some said it had been owned by the widow Paris, and that she had turned it loose when she had forsworn the Voodoo; others said that it was the old Marie, who had not died at all; and there were some who whispered that this was not so, that it was Marie Laveau herself who had taken this form and was waiting – for what, they could not say.

But the whispers were muted and heard by few, for bad times were back; the boll weevil had arrived, toppling King Cotton and the prosperity of the city with it. The city roared its rage against this new blow the Fates had imposed on it. It was struggle again, want again, fear again. The blacks in the so-well-named section of the city called Perdido wailed their fresh sorrows to Voodoo rhythms on the new instruments that this mechanized age had put into their hands, and a new music was born. It was a music that spread through the city like a fever, and which added to the cacophony that so offended the aging Emile.

In his eightieth year, over the protests of his family, he moved out of his great mansion in the Garden District and went back to the house on Royal. 'I intend to spend my last years in peace and quiet,' he announced firmly. 'I have earned it.' And no one could gainsay that.

The years did not greatly alter him. The war had worked its ravages early, but then it was as if the process of decay had stopped. His hair kept its reddish tone, his flesh did not drop away, and the pale skin remained unblotched with the telltale spots of age. Only in the mid 1880s had he become a stooped, elderly man, as if the many burdens he had shouldered in his life were physically bearing him down. He did not mind not looking the world square in the face, since for him there had long ceased to be anything he cared to look at.

It saddened him to see what had happened to the French Quarter: a whole block between Royal and Chartres torn down; the St Louis Hotel, which had once housed so proudly the government of Louisiana, now an empty, decrepit ruin; a Negro orphanage housed in the old Orleans Theatre; the list of ruin was endless. The hotel that had been built on the site of the Montal mansion had burned, and another after that. Now a shabby huddle of shanties stood on the corner opposite the French Opera House, itself far gone in decay. It was beyond the power of one man to halt the tide of ruin. Emile did what he could, and lavished his money to help what few old families there were left to keep up their houses; but too many were gone, too many had fled. The Anglos had triumphed, and he recognized that the future of the city lay beyond the confines of the quarter, just as the power did. Now all that was left for the Vieux Carré was melancholy – and memories.

In 1910 he died as decorously as he had lived, preceding his elder sister by precisely a week. On his deathbed he had been surrounded by his children, grandchildren, and great-grandchildren. Encomiums after his death praised him for his great devotion to his family – even his dying words, they said, had been for his wife. They reported correctly, for, as

the light faded from the hazel eyes, he had looked to where his aged wife stood by the bedside. 'Marie? Marie, my dearest, is that you?' he had muttered urgently. And then he had died. How fitting, his children murmured; only his widow was certain in her heart of hearts that his words were not for her.

He was buried with all the pomp and circumstance the mighty name of Valdoux required. And the city surged on and forgot. Gaston Valdoux continued in his father's footsteps, honouring, among many other things, the strange summons of the talisman. He would look with curiosity at the signature that came with it. 'Marie Laveau', he would murmur, 'surely she is dead. Who is *this* Marie Laveau?' But there was no answer. To New Orleans she had become a ghost as insubstantial as a mist hovering over the bayou.

Chapter Forty-eight

Jameson Reed stepped out of the *Times-Picayune* building and paused for a moment at its busy entrance. He adjusted his stiff celluloid collar a little more comfortably, fingered his dotted bowtie, and carefully tipped his new hat towards the back of his head, as he had seen the older reporters do. Thus armed against the world, he stepped down into the bright spring sunshine and sauntered jauntily off down Camp Street towards Canal.

At that precise moment he would not have changed places with anyone in the world. It was Carnival, tomorrow was Mardi Gras, God was in His Heaven, and, if all was not right with the world, it most certainly was with New Orleans in general, and with Jameson Reed in particular. To be eighteen in the New Orleans spring, to be a cub reporter on the famous *Picayune*, and a cub reporter who had already achieved his first byline – truly this was Heaven.

Lovingly he fingered the precious clipping nestled in his coat pocket. He was of an age when hero-worship came easy – and in his case his unusual brand of it had already paid a handsome dividend. LAFCADIO HEARN – THE GENIUS THAT FLOWERED IN NEW ORLEANS, proclaimed the headline. The desk editor had liked it, the news editor had condoned it, and the senior editor had been amused by it. Why not, indeed? For he had poured his heart and soul into it.

He, Jameson Reed, was going to be as great a writer as his hero, as great an adventurer. Although he had been only four when Lafcadio Hearn died in faraway Japan, he felt he knew him as well as he did his own father – better, perhaps. But to have seen him, to have met him as he roamed these very streets . . .

He strolled on towards his routine assignment, building beautiful castles in the air, dreaming magnificent dreams, unaware that his steps were being dogged by a black shadow. As he stopped at the busy intersection of Canal, the black shadow caught up with him and materialized at his side as a middle-aged black man.

' 'Scuse me,' he said questioningly, thrusting out a tattered duplicate of the precious news article, 'but ya wrote dis here?'

'I did, indeed,' Jameson agreed, his chest expanding an inch or two more.

'Sho' are a *young* one,' the man muttered suspiciously. Then: 'But if ya is de Jameson Reed lak it say here, Ah got a message fo' ya. A lady who knew dis here Lafcadio right well wants to talk to ya – says you'll be real interested in what she has to tell.'

'Someone who *knew* him! Here in the city?' Jameson said excitedly. 'Where? When can I see her?'

'Right now, if ya want – Ah'll take ya right to her.'

All thoughts of his routine assignment disappeared in smoke. Who needed to go to the funeral of a leading citizen when there was such a hot story in the making! His heart soared to the skies. 'Well, what are we waiting for? Let's go!' Jameson said, trying to sound hard-boiled, but failing miserably in the attempt as it came out as an excited stutter.

The Negro nodded, then beckoned Reed to follow him. They crossed Canal and plunged into the gloomy confines of Basin Street, from which the noise and hustle of yesteryear had disappeared. Ever since the city fathers had clamped down on Storyville the previous year, everything – from the gaudiest, most magnificent brothels to the humblest shanty-cribs – had been shuttered and silent. The city fathers had not done so with any good grace; they had been forced into it by the federal government. The war was on, and war was a serious business, as everyone knew, so the secretary of the navy and the secretary of the army had both decreed that prostitution be forbidden within five miles of any army cantonment or a port. In vain did the city fathers protest that nowhere was there to be found a better-regulated area of sin than Storyville – it had to go, said the government. And go it had.

424

When it had been open, Jameson Reed had been forbidden to go there. Now that it was closed, he found the shuttered houses cold and slightly ominous. He tried to pump the black man for information to calm his own fears, but all the Negro would say was, 'Ah don' know nothin'. Ya'll have to ask the lady.'

They were out of Basin Street and on North Rampart, and Jameson was beginning to feel downright uneasy. There was not a white face to be seen; it was known as one of the worst slums in the city. And with all the racial trouble there had been of late, the glances he was getting from passersby and the people sitting out on their steps were actively hostile. Was he walking into a setup of some kind? But what would they hope to get? He fingered his cheap pocket watch and asked uneasily, 'Where is this place? Is it much farther?'

'Not much,' the Negro assured, then quickened his pace as several Negro youths jostled them meaningfully on the narrow pavement. He scooted up a couple of steps and stopped before a door of peeling green paint. 'Right in here.' He opened it and beckoned Jameson inside. When he was in the narrow hallway, the Negro muttered, 'Stay here a minute. Ah'll tell her you're here.' And he slipped through the door to the left of the entrance.

Jameson looked about him, trying to calm his nerves, observing the scene. There was a murmur of voices from somewhere in the rear of the house, an overpowering smell of gumbo cooking, and a lower murmur of voices from the front room. The figure of a very fat mulatto woman appeared in the passage at the back and then popped back in as she caught sight of him. The door to the front room opened.

'Ya can go in now,' the Negro summoned, then slipped away out the front door.

As Jameson went in, he became more anxious. The room was very dark, its shutters closed, and the only illumination came from a single candle that guttered on a small table near the door. The room smelled of old age and decay, mixed with a cloying fragrance he could not identify, but which was

425

something like incense. It was also very hot, the heat steaming from a small fire glowing dimly in the grate, and he felt sweat break out all over his body.

'Sit down by the light, Mr Reed,' a voice commanded. 'You will need it to make notes. I apologize for the darkness, but my eyes can no longer tolerate the light. I also apologize for the heat, which you may find uncomfortable, but which my old bones require.'

Jameson did as he was bid and peered into the darkness. The voice emanated from what looked like a bundle of old clothes seated in an armchair near the fire; no feature of the woman speaking was visible, for even the head was swathed in a shawl. The voice was weak but clear, with a slight, indefinable accent, and it had a curious disembodied quality, as if it were emanating from some source other than the muffled figure. His sense of unease increased and he began to sweat even more profusely.

'I presume you have your reporter's notebook with you,' the voice went on. 'Take as many notes as you want, but, since my strength is limited and I have much to say, I will do most of the talking. I do not think you will be bored, though I do not intend to speak much of Lafcadio – just enough to satisfy you that I have not brought you here on a wild-goose chase.'

Reed nodded dumbly and pulled out his notebook. 'You actually knew him while he lived here?' he managed to blurt out.

'Oh, yes – very intimately, as I believe he has written. I was his mistress for years. I am Marie Laveau. Does the name mean anything to you, Mr Reed?'

James gathered his scattered wits together. 'Marie Laveau?' Of course the name was familiar. Now, what had Lafcadio said about her?

'I believe he referred to me as a vampire.' There was a note of wry amusement in the weak voice as it answered his unspoken thought. 'But you are too much of a man of the world to take such an allegation at its face value, Mr Reed.'

'Oh, no ... er ... I mean yes. Marie Laveau – yes, of course, I have read of you, but, but ...'

426

'But you thought I was dead? No, Mr Reed, as you see, I am not, though I am very old – eighty-eight to be exact. Lafcadio was more than twenty years my junior at the time of our love affair; however, it did not seem to matter at the time . . .' The voice died away for a moment, and added in a mutter, as if to itself, 'I had no idea it would take this long – all a question of time and balance – so many failures – but the moment comes now, the final moment . . .' Then louder: 'The fact is that I shall be here but a short while more, and before I go I must make one last attempt to set some matters right. To establish my credibility, I will tell you many things that you will not find in any open source, but if you dig deep enough into the files and records of this city for the past seventy-five years, you will discover I speak the truth. Now, to begin . . .'

Jameson's pencil flew as she began to recount old scandals, old mysteries – names, famous and infamous, dates, places . . . After a while he became so hypnotized by the quiet, insistent voice that his pencil faltered and he just sat and listened in growing amazement and excitement. Sometimes she spoke of Lafcadio, but nothing of what she said fitted in with Jameson's previous conception of his hero, and he was seized with inner dismay. But he could not stop listening; he could not even doubt . . .

'The one thing I would very much like for you to do is to clear a man's name.' The voice seemed to grow stronger. 'The man was Aristide Sautelle. And if you look it up, you will find it recorded that he took his own life after confessing to the sordid murder of a mulatto girl, Nicole Martins. This is not so. He confessed to the murder only to save another man, wrongfully accused, from the gallows. Both he and I knew the real murderer, who had confessed his crime to him, but we had no proof of that. He was a powerful man in this city by the name of St Regis Montal, and he had killed others, as well. You may think this is a strange thing for me to care about after so long, but I do, and I should very much like you to try and publish the truth of the matter.'

None of the names meant anything to Jameson, but he was so fired by enthusiasm by this time that he started up out of his chair. 'Publish – why, of course!' he cried. 'After I write what you've told me today, I can publish anything! I'll be famous!'

'You may not find it quite as you expect.' Again there was a hint of amusement in the aged voice. 'But sit down, young man. I have not finished.'

He sat.

'You may have remembered by this time that I had a certain reputation in the past of foretelling people's futures. I think I can say that today will indeed be a turning point in your life, and I hope for your sake, and for the sake of Aristide Sautelle, that it will be as you say. But you have been a good listener, Mr Reed, so I will tell you some more: not of what has been – that no longer matters – but of what is to come. I can give you no exact times and dates – that is not how the knowledge comes – but only the general sweep of what will be. This war, in which we are at present involved, and in which we will so shortly be victorious, is supposed to be a war to end wars. This is not so. Within a generation there will be an even greater one. That, too, we will win, but only after a force of fire is unleashed, which, if not contained, may well doom all of mankind. And in between these wars, after a great plague sweeps the world before this very year is out, this country and this city will flourish as they have never flourished before. They will rise to a great height only to crash within a decade to depths of misery not as yet seen, and only by the means of the second war will they regain their strength. But do not ever fear for yourself; in all this I see no great ill to you. You may think these wild words, but remember them – and with them, remember me.' The voice broke. After a little silence, she said faintly, 'I am very tired now. You had better go.'

Released from the spell of her flow of words, Jameson rose slowly to his feet. 'Well . . . er . . . thank you very much, Marie Laveau,' he stuttered, and he went towards her, meaning to shake her hand.

She shrank from him and commanded, 'Don't touch me! Don't come any nearer!'

An ember dropped from the fire, creating a small flare of

light, which illumined the face for a brief moment and stopped him dead in his tracks. It was like looking into the face of a living mummy, so shrunk and shrivelled it was, but out of which a pair of startlingly brilliant dark eyes peered and pierced him. It was not their brilliance that so transfixed him, but the remarkable pupils, which, at the sudden light, had constricted into half-moons, like a cat's; suddenly he was very afraid of them and what he saw in them.

The brief flame died, leaving the figure huddled and shadowed. 'You must go,' it insisted.

'I only wanted to ... er ... thank you,' he stammered. 'May I see you again?'

'Sometime, perhaps' – the voice was faint and detached – 'but not here. I shall not be here.'

'Then where?'

'That is for you to find out if it is so to be.' The voice was dismissive. 'Good-bye, Mr Reed. Remember that you are my last testament. Remember that!'

This startled him, and he was further startled when he let himself out of the house to find that it was almost dusk. He had been in the house for hours, and yet it had felt like so many minutes.

After the cloying atmosphere of the room, the fresh air made him feel light-headed, and he raced back through the darkening, threatening streets to the well-lighted bustle of Canal Street. Only then did he stop to draw a deep breath and let his thoughts expand.

Tomorrow – ah, yes, tomorrow was Mardi Gras, the time to rejoice; and tomorrow he would be famous . . .!

Chapter Forty-nine

With all thoughts of the frenzied merry-making around him banished, Jameson Reed had gone back to the office and had spent hours in the morgue examining old news clippings and yellowing files. He found enough to convince him that what he had been told by the strange old woman was the truth, and he cursed himself for not having taken more complete notes. After this he raced back to his room in a boarding house in the Irish Channel area and pounded away on his small portable typewriter until the thin dawn of Mardi Gras broke clear. He was light-headed with weariness and hunger, but this was no time for sleeping or eating. Gulping down another cup of the thick black coffee that had kept him going through the night, he gathered up the precious sheets of manuscript with shaking hands and hurried back to the office through the wakening streets. The flags of Carnival – purple, gold, and green – billowed majestically in the air, and in his mind trumpets flourished in endless fanfare. This, this was the day . . .

'Where the hell have you been?' The desk-editor was not in the best of tempers after a heavy night. He took in the white, sweating face and the dark-circled eyes of the young reporter and barked, 'Hell, boy, this is no time to go on a bender! Where the devil is that copy on the Parise funeral? It's missed this edition; we'll have to shove it in the next one and hope the relatives won't notice.'

Jameson ignored him. He slapped the thick sheaf of papers down on the desk and, stepping back, indicated them with a trembling hand. 'Read this!' he choked out. 'The scoop of the century! It'll knock the city for a loop! Go on, read it!'

The editor picked up the top sheet and his eyes widened as he saw the headline. VOODOO QUEEN TELLS ALL, it screamed.

He glanced suspiciously at the sweating boy. 'You putting
me on?' he demanded with narrowing eyes.

'No! God's truth – it's the real McCoy! The low-down on
every major scandal in the city for the past fifty years! *Read*
it!' Jameson urged.

The editor frowned and turned back to the manuscript.
As he read on, his face became sterner, his lips more and
more compressed. When he finished, he got up and said in a
carefully controlled voice, 'I think the copy-editor had better see this.'

He was gone a few seconds and came back with the copy-
editor, also solemn-faced, who went through the same
process as Jameson waited in a mounting agony of suspense.
When he had finished, he cast a curious eye at Jameson and
said to his colleague, 'Well, I see what you mean. Let's all go
see the senior editor – I feel he should be in on this.'

They all trooped across the humming newsroom to the
senior editor's office. 'Something here we'd like you to see,
Bill,' the copy-editor announced. 'Young Reed here just
brought it in.' A glance passed between the three older men,
and the senior editor began to read, the two others peering
over his shoulder as he turned over the pages. By this time
Jameson was almost suffocating with anxiety and excitement.

The senior editor finished the final page, tidied the manuscript into a neat pile, and said in a dry voice, 'Well, thank
you, gentlemen, for bringing me this. I wouldn't have missed
it for the world.' His voice quavered and broke, and he
began to chuckle; the chuckle turned to a laugh, the laugh to
a roar, as all three of them doubled over in gales of helpless
laughter, the tears rolling down their cheeks, their hands
clutching at aching sides.

Jameson looked at them with incomprehension, a slow
flush mounting his pale face. 'What is it?' he stammered. 'I
don't understand. What's so funny?'

'Funny! Oh, boy, don't!' the desk-editor choked out. 'It's a setup, kid, a setup! Who do you think did it? The *Item* crowd?' he gasped to the copy-editor. 'Sounds like them – ho-ho-ho!' He doubled over again.

Jameson's temper began to rise. 'Setup!' he shouted. 'Hell, no! I tell you I *saw* her! I interviewed her! I've checked the stories – they're true!'

'Oh, kid!' The senior editor mopped his streaming eyes. 'If you interviewed her, that's the dandiest bit of reporting on a ghost I ever did see! She dropped dead of a heart attack more'n twenty years ago.'

'No – you're wrong about that, Bill. That was a sister. The Voodoo dame drowned in the lake a couple of years after that.' This was the copy-editor.

'No, Joe, that's wrong, too – she was drowned, sure, but that was before the other dame died,' the desk-editor gasped. They began to argue amiably, with one another.

Jameson listened to them in growing horror. They didn't believe him – they didn't believe a word he'd written! 'But it's not true – none of what you are saying is true!' he cried. 'She told me all about those stories, but I tell you I saw her *in person* yesterday. She's very old, but she is *alive*.'

The senior editor sobered a little. 'All right, son, tell us *all* about it,' he said with a happy sigh, and winked at the others. 'Tell us how it all came about.'

Jameson stammered out the whole story, as the three of them continued to grin like a trio of Cheshire cats.

At the end of Jameson's desperate recital, the desk-editor began to chuckle again. 'So you went to an unspecified house on Rampart Street, and you had an interview in a darkened room with a woman whose face you did not see at *any* time, who *said* she was Marie Laveau and fed you a lot of garbage about long-dead news. Oh, boy! Can't you *see* it was a setup? I'm willing to bet it was the *Item* crowd,' he offered to the other two.

'Yeah. Probably got the idea from that damned fool story on Hearn I allowed to go through,' the senior editor agreed, 'and hoped we'd take the bait.'

'What do you mean, "damned fool story"!' Jameson exploded indignantly.

The senior editor rubbed at his bleary eyes. 'Oh, son, I only let that moonlight-and-roses crap of yours go through because it's what the public likes to hear – there was no truth in it. My father worked here on the *Times* in the old days with Hearn, and he used to say he was the most unpleasant son-of-a-bitch he'd ever met. He wasn't even much of a writer, come to that. He never made it here at all. Only coloured people would have anything to do with him; he never could get on with his own kind.'

Jameson's dream castles were crumbling around his ears, but he couldn't give up that easily. 'That's what she said,' he muttered stubbornly. 'Everything she said checks out, I tell you.'

'Well, of course it would.' The desk editor was beginning to sound irritated. 'If you could find the stories in the files, someone else could, too.'

'But they weren't the *way* she told them,' Jameson said heatedly. 'I can do even more checking, but . . .'

'Oh, save it! Other people have imaginations, too, you know. If they're good enough to think up a joke like this, they're good enough to alter things just enough to get you on the hook, boy.'

'But my story,' Jameson pleaded, 'what about that?'

'Sorry, kid, but this is what's going to happen to your story,' the senior editor said firmly, dumping the precious papers into his wastebasket. 'I'm not going to make the *Times* the laughingstock of the city, Mardi Gras time or no Mardi Gras! Forget it, and write it off to experience. And let this be a lesson to you – for if you can't figure out when you're being conned in this game, you're never going to get very far.'

Jameson's rage exploded. 'I'll *prove* it to you! I'll find Marie Laveau and bring her here, even if I have to carry her so she can tell you herself!'

The desk-editor began to chortle again. 'You do that, boy. Start in St Louis number one – that's where she's buried.'

'No, no! That's the old one – the mother. This one was buried in St Louis number two.'

'No, she wasn't. She was drowned, and they never did find the body.'

They all began to argue again, but Jameson did not wait to hear. He fled in fury in search of his prey. After some argument he managed to convince another cub reporter to accompany him on his quest. 'It's a big story,' he pleaded. 'And I'm going to need a witness.'

They struggled through the milling crowds, already gathering for the parades, over the same path he had taken the day before until they reached Rampart Street. 'It should be easy to spot,' Jameson said eagerly. 'The downstairs window shutters will be closed, and the door's green.'

'Don't you know the number?'

'No,' he confessed. 'I was taken there, so I never thought to look. But it'll be easy enough to find – you'll see!'

It wasn't. Though they searched Rampart right down to the Esplanade, no house on the left side had its shutters closed. Nervously, Jameson began to retrace his steps. 'Maybe they've opened up because of Carnival,' he muttered, looking up at the pathetic fringes of purple, yellow, and green coloured paper that fluttered feebly from the shabby houses. 'Just keep looking for a green door.'

'Is this going to take long?' His friend was restive. 'The parades'll be starting soon, and I don't want to miss them.'

'No, not long, I promise. Look – that's it! I'm almost certain!' He ran up the steps and pounded desperately on the peeling door. There was no answer for a long time. Then finally the door opened a crack to reveal the elderly mulatto woman he had seen the day before. She started back and went to slam the door, but he stuck his foot in it. 'This is it!' he yelled excitedly. 'Help me, Rob! I saw this one yesterday! Let me in! I've got to see Marie Laveau! It's very urgent!' he appealed through the crack. Nothing happened as the woman held the door against him, and she could be heard muttering to someone behind her. 'Let me in!' he called again. 'I'm a reporter from the *Times*. If you don't open up, I'll get the police!'

'Here, steady now, Jamey,' Rob whispered in alarm.

'That's no way to win friends and influence people around here.'

'I don't care! I've *got* to see her!' To his relief, the door swung open wider and a mulatto man of late middle age stood on the threshold.

'What is all this?' he demanded. 'There's no Marie Laveau here – and I ought to know, since this here is my house.'

'And what might your name be?' Jameson reached for his notebook. He was trembling with anger and excitement.

'William LeBlanc – William LeBlanc, *Junior*,' the man said dryly. 'An' I live here, like my father befo' me, an' there ain't no Marie Laveau here.'

'And I tell you I spoke to her here yesterday in that very room!' Jameson pointed a shaking finger at the closed door. 'And I demand to be allowed in!'

The man shrugged. 'If it'll get rid o' you – go ahead an' see for yo'self.' He opened the door wide and stepped aside.

James rushed in, his friend hard on his heels. The bright sun streamed in through dusty panes upon empty desolation: a few sticks of rickety antique furniture, the pale blue upholstery grimy and shredded, standing on the threadbare ghost of a rose carpet. There was a gaping hole in the ceiling where some fixture had been removed, and the only intact thing in the room was the grey marble fireplace that stretched in dusty emptiness above a clean-swept hearth.

'Well?' Rob demanded at Jameson's side. 'How about it, Jamey?'

'It's the same – I swear it!' He looked around desperately, trying to conjure up the images of yesterday in his mind. 'She was sitting in that armchair over near the grate – the one that doesn't look quite as dirty as the others. There were other things, too, things that aren't here now. There was a marquetry workbox on the table, and the candlestick was on ... that's not here. And something else – a picture; I spotted it when the fire flared up once.' He turned in time to see the mulatto cast an instinctive glance to the left of the fireplace. 'Ah-ha! I saw you!' he shouted in triumph. 'You looked right to where it was! A watercolour, it was – looked like the old Wishing Tree. Don't try to tell me it wasn't here!'

The coloured man looked at him impassively. 'Mister, I don't know what you're talkin' 'bout. But, as you can see, there ain't no one here now, so I'll trouble you to take yourself off – or *I'll* call the police.'

'Come on.' Rob tugged at the reluctant Jameson. 'You may be right, but let's get out of here, for Pete's sake!'

In helpless frustration, Jameson saw the door close on them. 'I can't let it go at that . . .' he started to say, when he spotted coming towards them the black man who had been his guide and who was now clutching a small boy by the hand. 'That's him!' he yelled. 'Come on! Don't let him get away! We'll get the truth out of him!'

The man stopped, wheeled, and, shoving the boy away from him, started to run towards the crowd pressing in upon Orleans Street.

'You get the kid! I'll get him!' Jameson yelled. And they set off in hot pursuit.

The man was surprisingly fleet of foot, but desperation put wings on Jameson's feet and he kept close behind him until they got to the densely packed area of Orleans. Then the crowds pressed in around them. Jameson's new hat went, snatched off by a drunken reveller, and his clothes were almost torn off his back as he forced his way unheeding through the throng, his eyes fixed frantically on the bright yellow shirt the Negro was wearing. A roar went up from the crowd as the vanguard of the Comus procession was sighted, and they began to surge. Jameson battled on, and all went well until Royal was reached, then a trio of brightly dressed masquers seized him and whirled him into an impromptu dance. By the time he had fought himself free of their clutches the yellow shirt had disappeared.

With black desolation in his heart, Jameson began to stagger haphazardly onwards – seeking, a hopeless wanderer. Comus and his court in cloth of silver passed; Rex in cloth of gold; Mystic in purple; Momus in blue. Jameson did not see them as the crowds around him went wild. 'If Ever I Ceased to Love,' the song of Carnival, beat at his brain from brass and wind and drum until his senses reeled. He was peppered with favours thrown from the floats, and one hit him in the eye, bringing forth blinding tears that were not far below the surface. When his legs could no longer support him, he leaned in weakness against a building and despair seized him. The gay banners of Carnival mocked; the fanfare of trumpets muted, dying. He cursed Heaven and Earth; he cursed Marie Laveau; he even cursed his own white skin. She had sunk behind the impenetrable barrier of the black world again, and he, a white man, would never find her now.

Chapter Fifty

It had been too good a story to keep quiet, and within a week Jameson Reed was the laughingstock of every newsroom in New Orleans. He bore the constant ribbing of his fellow reporters in grim silence, knowing that to react would only continue the process forever and that he would then have no hope of living it down. Finally, tiring of the unrewarded sport, his colleagues turned to fresh game and he was allowed to pick up the fragments of his dreams in peace. He was certain only of one thing; he was on to something remarkable, and he would not give up on it.

A slender thread of hope appeared as he continued to delve into the records. A 'chatty' article on Voodoo related the story of how a white girl, Louise Walters, found the Voodoo Queen in a half-drowned condition in Bayou St John. 'Louise, now Mrs Arnold Spier, related many interesting anecdotes about the late Voodoo Queen, whom she knew well in her youth,' the article babbled with infuriating vagueness, 'but Mrs Spier, who is now a practicing Baptist, has long since put such heathen superstitions behind her.'

A white woman! It was a very long shot, indeed, but he would try it. At least she might be willing to talk to him.

After some more investigating, he came up with the fact that Arnold Spier was now the late Arnold Spier. But on the off-chance that the address in a working-class suburb given for him in an old city directory was still the family home, Reed went to check it out. It wasn't, but after some reflection on the part of the current lady of the house, he was directed to an equally humble abode two streets away. 'I'm almost as sure as I can be that she moved there with her daughter when her husband passed on. Why don't you try that? Number ten, it is.'

He did, and this time his luck held. The door was opened to him by a very faded, fair woman, clad in shabby black, whose lined face and sad eyes proclaimed a far-from-easy life. 'Mrs Spier?' he inquired, politely doffing his hat. And at her nod, he went on: 'Formerly Louise Walters, the friend of Marie Laveau?'

An alarmed and guarded expression came over her face, and she cast a quick, nervous glance over her shoulder to where he could hear voices coming from the rear of the small house. 'Are you a reporter?' she whispered. 'I'm sorry I can't tell you anything – my daughter is dead-set against ...'

'Madam,' he interrupted, 'yes, I am a reporter, but I swear I am not here to write about you or Marie Laveau. However, I am in desperate need of some information, and you are my only hope. I just want to *talk* to you about her. *Please!* It is very important.'

A gleam of curiosity entered the faded blue eyes. 'I can't talk to you here,' she whispered, 'but there's a small park down the road a piece. Go there and I'll meet you in half an hour. I usually go for a bit of a walk just about now, so they won't be any the wiser.' Again she cast a haunted glance over her shoulder and closed the door on him.

He paced the littered, depressing stretch of grass, scattered around which were a few benches, until her black-clad figure came into sight. She greeted him with a timid smile and sat down on one of the benches, panting slightly. 'What is it? What do you want to know?' she asked.

He was in a quandary, since he did not want to scare his very timid informant. 'Well ... er ... suppose you start by telling me about your friendship with her,' he said lamely.

'You swear you aren't going to put this in your paper?' she said in a frightened whisper.

'No, definitely not. This is what is known as a privileged communication.' He tried to sound important. 'Anything you tell me will be held in the strictest confidence.'

She relaxed a little. 'I really don't know where to begin ... er ... Mr Reed, is it? She was always so kind to me ...' She retold the story, rambling through what he had already read

439

of her finding Marie Laveau and the beginning of their strange friendship. 'She taught me to tell fortunes.' A faint flush of pleasure came over the worn face. 'I enjoyed that. And she taught me how to make simple potions to help people, but I didn't have any real gifts along those lines. She soon saw that, but it didn't make any difference to her. She liked me. And I think she was lonely.'

'And did she have any other white friends?' Jameson said cautiously.

'No, I don't think so – none that I ever saw, anyway.'

'But you were hers because you saved her life?'

'Partly, and also because she said I reminded her of her daughter.'

This came as a shock. 'Marie Laveau had a daughter – *here*?' He tried not to sound too excited.

She looked confused. 'No, not here. She never told me what happened or where the daughter was or anything – just that I looked like her.'

'Did she say anything about the father?' He was having a hard time controlling the excitement in his voice.

'No – though she *was* married; I remembered that. Once when we were passing Our Lady of Guadalupe – you know that old place in the French Quarter? – she said to me, "That's where I was married." It was just before I got married myself.' Her face clouded. 'She was against that, and I don't think I'd have gone through with it if she hadn't gone away and I didn't see her again for so long.'

'Where did she go?'

'Out of the country – those islands in the south somewhere. "Don't rush things," she said to me. "Wait till I get back." ' The faded face convulsed. 'I wish I had,' Louise Spier muttered. 'But she was gone, and Arnie was being so pressing, but I wish I had . . .'

'But you heard from her after?' Jameson urged.

She evaded the question. 'Arnold made me give it all up. Devil's work, he said it was. Not that I ever had anything to do with those Voodoos – she wouldn't have that at all. All I did was to try and help people, but he wouldn't have any of it. A strict Baptist, he was, and my daughter is just the same.

440

But there was no harm in what I did.' Her voice rose queru-
lously.

'But you *did* hear from her after that?' Jameson insisted.

'Yes, sometimes,' she muttered, 'but she saw how it was
with Arnie, so she left me alone – she didn't want to make
trouble for me.'

Then he forced himself to ask the all-important question.
'Where is she? Where can I find her?'

Her eyes flickered away from his. 'Why, how should I
know? She was very old. She's dead, I suppose.' He was
certain she was lying.

'Well, then, it must have been very recent,' he said deliberately, 'because I saw her not more than six weeks ago in
the old house that used to belong to her on Rampart Street –
and I *must* find her again.'

She stared at him like a frightened rabbit, but said
nothing.

He took another tack. 'You see, she was telling my future
and then we got interrupted, so we never finished. I don't
suppose you'd tell my fortune, would you? I'd gladly pay –
say, five dollars?'

The prospect of the money brought a faint gleam to her
eyes and she seemed to relax a little. 'Oh, dear, I don't know.
I haven't done it for such a long time, and I never was anywhere near as good as she was . . .'

'I really would appreciate it,' he said earnestly, trying to
win back her trust.

'I tell the cards,' she confided. Then she glanced at a
pretty gold-and-blue enamel fob watch she had pinned to her
bodice. 'She gave me this.' She touched it gently. 'As it
happens, the house will be empty now – my daughter goes
out to see her sister today, and the rest are working.' She
hesitated. 'If you'd care to come back with me, I'd tell you as
well as I could.'

'Good. Then let's go.' He assisted her up, then talked of
noncommittal things until they got back to the down-at-the-
heels dwelling.

After Louise had cautiously checked to see if the house
was indeed empty, she ushered Reed through into a small

room at the back crammed full of furniture, the tops of every flat surface crowded with boxes and knick-knacks of all kinds. Louise Spier gave a helpless glance at the confusion and said apologetically, 'I kept all my best things from the old house, but I can't seem to get organized in this small place. Sit down a minute. I know I kept my cards. They ought to be in one of these boxes here . . .' She bustled over and started to rummage through boxes on the chest of drawers. Her efforts dislodged a pile of papers that cascaded unheeded to the floor. Jameson found himself gazing at an object that had been masked by the papers but which he recognized – it was a marquetry workbox.

He jumped to his feet. 'Mrs Spier, you've been lying to me!' he thundered. 'You *have* been in contact with her! You must know where she is!'

She whirled around, and when she saw what he was looking at, she went deathly pale. 'No – I swear!' she gasped.

'Then how did you come by that box, which I saw in her room not six weeks ago?' he thundered on.

'But I didn't *see* her.' She began to sob, plucking at the fallen papers and camouflaging the box again. 'This was brought to me, and my daughter mustn't know . . .'

'There must have been a message, a note!' he insisted.

'It was brought by a nigger. All he said was "Marie Laveau wants you to have this and to remember her. Her time approaches." ' She gulped convulsively. 'So, you see, she *must* be dead; otherwise, she'd never have given it away; it was her grandmother's – one of the things she cherished most.'

'Mrs Spier,' Reed said with deliberate cruelty, 'this is obviously a news story of importance, because she was presumed dead years ago. Unless you tell me *all* you know, with no reservations, I'm afraid my pledge of silence no longer holds. *Where* was she?'

'I don't know – I swear it!' Louise whispered. 'And you *promised* . . . If she's not in the Rampart Street house, I don't know where she would be. Maison Blanche, where I used to go, was sold years and years ago.'

'Then *think*! There must be other places she went; other

442

places and people you knew about – who her Negro friends were, for instance.'

She looked at him like a trapped animal. 'There was one place,' she said in a frightened whisper, 'a shack out on Bayou Sauvage – she took me there a few times. It belonged to an ol' *hungan* named Dan – he's dead now. She said it was a place of power – Voodoo power, she meant.'

'Could you take me there?'

'I don't know that I could find it – it's been so long,' she whimpered.

'Well, you must try. It's vital.' Although Jameson felt sorry for his victim, he had to continue. 'And another thing: *Why* did she disappear for all those years? Why has she been hiding all this time? There *has* to be a reason.'

A puzzled expression came into her face. 'I don't know for sure,' she muttered. 'At first, I think, she was afraid of someone, but after a while it wasn't that anymore. I think it was something she had been trying to do. Once she said to me, "If my mother could do it, I can, too. It's a question of the right time and the right balance." But I don't know what she meant. Oh, Mr Reed, you won't break your promise, will you? I've told you all I know!'

Jameson relented. 'Not if you do your best to show me this place on Bayou Sauvage, and if you can tell me anything else that might help. Could you show me tomorrow if I get a car?'

Finally, after another anguished glance at the fob watch, she gave in. 'My son-in-law will be home from work soon,' she moaned. 'He mustn't find you here. Please go!'

'Then I'll pick you up at ten tomorrow?' he queried as she almost pushed him out of the overcrowded room.

'Yes, yes. I'll do the best I can to find it.'

'Just tell them I'm the son of an old friend taking you for a ride in the country,' he counselled as she went to close the front door on him. And there was a gleam of excitement in the sad eyes as she nodded and locked it after him.

He spent a busy day checking in the records of Our Lady of Guadalupe. He found the marriage record easily enough. 'Nils Andersen, coloured,' he snorted to himself. 'In a pig's eye! So that's where the blue-eyed blonde came from.' And a short while later he found the baptismal record of one Ingrid Andersen, daughter of Marie Laveau and Nils Andersen, with the Rampart Street address added. It was another dead end, but he noted down all the data – there couldn't have been that many Nils Andersens in New Orleans before the war; there would have to be some faint trail there for him to follow.

Reed managed to borrow a Model-T from a more affluent friend. At the appointed hour, he picked up a visibly excited Louise Spier. She was still in her rusty black attire, but she had added a wide, much beflowered, old spring hat to her ensemble, which lent an air of pathetic jauntiness to her frail figure.

The hat presented certain problems in the open car, and Louise was constantly clutching at it with little squeaks as Jameson drove at a decorous speed through the outskirts of the city towards the wilder reaches of the lake. It precluded any sustained conversation, but she was so obviously enjoying this departure from her dreary routine that he held his peace until they were at Bayou Sauvage. Then he stopped the car and gently insisted she remove the problematic hat.

By this time she was so excited that she did not even demur, but, removing it, said happily, 'We keep on this road until we come to a big red barn; that's where we turn on to a cart track.'

They found the barn, far gone in decay but still recognizable, and jolted on to the narrow cart track. Half a mile down, it forked into three separate, even narrower tracks.

She looked at them helplessly. 'I don't know,' she faltered. 'I don't know which ...' Two of them were evidently still well travelled, the third almost overgrown.

'We'll try them all,' he vowed, 'but the least travelled one first.'

They bumped down the almost hidden trail, bushes and rushes tearing at the car, as the soggy ground quaked ominously beneath the wheels. Suddenly Louise let out a joyous squeak: 'There it is!' And she pointed at a ruinous shack standing almost on the bayou's edge.

'Just as well,' he said with a relieved sigh. 'I couldn't have got much farther in this swamp. We'll walk the rest of the way.'

'Yes, yes, that's it – I'm sure of it.' She hurried ahead of him, 'I remember *Hungan* Dan saying it was built by an old Voodoo named Crocodile – oh, way, way back.' But when they came up to its blank, shuttered windows, she stopped and faltered. 'There's no one there. See? It's all closed up. I don't want to go any farther.'

'Come on. We've come this far; we might as well see.' He went up to the weathered door and tapped on it; with a creak it swung open on emptiness. He heard Mrs Spier breathing hard behind him, and then he heard a sudden gasp as she took in the contents of the hut. The floor and walls were decorated with many-coloured chalks in a series of bizarre designs which dizzied the mind with the strange optical illusion of limitless space they created. The focal point of the designs was a white sheet edged by the guttered remains of a multitude of candles. Lying on it, as if dropped suddenly from an unseen hand, lay a metal bell and a bead-covered gourd.

'Voodoo!' The voice behind him was hoarse. 'And those things are hers – she showed me them many a time.'

Jameson stepped inside, and the moment he crossed the threshold he was aware of two things – a strange electric vibrancy to the air, and the same odd aroma he had smelled in the room on Rampart Street. 'Look at the candles,' he muttered. 'How strange they are! They look as if they have been blasted *outwards* from the sheet.'

Mrs Spier was peering in with wide, frightened eyes, but would not venture farther. 'What's that in the corner?' She pointed with a trembling finger.

He went over to an untidy mound of old clothes; he picked up a shawl and a faded pale blue dress, partially burned. He held them up. 'Do you recognize them?' She shook her head as he gazed at them. 'I'm almost certain it's the same shawl,' he murmured.

'There's something else on the floor,' she quavered. A blackened piece of paper lay beneath the clothes. He took it up and turned it over. It crumbled under his touch, but not before he saw it was a watercolour painting of the Wishing Tree. 'It's the picture of the tree, isn't it?' The hushed voice came from the door. 'Then she *is* gone – I'm sure of it now.'

Reed looked at the clothes with a puzzled frown. 'But I don't understand. Why are her clothes here?'

There was a hint of impatience in Louise Spier's voice. 'If she was doing a Voodoo rite, she'd be naked.'

'And after?'

She was frightened again. 'We'd better look around,' she whispered. 'The designs go on out here.'

After a baffled glance at the enigmatic contents of the hut, Reed joined Mrs Spier outside. She pointed to a narrow pathway that had been carved in the undergrowth leading away from the hut, and on the raw, wet earth beneath were sinuous designs in the mud. 'I think that's what they call a Path of Power,' the trembling woman said. 'She showed me in a book once . . .'

He followed the narrow trail with her close on his heels, and the grasses and reeds on either side had the same seared and blasted outward look as the candles had had. The ground got soggier and sucked treacherously at his feet until he found he was gazing down into the black, still waters of the bayou. There was a little sob behind him. 'If she went in there, there'll never be a trace found – not with the crabs and all.'

There was a strange feeling of desolation in his heart as he gazed at the end of the trail and the end of his hopes, but then his mind was set spinning. While the designs in the mud path had been sharp and clear, there had at no place along the way been so much as a hint of a footprint! He looked back to see their own prints firmly and deeply marked, and his wonder grew. 'Well, let's get back,' he said grimly. 'There's nothing more to do here.' He cast around the outside of the shanty for some other sign of a trail, but the undergrowth was unmarked, unbroken, save for that single sinister trail that led nowhere.

Wordlessly, he led the way back to the car and they drove in silence to the city. Louise Spier was crying quietly. When they got close to her house, she said drearily, 'Don't take me home – they mustn't see me like this. Take me to a friend's, my old neighbour, who lives two streets over. She's used to seeing me crying. I can stay there till it's over.' He followed her directions, and as she got out of the car her tears were dried, and she said, 'You will keep your bargain, Mr Reed?'

'Oh, yes. I'll make no mention of you – ever.'

A defiant look came into her reddened eyes. 'Whatever she was trying to do,' she whispered fiercely, 'I hope she succeeded. She was a woman like no other, Marie Laveau, and *I'll* never forget her, never!' And, squaring her shoulders, she went off without a backward look.

After Reed got back to his lodgings, he typed far into the night. When he had finished, he read carefully through what he had written, then sighed and tore the papers into small pieces. 'My greatest story, and it will never see the light of day,' he murmured as he dropped them into his wastebasket. 'My story without an ending. I was to be your last testament, Marie Laveau, but a testament to what? I mean to find the answer before I die, I mean to find the truth – I promise you that!'

Epilogue
The Present

Chapter Fifty-one

Jameson Reed had come home at last. He supposed it was to die, though the thought of death had long since ceased to hold any terrors for him. He had been through so much and learned so much, that this transition of his aged self into some other state seemed of little importance. It was just some animal instinct, he surmised, that brought him back to the city of his birth to finish the cycle.

His had been a success story. The first break had come when he had predicted the great Spanish flu plague a month before it had begun. He had built from there, using the strange knowledge he had been given in that room of dancing shadows to build success on success. When others had been speculating madly in the '20s, he had conservatively saved his money; and when the crash had come, he had profited from it by buying large chunks of property and land for the proverbial song. He still owned three large houses in the Garden District, which, besides being worth their weight in gold, housed his widower son – with whom he would share his remaining days – and two of his married grandsons.

He had gone to Europe in World War II as a foreign correspondent and, after falling hopelessly in love with Paris, had stayed there after the war had ended, as happy an expatriate as it was possible to find. There had been frequent trips back during the years his own children were growing up, of course, but since the death of his wife and his children's marriages, there had been less and less occasion to visit the not very appealing America of the '60s and '70s, even after his retirement. Now, in the new '80s, something drew him irresistibly back: some unfinished business of living, or possibly of dying.

He felt a little like Rip Van Winkle as his grandsons toured him dutifully around the new New Orleans, which, in its newest burst of prosperity, seemed determined to hurl itself upward into the clouds. He did not like much of what he saw: the dreary brick blocks of low-cost housing that stood on what once was Storyville; the multi-laned highway, which was now all that was left of Rampart; the crass commercialism of much of the French Quarter. It was with relief that he would escape back to the tranquillity of the large house in the Garden District, its trees and shrubs forming bowers and screening it effectively from the large tourist buses that would crawl through the quiet streets with thunderous reminders of what had become New Orleans's foremost industry.

His return was not all bad. There was so much he had to catch up on: books and papers that had been stored in the attic for thirty or more years; discovering what had happened to his friends (mostly dead), his family, and, indeed, to America during his long exile. Through his grandsons, in really getting to know them, he would in the little time left to him find out where it was all heading, what it had all been about.

In sorting his papers, he came across a folder which released in him a flood of memories and intensified the feeling that there was at least one thing that remained for him to do. It was a folder labelled 'Marie Laveau'. Over a period of years after the enigma of Bayou Sauvage, he had probed along a very hazy trail. He had traced the Nils Andersen of the marriage record to Chicago, and had found there the marriage record of an Ingrid Andersen to a Charles Ballou of Rhode Island. There the trail would have petered out had it not been for a stroke of luck. He had heard of an aged woman, a Georgina Laveau, who claimed to have been a Voodoo Queen and kin to the two great Maries. Interviewing her, Reed had heard a strange tale about a ward of the younger Marie, who had been a descendant – albeit an illegitimate one – of the once mighty New Orleans family of Montal: a coloured girl who had gone north and married a white man in Chicago.

The odd coincidence of place had once more sent him on

452

a genealogical trace, and he had come across the further interesting fact that one of Claire Agnelli's numerous progeny had married a Claire Ballou from Rhode Island and had gone east. Among their resulting family – many of whom seemed to have died in infancy – was one, Esther, whose birthdate he had underlined in red ink. He stared at it back through the tunnel of the years in puzzlement: Why had he done that? After a mental struggle he remembered; the child had been born just two weeks before his strange visit to the shack on Bayou Sauvage, and the fact coincided with a wild speculation he had made after his own deep reseach into Voodoo. Still, he had got no further. He sighed and went to put the folder away, but before closing the folder he noted that he had made one of his last entries before going overseas to cover the war in Europe. In 1940 Esther Agnelli had married one Ernest Simpson of Boston, Massachusetts.

The old interest sparked, he made some inquiries about Voodoo in the modern New Orleans, and he was surprised to find that, in spite of the fact that Voodoo had long since been recognized as an established church and was flourishing elsewhere in America, there was no such church in New Orleans; for this springing city, it had merely become a facet of its colourful past.

The present claimed Reed also. His son Richard announced somewhat grumpily the imminent arrival of a granddaughter Jameson had never seen. She was the daughter of his younger son, who had ended up in California as a screenwriter, an occupation Reed's eldest son regarded with marked suspicion. His eldest son had early joined the mighty Valdoux bank and had quickly settled into the conservative tradition of that august institution.

'Of course, Don has had all sorts of trouble with his family,' Richard snorted to his father. 'But what would you expect, brought up in the sort of atmosphere that prevails out there? This youngest daughter of his, Grace, for instance – *what* a handful! Always involved with Women's Lib and protest movements and such nonsense. Don seems positively relieved now that he has channelled her energies at last into this Spiritual Revitalization movement – of all things!'

'And what might that be?' Jameson was short, for sometimes he found his son's pomposity irksome.

'You haven't heard of it? Good heavens! Well, I suppose it hasn't hit Europe yet, but it's been sweeping America like a flash flood. It has put outfits like Sun Myung Moon's completely out of business, and has even made a sizable dent in the big evangelists' followings. Quite an amazing phenomenon, really – started up in a small way about eight years ago, and five years ago it really started to snowball. Run by a couple of northern women – latter-day Mary Baker Eddys, modern style. They seem to be sweeping up everybody: the charismatics, the Jesus movement, the Women's Libbers, the Grey Panthers, the black groups – you name it; they've converted it. The older one, an Esther Vincent, is a doctor – marvellous healer, supposedly; but it's the younger one, a Mary Updyke, who really brings them in – one of those personalities that won't stop; she keeps predicting things that always pan out in some odd way. Even the politicians are beginning to take them very seriously, for what they say today, their followers tend to do tomorrow. This is the first time they've hit New Orleans; never been here before for some odd reason – but now it's by popular demand.'

'Oh, really?' Jameson was mildly interested. 'And how is Grace involved with them?'

'On the staff of one of them – the younger one. PR, I think. Anyway, I'm sure she'll tell you all about it tomorrow. The few times I've seen her lately she rarely stops talking, and this spiritual thing is her only subject.'

With Jameson it was a case of love at first sight. He liked everything about Grace Reed, from the top of her neatly coiffed head to her elegantly shod toes. What he liked most was her enthusiasm, her zest for life, which he had found somewhat lacking in his more orthodox grandsons.

He was an immediate hit with her, too. Taken aback by his profound ignorance, she quickly and at length rectified it. 'You've got to get with it, Jamey!' she bubbled irreverently. 'You simply have to come to the rally tomorrow. That's why I'm here. It'll be in the Superdome, and so I'm sure I can squeeze you in somewhere, though I'm told they'll be coming in from all over the South; there's not a room to be had in the city – which is why I'm staying here,' she added with an impish twinkle. 'Otherwise, Uncle Dick doesn't approve of me, and vice-versa.'

'Well, I don't think at my age I'm up to that sort of thing – the old pump's not what it was,' Jameson explained cheerfully. 'Are you *really* expecting to fill the Superdome?'

'Why, of course! And it is never too late – honestly, you just haven't lived until you've experienced the Simpson sisters.'

'*Who* did you say?' Jameson said sharply.

'The Simpson sisters – Esther Vincent and Mary Updyke. They are old-fashioned enough to use their married names, but in the inner circle that's what we always call them.'

'And where did you say they were from?'

'From Boston. Both of them went to Radcliffe. Why, Jamey, is anything the matter? You've gone quite pale!'

The coincidence was too fantastic; it just could not be; yet he must find out. 'No, nothing's the matter,' he muttered. 'But I've changed my mind. I would like to come. Any chance of meeting these paragons of yours?'

'Why, sure – no sweat!' Again she grinned. 'That's what we PR types are for – getting important people to meet important people.'

'There's nothing important about a retired old hack journalist,' he protested, secretly delighted with the flattery.

'Nonsense!' she said staunchly. 'You were one of the best – and pretty good yourself at predicting the future, come to that. You should get on like a house on fire with Mary Updyke.'

Jameson looked forward to the morrow with a mixture of trepidation and excitement, his own mixed feelings helped little by the carping of his son. 'Really, I think this town has taken leave of its senses!' the latter had fumed. 'I've just learned that Gaston Valdoux – he's the present head of Valdoux Enterprises – has pledged an enormous sum to the

Spiritual Revitalization of America cause. That Updyke woman must have smitten him with her womanly charms – quite a womanizer, you know. Takes after his grandfather that way. Do you remember him?'

James remembered; that was his trouble – he was remembering altogether too much. On an impulse he bundled up his file on Marie Laveau and stuffed it in a big manila envelope – there was one question he was burning to ask the Simpson sisters.

When he got to the Superdome, however, his excitement failed him; people scurried into the enormous flying-saucer shape of the Superdome like lines of ants, not in crowds, but in hordes. 'If this is going to be as long a session as you predicted,' he said to his granddaughter, 'I think I'll just sit out here for a bit and come on in later.'

'Are you sure you'll be all right?' Grace Reed said anxiously. 'You're still looking a bit on the peaked side.'

'No, I'm fine, just fine. You go on and do your thing,' he told her. 'Give me my ticket and I'll meet up with you later. Okay?'

She gave him the ticket. 'I'm afraid it's in one of the upper tiers,' she apologized. 'It was the best I could do at such short notice. I'm afraid I'm a very *junior* PR type, so I don't carry much clout. But as soon as the meeting is over, go to the manager's suite – see, here's a special pass for that. The ushers will show you where it is. I'll meet you there. They always have a sort of VIP get-together afterwards, and you can meet them then. 'Bye, Jamey.' She gave him a hurried peck on the forehead and was gone, clutching a huge bulging briefcase.

He admired the slim, vibrant outline of her figure until it was swallowed up by the huge buildings. Then he turned his attention to the waves of people hurrying by; they were of all shapes, colours, and conditions, young, old, rich, poor – all rushing with the same expression of tense, almost grim, expectancy. The horde gradually thinned to a crowd, then to a trickle, then stopped altogether; the building having swallowed them all sat as quiet as a gorged monster.

The Superdome was one of the few modern buildings in

the city of which he thoroughly approved, and in his present state of mind he would not have been at all surprised if this daring glimpse of the future had slowly lifted from its immense launching pad and drifted upwards out of sight. He must have dozed off for a while, for when he came to again it was dark, the outline of the Superdome framed by the huge arc lights. He felt refreshed and buoyed by a new vigour, so he scrambled out of the car and found his way with some difficulty to the appointed tier and seat.

His late coming went completely unnoticed, and what first struck him about the packed auditorium was its quietness. It was as if the whole audience was holding its breath, its total attention focused on the dais, which was spotlighted at the scoreboard end of the arena. Trying to adjust himself to his surroundings, he looked at the faces of his neighbours, and was surprised, almost shocked, by what he saw. All the tense grimness had gone, and the faces were smooth and bland, many with the faint smiles of the satiated and content. He struggled to bring the figures on the dais into focus, but he was so far away that, even with binoculars, he could not bring them into sharp definition; the figures remained hazy and wavering to his fading sight. All he could make out was that one was tall and with dark hair that held a reddish glint under the lights; she was dressed in a long purple evening gown. The other was much smaller and frailer, with fair hair, and dressed all in white. It was she who was addressing the rapt crowd. After a while he gave up trying to make out her face and tried instead to concentrate on what she was saying.

The clear, high voice came with but little distortion over the PA system; she was talking of spiritual strength, spiritual growth, self-knowledge, self-help. *She's telling them what they want to hear*, he thought; *this is nothing very new or startling*. Yet, in spite of himself he found he was listening with the same alert intentness of his neighbours. The clear voice fell silent for a moment, then said, 'The hour grows late, and tomorrow the struggle for all that we dream begins anew, so we will conclude with the focus of our fight – we will sing "America".'

It was as if she had pressed some electric release; the

whole audience surged to its feet and burst full-throated into the old, worn lyrics. There was no music, no one was singing in time or even in tune, but they were singing with every atom of their strength. Jameson found himself croaking the lyrics with tears pouring down his cheeks. *It's come, I'm senile,* flashed through his mind, but then he saw that the faces surrounding him were also streaming with facile tears; it was an outlet of emotions the like of which he had never witnessed before. The song ended, the lights on the central dais went out, and when they came on again it was empty. A communal sigh heaved and swelled through the vast crowd and the tier lights went on. It was over.

Jameson stayed in his seat as the crowd flowed silently past him to the exits. He felt stunned with the emotional impact of the evening. *There hasn't been anything like this since the Nuremberg rallies,* he thought, and this disquieting reflection snapped the spell he had been under. Slowly he made his way to the elevator and took it to the appointed floor. When he got to the door of the manager's office, closely guarded by two very tough-looking security police, he almost turned tail to go unnoticed back to the car, but the stubborn streak that had made him such a good newspaperman drove him on. He still had to ask that question.

His pass was an 'open Sesame' to a suite of rooms done in a severely modern style. They were only moderately crowded. There was no sign of Grace, so he made his way to the bar that was operating at one end and fortified himself with a Scotch and soda. He was thankful to see the Spiritual Revitalization movement was not a 'dry' one.

Grace came hurrying up, eager expectation on her young face. 'How was it? Did it turn you on?' she demanded breathlessly. 'Did you enjoy it?'

Misgivings came to him again as he looked at her vulnerable face. 'What I saw was very interesting, though I only came in at the very end. Fell asleep out in the car, I'm afraid,' he apologized.

'Oh, then you missed all the excitement! It was a smashing success – one of the best we've ever had!' She was visibly disappointed. 'Still, come and meet them; they're even better at close quarters.' She craned around. 'Hmm, Mary seems a bit deluged at the moment. Come and meet Esther Vincent. She can probably answer those questions you mentioned.'

Grace towed him firmly by the hand towards where the tall, handsome, chestnut-haired woman was talking to a small group. 'Dr Vincent, I'd like you to meet my grandfather, Jameson Reed, the newsman,' Grace broke in shamelessly. 'He's got some question he's dying to ask you.'

A pair of shrewd hazel eyes, which were more amber than green, appraised him. 'Why, of course, Grace. I had no idea you had such a distinguished grandfather. Delighted to meet you, Mr Reed. What can I do for you?' she was smoothly diplomatic.

Jameson felt a strange sense of disappointment, but the newsman in him rose to the occasion. 'I just wondered if you would be good enough to satisfy an old genealogist's curiosity. Are you the daughter of Ernest Simpson of Boston?'

'Why, yes.' She sounded a little startled.

'And of Esther Agnelli?'

'Good heavens, yes! I'm named after her. Did you know my parents, then?'

He sidestepped the question. 'In a way, but I left the country shortly after their marriage and I'm afraid I lost touch. I had no idea they had had such a talented family. Are there any more of you?'

She looked a little puzzled. 'No. We did have an older brother who died young, but now there are just Mary and myself.'

'And do your remarkable gifts come from your mother?' He tried to sound casual.

There was a guarded expression in her eyes. 'Why, I'm afraid on that I have no idea. I was only seven when my mother died while giving birth to Mary. I believe she was indeed a remarkable woman, but, naturally, I do not remember a great deal about her. Why do you ask, Mr Reed?'

He looked at her levelly, seeking, hoping, for something he did not see. 'It's just that your mother's family was noted for its remarkable women in the past, so naturally I was

459

interested in the connection. Particularly,' he added, 'since it has its roots in this very city.'

Her eyes were wary now. 'Indeed. I had no idea. You evidently have gone deeply into our history, Mr Reed. You must come and meet my sister. She will be most interested.' She looked around and let out a little cluck of impatience. 'Ah, there she is, talking with Gaston Valdoux again! Well, he has monopolized her long enough. We'll break it up. Since Mary has been a widow, this has been a constant threat ...'

With an imperative gesture, she propelled him towards the slight, fair woman standing by a window and screened protectively by a broad, stocky figure. 'Mr Valdoux,' Esther Vincent trumpeted, 'I'm sure you will excuse us, but there is someone here Mary simply must meet.'

Gaston Valdoux grudgingly gave in, for Esther Vincent was not a woman whose edicts were ever questioned, and she went on: 'Mary, this is Jameson Reed – Grace's grandfather – whom I'm sure you've heard of for his noted newspaper career, but he is also a genealogist and has been telling me the most fascinating things about our family tree. I'm sure you'll want to hear them firsthand.' There was almost a note of warning in the deep voice.

The fair figure turned to him, and Jameson gazed into brilliant dark brown eyes. A sense of suffocating excitement welled up in him. 'So you have interested yourself in our family tree, Mr Reed. I had no idea we were that noteworthy,' the cool voice challenged. 'And what did you find that was so exciting?'

Jameson fumbled in his inside pocket for the thick wad of papers. 'Well, Mrs Updyke, it is a very long story that goes a long way back, and which I will not bore you with now. But it is all here.' He put the packet of papers into the slim hands and looked directly at her. 'The most remarkable story of my career, and yet one which will never see the light of day. However, it's a story that has a happy ending, I think, and I do so like happy endings. Don't you?'

She looked at him in silence for a moment. 'Everybody does, don't they?'

'Yes, but only you and I know this one, and soon only you will know it. I have fulfilled a long-standing commission, a long-standing debt – this is *my* testament, Mary Updyke.'

She withdrew the folder a little way from its packet and saw the superscription. She slid it back in again. 'You seem very sure of yourself, Mr Reed – but it ends here.' It was a statement, not a question.

'Yes, it ends here, and it has been a very long search – your mother was a very remarkable woman.'

'My mother!' She gave a little amused laugh and gazed directly at him. As she did so, the pupils of her remarkable eyes contracted into half-moons like a cat's. Jameson gasped, and with this new and final certainty came an agonizing pain that shot up his left arm and clutched at his failing heart. He reeled against the wall with the force of it, and she cried out, 'You're ill! I'll get my sister!'

'No!' he managed to gasp out. 'It will pass. My life is not quite over yet, but I'm almost done. One last question: Grace – she will be all right, won't she?' It was almost a plea.

'You have no need to fear for her, Mr Reed,' Mary Updyke said softly. 'As you should well know by now, I have always taken care of my friends.'

BESTSELLERS AVAILABLE IN GRANADA PAPERBACKS

Leslie Waller

The Swiss Account	£1.25	☐
The 'K' Assignment	50p	☐
Number One	85p	☐
A Change in the Wind	40p	☐
The American	75p	☐
The Family	£1.25	☐
The Banker	£1.25	☐
The Coast of Fear	60p	☐

Patrick Mann

The Vacancy	60p	☐
Dog Day Afternoon	60p	☐

All these books are available at your local bookshop or newsagent, or can be ordered direct from the publisher. Just tick the titles you want and fill in the form below.

Name ....

Address..

....

Write to Granada Cash Sales, PO Box 11, Falmouth, Cornwall TR10 9EN.

Please enclose remittance to the value of the cover price plus:

UK: 30p for the first book, 15p for the second book plus 12p per copy for each additional book ordered to a maximum charge of £1.29.

BFPO and EIRE: 30p for the first book, 15p for the second book plus 12p per copy for the next 7 books, thereafter 6p per book.

OVERSEAS: 50p for the first book and 15p for each additional book.

Granada Publishing reserve the right to show new retail prices on covers, which may differ from those previously advertised in the text or elsewhere.

BESTSELLERS AVAILABLE IN GRANADA PAPERBACKS

Emmanuelle Arsan

Emmanuelle	£1.25 ☐
Emmanuelle 2	£1.25 ☐
Laure	95p ☐
Nea	£1.25 ☐

Jonathan Black

Ride the Golden Tiger	80p ☐
Oil	£1.25 ☐
The World Rapers	£1.25 ☐
The House on the Hill	£1.25 ☐

Herbert Kastle

Hot Prowl	60p ☐
Cross-Country	£1.25 ☐
The World They Wanted	75p ☐
Little Love	85p ☐
Millionaires	75p ☐
Miami Golden Boy	95p ☐
The Movie Maker	£1.50 ☐
The Gang	95p ☐
Countdown to Murder	75p ☐
The Three Lives of Edward Berner	85p ☐

Calder Willingham

The Big Nickel	75p ☐
Rambling Rose	50p ☐
End as a Man	£1.25 ☐
To Eat a Peach	75p ☐
Geraldine Bradshaw	40p ☐
Eternal Fire	£1.50 ☐
Providence Island	£1.50 ☐
Reach to the Stars	95p ☐